EUROPE

A Continental Overview of Environmental Issues

THE WORLD'S ENVIRONMENTS

KEVIN HILLSTROM AND
LAURIE COLLIER HILLSTROM, SERIES EDITORS

Global warming, rain forest destruction, mass extinction, overpopulation—the environmental problems facing our planet are immense and complex.

ABC-CLIO's series The World's Environments offers students and general readers a handle on the key issues, events, and people.

The six titles in the series examine the unique—and common—problems facing the environments of every continent on Earth and the ingenious ways local people are attempting to address them. Titles in this series:

Africa and the Middle East

Asia

Australia, Oceania, and Antarctica

Europe

Latin America and the Caribbean

North America

EUROPE

A Continental Overview of Environmental Issues

KEVIN HILLSTROM
LAURIE COLLIER HILLSTROM

ABC CLIO
Santa Barbara, California
Denver, Colorado Oxford, England

Library of Congress Cataloging-in-Publication Data

Hillstrom, Kevin, 1963–
Europe : a continental overview of environmental issues / Kevin Hillstrom, Laurie Collier Hillstrom.
p. cm. — (The world's environments)
Includes bibliographical references and index.
ISBN 1-57607-686-5 (acid-free paper) — ISBN 1-57607-687-3 (eBook)
1. Europe—Environmental conditions. 2. Environmental degradation—Europe. 3. Environmental protection—Europe. 4. Conservation of natural resources—Europe. I. Hillstrom, Laurie Collier, 1965– II. Title. II. Series: Hillstrom, Kevin, 1963– . World's environments.

GE160.E75H55 2003
363.7'0094—dc21 2002156275

07 06 05 04 03 10 9 8 7 6 5 4 3 2 1

This book is also available on the World Wide Web as an eBook.
Visit http://www.abc-clio.com for details.

ABC-CLIO, Inc.
130 Cremona Drive, P.O. Box 1911
Santa Barbara, California 93116–1911

This book is printed on acid-free paper ♾.
Manufactured in the United States of America

Contents

List of Tables and Figures

Tables

Figures

Introduction

The World's Environments

As the nations of the world enter the twenty-first century, they confront a host of environmental issues that demand attention. Some of these issues—pollution of freshwater and marine resources, degradation of wildlife habitat, escalating human population densities that place crushing demands on finite environmental resources—have troubled the world for generations, and they continue to defy easy solutions. Other issues—global climate change, the potential risks and rewards of genetically modified crops and other organisms, unsustainable consumption of freshwater resources—are of more recent vintage. Together, these issues pose a formidable challenge to our hopes of building a prosperous world community in the new millennium, especially since environmental protection remains a low priority in many countries. But despite an abundance of troubling environmental indicators, positive steps are being taken at the local, regional, national, and international levels to implement new models of environmental stewardship that strike an appropriate balance between economic advancement and resource protection. In some places, these efforts have achieved striking success. There is reason to hope that this new vision of environmental sustainability will take root all around the globe in the coming years.

The World's Environments series is a general reference resource that provides a comprehensive assessment of our progress to date in meeting the numerous environmental challenges of the twenty-first century. It offers detailed, current information on vital environmental trends and issues facing nations around the globe. The series consists of six volumes, each of which addresses conservation issues and the state of the environment in a specific region of the world: individual volumes for *Asia, Europe,* and *North America,* published in spring 2003, will be joined by *Africa and the Middle East; Australia, Oceania, and Antarctica;* and *Latin America and the Caribbean* in the fall of the same year.

Each volume of The World's Environments includes coverage of issues unique to that region of the world in such realms as habitat destruction, water pollution, depletion of natural resources, energy consumption, and development. In addition, each volume provides an overview of the region's response to environmental matters of worldwide concern, such as global warming. Information on these complex issues is presented in a manner that is informative, interesting, and understandable to a general readership. Moreover, each book in the series has been produced with an emphasis on objectivity and utilization of the latest environmental data from government agencies, nongovernmental organizations (NGOs), and international environmental research agencies, such as the various research branches of the United Nations.

Organization

Each of the six volumes of The World's Environments consists of ten chapters devoted to the following major environmental issues:

Population and Land Use. This chapter includes continental population trends, socioeconomic background of the populace, prevailing consumption patterns, and development and sprawl issues.

Biodiversity. This chapter reports on the status of flora and fauna and the habitat upon which it depends for survival. Areas of coverage include the impact of alien species on native plants and animals, the consequences of deforestation and other forms of habitat degradation, and the effects of the international wildlife trade.

Parks, Preserves, and Protected Areas. This chapter describes the size, status, and biological richness of area park systems, preserves, and wilderness areas and their importance to regional biodiversity.

Forests. Issues covered in this chapter include the extent and status of forest resources, the importance of forestland as habitat, and prevailing forest management practices.

Agriculture. This chapter is devoted to dominant farming practices and their impact on local, regional, and national ecosystems. Subjects of special significance in this chapter include levels of freshwater consumption for irrigation, farming policies, reliance on and attitudes toward genetically modified foods, and ranching.

Freshwater. This chapter provides detailed coverage of the ecological health of rivers, lakes, and groundwater resources, extending special attention to pollution and consumption issues.

Oceans and Coastal Areas. This chapter explores the ecological health of continental marine areas. Principal areas of coverage include the current state of (and projected outlook for) area fisheries, coral reef conservation, coastal habitat loss from development and erosion, and water quality trends in estuaries and other coastal regions.

Energy and Transportation. This chapter assesses historic and emerging trends in regional energy use and transportation, with an emphasis on the environmental and economic benefits and drawbacks associated with energy sources ranging from fossil fuels to nuclear power to renewable technologies.

Air Quality and the Atmosphere. This chapter reports on the current state of and future outlook for air quality in the region under discussion. Areas of discussion include emissions responsible for air pollution problems like acid rain and smog, as well as analysis of regional contributions to global warming and ozone loss.

Environmental Activism. This chapter provides a summary of the history of environmental activism in the region under discussion.

In addition, each volume of The World's Environments contains sidebars that provide readers with information on key individuals, organizations, projects, events, and controversies associated with specific environmental issues. By focusing attention on specific environmental "flashpoints"—the status of a single threatened species, the future of a specific wilderness area targeted for oil exploration, the struggles of a single village to adopt environmentally sustainable farming practices—many of these sidebars also shed light on larger environmental issues. Finally, each volume of the series includes a general index containing citations to issues, events, and people discussed in the book, as well as supplemental tables, graphs, charts, maps, and photographs.

Coverage by Geographic Region

Each of the six volumes of The World's Environments focuses on a single region of the world: Africa and the Middle East; Asia; Australia, Oceania, and Antarctica; Europe; Latin America; and North America. In most instances, the arrangement of coverage within these volumes was obvious, in accordance with widely recognized geographic divisions. But placement of a few countries was more problematic. Mexico, for instance, is recognized both as a part of North America and as the northernmost state in Latin America. Moreover, some international environmental research agencies (both governmental and nongovernmental) place data on Mexico under the North American umbrella, while others classify it among Central American and Caribbean nations. We ultimately decided to place Mexico in the Latin America volume, which covers Central and South America, in recognition of its significant social, economic, climatic, and environmental commonalities with those regions.

Similarly, environmental data on the vast Russian Federation, which sprawls over northern reaches of both Europe and Asia, is sometimes found in resources on Asia, and at other times in assessments of Europe's environment. Since most of Russia's population is located in the western end of its territory, we decided to cover the country's environmental issues in The World's Environments Europe volume, though occasional references to environmental conditions in the Russian Far East do appear in the Asia volume.

Finally, we decided to expand coverage in the Africa volume to cover environmental issues of the Middle East—also sometimes known as West Asia. This decision was made partly out of a recognition that the nations of Africa and the Middle East share many of the same environmental challenges—extremely limited freshwater supplies, for instance—and partly because of the space required in the Asia volume to fully explicate the multitude of grave environmental problems confronting Asia's central, southern, and eastern reaches. Coverage of other nations that straddle continental boundaries—such as the countries of the Caucasus region—are also concentrated in one volume, though references to some nations may appear elsewhere in the series.

Following is an internal breakdown of the volume-by-volume coverage for The World's Environments. This is followed in turn by two overview maps for the current volume, one showing country locations and key cities and the other indicating physical features.

Africa and the Middle East

Middle East and North Africa:

Algeria
Bahrain
Cyprus
Egypt
Gaza
Iraq
Israel
Jordan
Kuwait
Lebanon
Libya
Morocco
Oman
Qatar
Saudi Arabia
Syrian Arab Republic
Tunisia
Turkey
United Arab Emirates
West Bank
Yemen

Sub-Saharan Africa:

Angola
Benin
Botswana
Burkina Faso
Burundi
Cameroon
Central African Republic
Chad
Congo, Republic of the
Congo, Democratic Republic of (Zaire)
Côte d'Ivoire
Equatorial Guinea
Eritrea
Ethiopia
Gabon
Gambia
Ghana
Guinea
Guinea-Bissau
Kenya
Lesotho
Liberia
Madagascar
Malawi
Mali
Mauritania
Mozambique
Namibia
Niger
Nigeria
Rwanda
Senegal
Sierra Leone
Somalia
South Africa
Sudan
Tanzania
Togo
Uganda
Zambia
Zimbabwe

Asia

Afghanistan
Armenia
Azerbaijan

Bangladesh
Bhutan
Cambodia
China
Georgia
India
Indonesia
Iran
Japan
Kazakhstan
Korea, Democratic People's Republic of (North)
Korea, Republic of (South)
Kyrgyzstan
Lao People's Democratic Republic
Malaysia
Mongolia
Myanmar (Burma)
Nepal
Pakistan
Philippines
Singapore
Sri Lanka
Tajikistan
Thailand
Turkmenistan
Uzbekistan
Vietnam

Australia, Oceania, and Antarctica
Australia
Cook Islands
Fiji
French Polynesia
Guam
Kiribati
Nauru
New Caledonia
Northern Mariana Islands
Marshall Islands
Federated States of Micronesia
New Guinea
New Zealand
Palau
Papua New Guinea
Pitcairn Island
Samoa
Solomon Islands
Tonga
Tuvalu
Vanuatu
Wallis and Futuna
various territories
(Note: Antarctica is discussed in a standalone chapter)

Europe
Albania
Austria
Belarus
Belgium
Bosnia and Herzegovina
Bulgaria
Croatia
Czech Republic
Denmark
Estonia
Finland
France
Germany
Greece
Hungary

Iceland
Ireland
Italy
Latvia
Lithuania
Republic of Macedonia
Moldova
Netherlands
Norway
Poland
Portugal
Romania
Russian Federation
Slovakia
Slovenia
Spain
Sweden
Switzerland
Ukraine
United Kingdom
Yugoslavia

Latin America and the Caribbean

Argentina
Belize
Bolivia
Brazil
Caribbean territories
Chile
Colombia
Costa Rica
Cuba
Dominican Republic
Ecuador
El Salvador
Guatemala
Guyana
Haiti
Honduras
Jamaica
Mexico
Nicaragua
Panama
Paraguay
Peru
Suriname
Trinidad and Tobago
Uruguay
Venezuela

North America

Canada
United States

Reykjavik
ICELAND
ATLANTIC
OCEAN
UNITED
KINGDOM
NORTH
SEA
NORWAY
Oslo
SWED
Stockh
DENMARK
Copenhagen
BALT
Dublin
IRELAND
London
Amsterdam
Berlin
NETHERLANDS
POLA
BELGIUM
Brussels
GERMANY
LUXEMBOURG
Pragu
Paris
CZECH R
LIECHTENSTEIN
Vienna
Bern
AUSTRIA
Brati
SWITZERLAND
SLOVENIA
FRANCE
Ljubljana
ITALY
CROATIA
MONACO
SAN
MARINO
Sara
PORTUGAL
Madrid
VATICAN CITY
Rome
Corsica
Lisbon
ANDORRA
SPAIN
BOSNIA &
HERZEGOVI
Sardinia
Balearic Is.
MEDITERRANEAN SEA
Sicily
MALTA

RUSSIAN FEDERATION
NLAND
elsinki
Tallinn
ESTONIA
Riga
LATVIA
Moscow
THUANIA
Vilnius
Minsk
BELARUS
saw
Kiev
UKRAINE
AKIA
MOLDOVA
est
Chisinau (Kishinev)
GARY
ROMANIA
CASPIAN SEA
Bucharest
Belgrade
GO-
VIA
BLACK SEA
BULGARIA
Sofia
Skopje
ACEDONIA
A
EECE
Athens
Crete

ARCTIC CIRCLE
NORWEGIAN SEA
Iceland
PRIME MERIDIAN
Faroe Is.
Shetland Is.
Orkney Is.
ATLANTIC OCEAN
Outer Hebrides
Highlands
NORTH SEA
Jutland
British Isles
Ireland
Irish Sea
Great Britain
Celtic Sea
English Channel
Ruhr Valley
Rhine
Elbe
Loire
Mt. Blanc
15,771 ft
(44,807 m)
ALPS
Bay of Biscay
Massif Central
Contabrian Mts.
Pyrenees
APENNINES
Riviera
Tagus
Iberian Peninsula
Corsica
Balearic Sea
Sardinia
Balearic Is.
Baetic Mts.
Strait of Gibraltar
Tyrrhenian Sea
MEDITERRANEAN SEA
Sicily
AFRICA

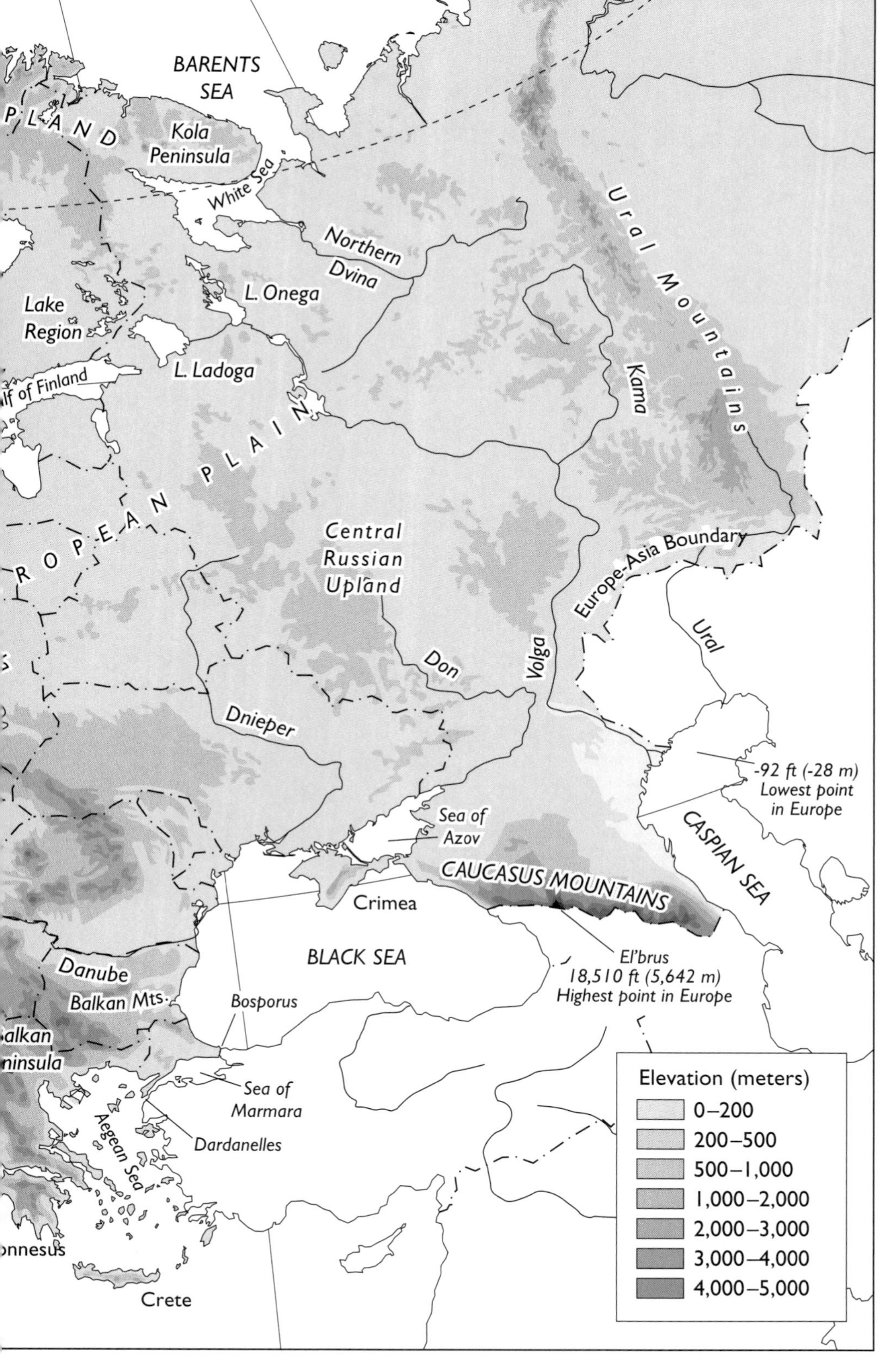
BARENTS SEA
PLAND
Kola Peninsula
White Sea
Northern Dvina
L. Onega
Lake Region
L. Ladoga
lf of Finland
ROPEAN PLAIN
Ural Mountains
Kama
Central Russian Upland
Europe-Asia Boundary
Ural
Don
Volga
Dnieper
-92 ft (-28 m) Lowest point in Europe
Sea of Azov
CASPIAN SEA
CAUCASUS MOUNTAINS
Crimea
BLACK SEA
El'brus 18,510 ft (5,642 m) Highest point in Europe
Danube
Balkan Mts.
Bosporus
alkan ninsula
Sea of Marmara
Aegean Sea
Dardanelles
onnesus
Crete
Elevation (meters)
0–200
200–500
500–1,000
1,000–2,000
2,000–3,000
3,000–4,000
4,000–5,000

Acknowledgments

The authors are indebted to many members of the ABC-CLIO family for their fine work on this series. Special thanks are due to Vicky Speck, Martha Whitt, and Kevin Downing. We would also like to extend special thanks to our advisory board members, whose painstaking reviews played a significant role in shaping the final content of each volume, and to the contributors who lent their expertise and talent to this project.

Biographical Notes

Authors

Kevin Hillstrom and **Laurie Hillstrom** have authored and edited award-winning reference books on a wide range of subjects, including American history, international environmental issues, environmental activism, outdoor travel, and business and industry. Works produced by the Hillstroms include *Environmental Leaders 1* and *2* (1997 and 2000), the four-volume *American Civil War Reference Library* (2000), the four-volume *Vietnam War Reference Library* (2000), *Paddling Michigan* (2001), *Encyclopedia of Small Business, 2d ed.* (2001), and *The Vietnam Experience: A Concise Encyclopedia of American Literature, Films, and Songs* (1998).

Advisory Board

J. David Allan received his B.Sc. (1966) from the University of British Columbia and his Ph.D. (1971) from the University of Michigan. He served on the Zoology faculty of the University of Maryland until 1990, when he moved to the University of Michigan, where he currently is Professor of Conservation Biology and Ecosystem Management in the School of Natural Resources and Environment. Dr. Allan specializes in the ecology and conservation of rivers. He is the author of *Stream Ecology* (1995) and coauthor (with C. E. Cushing) of *Streams: Their Ecology and Life* (2001). He has published extensively on topics in community ecology and the influence of land use on the ecological integrity of rivers. He serves or has served on committees for the North American Benthological Society, Ecological Society of America, and the American Society of Limnology and Oceanography. He serves or has served on the editorial board of the scientific journals *Freshwater Biology* and *Journal of the North American Benthological Society,* and on scientific advisory committees for the American Rivers and Nature Conservancy organizations.

DAVID LEONARD DOWNIE is Director of Education Partnerships for the Earth Institute at Columbia University, where he has conducted research and taught courses on international environmental politics since 1994. Educated at Duke University and the University of North Carolina, Dr. Downie is author of numerous scholarly publications on the Stockholm Convention, the Montreal Protocol, the United Nations Environment Program, and other topics in global environmental politics. From 1994 to 1999, Dr. Downie served as Director of Environmental Policy Studies at the School of International and Public Affairs at Columbia University.

SETH DUNN is a research associate at the Worldwatch Institute, where he investigates energy and climate policy and strategy. He has contributed to five editions of the institute's annual *State of the World* report, including most recently "Moving the Climate Change Agenda Forward" (2002). He has also authored four WorldWatch papers, including "Micropower: The Next Electrical Era" (2000), "Hydrogen Futures: Toward a Sustainable Energy System" (2001), and "Reading the Weathervane: Climate Policy from Rio to Johannesburg" (2002). His contributions to *World Watch* magazine include "Iceland's Hydrogen Experiment" (2000) and "King Coal's Weakening Grip on Power" (1999). He holds a B.A. in history and studies in the environment from Yale University.

YUMIKO KURA is a research associate in the World Resource Institute's Information Program. Her recent work focuses on coastal ecosystems, water resources, and global fisheries. She coauthored WRI's 2001 *Pilot Analysis of Global Ecosystems: Coastal Ecosystems,* which analyzes quantitative and qualitative information on the condition of the world's coastal ecosystems. Before joining WRI, she worked for Conservation International, World Bank, and World Wildlife Fund as a consultant. She is originally from Japan and has a master's degree in environmental science and policy from Clark University, Worcester, Massachusetts.

CARMEN REVENGA is a senior associate with the Information Program at the World Resources Institute. Her current work focuses on water resources, global fisheries, and species conservation. She specializes in environmental indicators that measure the condition of ecosystems at the global and regional level, and is also part of WRI's Global Forest Watch team, coordinating forest monitoring activities with Global Forest Watch partners in Chile. Ms. Revenga is lead author of the WRI report *Pilot Analysis of Global Ecosystems: Freshwater Systems* (2000) and a contributing author to the WRI's *Pilot Analysis of Global Ecosystems: Coastal Ecosystems* (2001). These two reports assess the condition of freshwater and coastal ecosystems as well as their capacity to continue to provide goods and services on which humans depend. Ms. Revenga is also the lead author of *Watersheds of the World: Ecological Value and Vulnerability* (1998), which is the first analysis of a wide range of global data at the watershed level. Before joining WRI in 1997, she worked as an environmental scientist with Science and Policy Associates, Inc., an environmental consulting firm in Washington, D.C. Her work covered topics in sustainable forestry and climate change.

Robin White is a senior associate with the World Resources Institute, an environmental think tank based in Washington, D.C. Her focus at WRI has been on the development of environmental indicators and statistics for use in the *World Resources Report* and in global ecosystems analysis. She was the lead author of the WRI report *Pilot Analysis of Global Ecosystems: Grassland Ecosystems* (2000), which analyzes quantitative information on the condition of the world's grasslands. Her current work focuses on developing an ecosystem goods and services approach to the analysis of the world's drylands. A recent publication regarding this work is WRI's Information Policy Brief, *An Ecosystem Approach to Drylands: Building Support for New Development Policies.* Ms. White completed her Ph.D. in geography at the University of Wisconsin, Madison, with a minor in wildlife ecology. Before joining WRI in 1996, she was a policy analyst with the U.S. Congress, Office of Technology Assessment.

Contributors

Kathryn Miles received her Ph.D. in literature from the University of Delaware and is currently an assistant professor of English and Environmental Studies at Unity College. She has worked as a freelance environmental writer for several newspapers and magazines, and has published on British modernism in academic journals. She is a member of ASLE (Association for the Study of Literature and the Environment), NAAGE (North American Alliance of Green Education), and the Virginia Woolf Society.

Andrew Park has an extensive background as a researcher and writer on conservation and forestry issues. After completing his B.Sc. in Biology at Simon Fraser University, he worked in forestry consulting for several years in British Columbia. He gained his Ph.D. in forest ecology from the University of Toronto in 2001 for work on forest regeneration in the pine-oak forests of Mexico's Sierra Madre Occidental. He is now investigating successional pathways in the northern boreal forest as a postdoctoral researcher with the Forest Ecology Research Group at the University of Quebec in Montreal. Although trained as a researcher, Park has broad and active interests in forest conservation worldwide. He has done ecology field work in Canada, Mexico, Brazil, and Bolivia, and his interests in social forestry and conservation have taken him as far afield as Malawi and Tanzania. In addition to a growing body of academic publications, Park has authored popular articles, reports for conservation groups, and is a published wildlife and environmental photographer.

Population and Land Use

Many of the nations of Europe are engaged in earnest efforts to establish sustainable practices in land use and the consumption of natural resources. But the continent, which is heavily industrialized and, on the whole, enjoys a higher standard of living than most other areas of the world, has thus far had only limited success in meeting these goals. Consumption trends among European cities and households continue to rise in many important respects, and experts contend that curbing the "ecological footprint" of tourism—which is vital to the economies of countless European communities and continues to increase in most areas—poses particularly vexing challenges. But while changes in land use may be an inevitable part of societal changes, European advocates of sustainable growth argue that the continent has the capacity to make these changes in ways that recognize nonproductive forms of land use, such as conservation of natural and cultural heritage (Jongman, *Ecological and Landscape Consequences of Land Use Change in Europe,* 1996).

Europe Sees Modest Levels of Population Growth and Economic Expansion

Europe has the highest overall population density of the world's continents. Approximately 730 million people lived across Europe in the mid-1990s, with the population distributed fairly evenly between the continent's fifteen European Union (EU) nations—Austria, Belgium, Denmark, Finland, France, Germany, the United Kingdom, Greece, Ireland, Italy, Luxembourg, the Netherlands, Portugal, Spain, and Sweden—and non-EU nations. The continent's population is also roughly balanced between the West, where the EU is concentrated, and Eastern and Central Europe.

Figure 1.1 Countries of the European Union

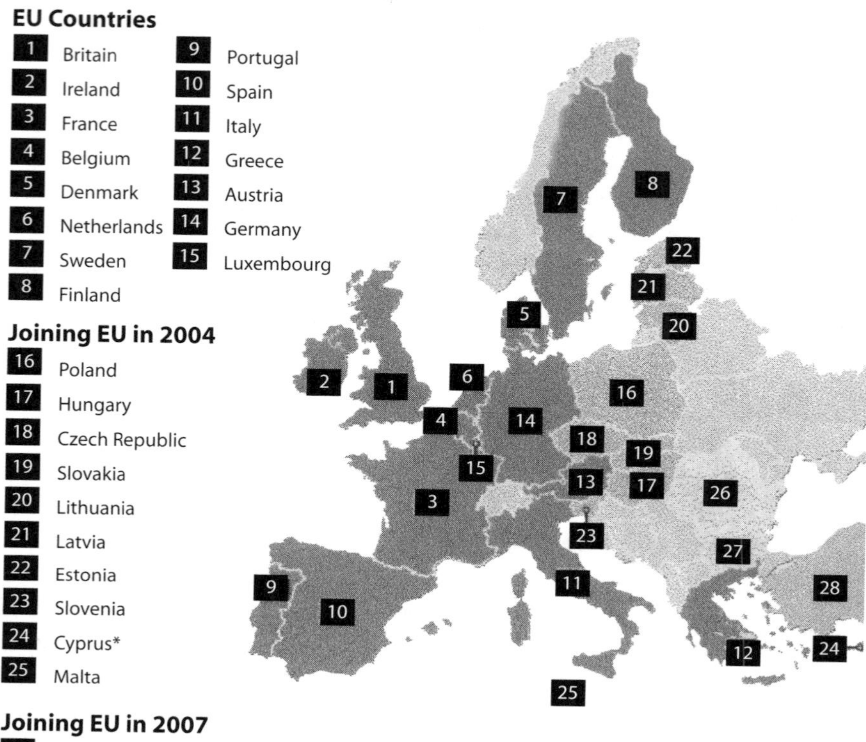

* Membership would effectively cover only the southern Greek Cypriot populated areas.

But while Europe is currently the most densely populated continent, its overall population growth is quite modest compared with other regions of the world. In 2000, for instance, the combined population of the fifteen nations of the European Union was 376.46 million, an increase of only 13 million people since 1990 (and only 1 million people since 1999). The citizens of the EU are living longer than did previous generations, thanks to advances in health care, nutrition, and other quality-of-life improvements, but they are also having fewer children. In 1999 there were just 266,000 more births than deaths in the European Union, the lowest figure since World War II. Some EU nations, such as Germany, Italy, and Spain, would actually be experiencing declines in the size of their populations were it not for steady influxes of immigrants from Eastern and Central Europe, and other regions of the world.

Life expectancy is lower in Central and Eastern Europe than in the West. Analysts attribute the difference to higher smoking rates, poor dietary practices, uneven medical care, and greater levels of air and water pollution in the Eastern and Central states. This health gap between the Western and Eastern reaches of the continent did not close appreciably during the 1990s, despite the introduction of various financial and medical aid programs in Eastern and Central European countries. In the early 1990s, for instance, the life expectancy for men in Eastern Europe actually declined from an average of sixty-eight years to sixty-six years, according to UN and World Bank analyses (UN Environment Programme, *Global Environment Outlook 2000*, 2000). At the regional level, this comparatively lower life expectancy, coupled with the migration of working-age men and women to EU countries in pursuit of improved socioeconomic status, has largely offset population gains from births, migration within the region, and so forth. In Russia, for instance, nearly half of all urban settlements experienced population loss from 1989 to 1996, a trend driven by dramatic declines in industrial production that forced many families to relocate (International Organization for Migration, *Report on Migration of Population in CIS Countries*, 1998).

Economic growth in much of Europe was moderate for much of the 1990s. Nations in Central and Eastern Europe suffered through particularly severe economic downturns in the early 1990s, when they made the difficult transition to new economic philosophies after decades of socialist rule. According to the European Environment Agency, the Gross Domestic Product (GDP) in Central and Eastern Europe (including the Newly Independent States of the former Soviet Union) fell by 32 percent between 1990 and 1994 (EEA, *Europe's Environment*, 1998).

Most of these countries entered this new political and economic era saddled with environmentally degraded lands, limited financial resources with which to establish new business enterprises or regulate the activities of existing ones, and highly urbanized populations that put severe strain on neglected infrastructure. The region's economic downturn was beneficial in one significant respect, however—it produced a significant decline in industrial pollution, creating healthier living conditions for human populations and relieving pressure on animal and plant species. But the barrage of factory closures decimated numerous towns and cities. From 1990 to 1996, for instance, Russia's overall industrial output fell by more than half, as apparel manufacturers and other businesses—primarily in light industry sectors—closed their doors.

By the late 1990s, however, a number of Central and East European states appeared to be on the path toward economic recovery, boosted by increased

Table 1.1 Demographic Indicators: European Countries

	Population (thousands)			*Average Annual Population Change (percent)*		*Percentage of Population in Specific Age Groups*			*Total Fertility Rate (average number of children per woman)*	
						Year 2000 (a)				
	1950	*2000 (a)*	*2025 (a)*	*1975–80*	*1995–00 (a)*	*<15*	*15–65*	*>65*	*1975–80*	*1995–00 (a)*
World	*2,521,495*	*6,055,049*	*7,823,703*	*1.7*	*1.3*	*30*	*63*	*7*	*3.9*	*2.7*
Europe	**547,053**	**728,416**	**701,734**	**0.5 b**	**0.0 b**	**17**	**68**	**15**	**2.0 b**	**1.4 b**
Albania	1,230	3,113	3,820	1.9	(0.4)	29	64	6	4.2	2.5
Austria	6,935	8,211	8,186	(0.1)	0.5	17	68	15	1.6	1.4
Belarus	7,745	10,236	9,496	0.6	(0.3)	19	68	14	2.1	1.4
Belgium	8,639	10,161	9,918	0.1	0.1	17	66	17	1.7	1.6
Bosnia and Herzegovina	2,661	3,972	4,324	0.9	3.0	19	71	10	2.2	1.4
Bulgaria	7,251	8,225	7,023	0.3	(0.7)	16	68	16	2.2	1.2
Croatia	3,850	4,473	4,193	0.5	(0.1)	17	68	15	2.0	1.6
Czech Republic	8,925	10,244	9,512	0.6	(0.2)	17	70	14	2.3	1.2
Denmark	4,271	5,293	5,238	0.2	0.3	18	67	15	1.7	1.7
Estonia	1,101	1,396	1,131	0.6	(1.2)	17	69	14	2.1	1.3
Finland	4,009	5,176	5,254	0.3	0.3	18	67	15	1.6	1.7
France	41,829	59,080	61,662	0.4	0.4	19	65	16	1.9	1.7
Germany	68,376	82,220	80,238	(0.1)	0.1	16	68	16	1.5	1.3
Greece	7,566	10,645	9,863	1.3	0.3	15	67	18	2.3	1.3
Hungary	9,338	10,036	8,900	0.3	(0.4)	17	68	15	2.1	1.4

(continues)

Table 1.1 Demographic Indicators: European Countries *(continued)*

	Population (thousands)			*Average Annual Population Change (percent)*		*Percentage of Population in Specific Age Groups*			*Total Fertility Rate (average number of children per woman)*	
						Year 2000 (a)				
	1950	*2000 (a)*	*2025 (a)*	*1975–80*	*1995–00 (a)*	*<15*	*15–65*	*>65*	*1975–80*	*1995–00 (a)*
Iceland	143	281	328	0.9	0.9	23	65	12	2.3	2.1
Ireland	2,969	3,730	4,404	1.4	0.7	21	67	11	3.5	1.9
Italy	47,104	57,298	51,270	0.4	(0.0)	14	68	18	1.9	1.2
Latvia	1,949	2,357	1,936	0.4	(1.5)	18	68	14	2.0	1.3
Lithuania	2,567	3,670	3,399	0.7	(0.3)	19	67	13	2.1	1.4
Macedonia, FYR	1,230	2,024	2,258	1.4	0.6	23	67	10	2.7	2.1
Moldova, Rep	2,341	4,380	4,547	0.9	0.0	23	67	10	2.4	1.8
Netherlands	10,114	15,786	15,782	0.7	0.4	18	68	14	1.6	1.5
Norway	3,265	4,465	4,817	0.4	0.5	20	65	15	1.8	1.9
Poland	24,824	38,765	39,069	0.9	0.1	19	69	12	2.3	1.5
Portugal	8,405	9,875	9,348	1.4	0.0	16	68	16	2.4	1.4
Romania	16,311	22,327	19,945	0.9	(0.4)	18	69	13	2.6	1.2
Russian Federation	102,192	146,934	137,933	0.6	(0.2)	18	69	13	1.9	1.3
Slovakia	3,463	5,387	5,393	1.0	0.1	20	69	11	2.5	1.4
Slovenia	1,473	1,986	1,818	1.0	(0.0)	16	70	14	2.2	1.3
Spain	28,009	39,630	36,658	1.1	0.0	15	68	17	2.6	1.2
Sweden	7,014	8,910	9,097	0.3	0.2	18	64	17	1.6	1.6
Switzerland	4,694	7,386	7,587	(0.1)	0.7	17	68	15	1.5	1.5
Ukraine	36,906	50,456	45,688	0.4	(0.4)	18	68	14	2.0	1.4
United Kingdom	50,616	58,830	59,961	0.0	0.2	19	65	16	1.7	1.7
Yugoslavia	7,131	10,640	10,844	0.9	0.1	20	67	13	2.4	1.8

SOURCE: United Nations Population Division.

NOTES: Negative values are shown in parentheses. "0" is either zero or less than one-half the unit of measure. "(0)" indicates a value less than zero and greater than negative one-half.

a. Data include projections based on 1990 base year population data. See the technical notes for more information. b. Regional totals were calculated by the data source.

foreign investment, development of rich natural resources such as oil and gas, and economic and political stabilization. This economic growth places the region on the cusp of important decisions about environmental policies. "The key challenge [facing these countries] is to strengthen environmental management now, in order to ensure that future growth is environmentally sustainable," stated one observer. "The alternative—economic growth now and clean up later—may appear in the short-term to be more expedient, but it is far too costly in the long-term, both environmentally and financially" (Von Ritter, "Europe and Central Asia Region: Transition toward a Healthier Environment," in Norsworthy, ed., *Rural Development, Natural Resources and the Environment,* 2000).

In Western Europe, recessionary conditions in the early 1990s curbed some types of consumption. Energy use, for instance, increased only slightly during this period. By the late 1990s, though, the regional economy was growing at an annual rate of 2.5 percent, lifted by the establishment of the Single Market and by tremendous growth in various service-oriented industries. The rapid expansion of the service sector may result in less environmental pressure than similar growth dominated by industrial activities, but tourism and transportation—which have powered much of the growth in the service sector—bring their own environmental baggage. Moreover, experts point out that a service economy that relies on increased imports of agricultural and industrial products simply shifts environmental pressures to other regions of the world (UN Environment Programme, *Global Environment Outlook 2000*).

Trends in European Household Consumption

Household consumption rates are rising rapidly in many areas of Europe, despite gains in energy efficiency and other types of resource use. This trend is particularly evident in Western Europe, where many people have significant levels of discretionary income. In fact, despite the relative stability of the population within the European Union and aforementioned efficiency gains, the combination of rising incomes and the proliferating number of households is expected to increase final consumption levels above current levels by as much as 50 percent between 1995 and 2010 (EEA, *Environment in the European Union at the Turn of the Century,* 1999).

Environmental experts are worried by such forecasts, for the household sector is already a major influence on the state of Europe's environment and natural resources. "Household expenditure is nearly twice what it was in 1980," reported the European Environment Agency (EEA) in *Environmental Signals 2001*. "This growth reflects aspirations for higher living standards and increased welfare which threaten the integrity of the environment. In particular, the sector contributes, directly or indirectly, to emissions of greenhouse gases, acidifying substances, tropospheric ozone precursors, nitrogen, phosphorus, and other pollutants; to energy and water use; and to waste."

In the realm of water use, for example, households accounted for about 10 percent of total water consumption in the European Union in the late 1990s, and some analysts believe that this percentage is considerably higher in arid or highly urbanized regions. EU households are also responsible for approximately 29 percent of final energy consumption (excluding energy used for transport), as household consumption increased by 4 percent between 1985 and 1998. This upward trend is particularly troubling because it occurred even though Western Europe made major strides in improving the energy efficiency of appliances, implementing higher energy standards for houses, and introducing more efficient home heating installations (Eurostat, *Consumers in Europe,* 2001; EEA, *Environmental Signals 2001,* 2000). These innovations have enabled Europe to realize a 22 percent reduction in energy required for space heating of new homes since 1985. But the sector's increased utilization of energy to operate appliances and heat larger and more numerous homes neutralized most of Europe's impressive energy efficiency gains. "Appliances are becoming more efficient, but households have more of them, their characteristics have changed (refrigerator/freezers instead of refrigerators, colour instead of black and white televisions), and they are used more often (especially washing machines and televisions)," stated the EEA. "A further factor has been the steady fall in domestic electricity prices—about 1 percent per year in real terms between 1985 and 1996" (EE, *Environmental Signals 2001,* 2000).

Households Increasing in Number, Decreasing in Size

As indicated, one of the key factors in the overall growth of consumption by Europe's household sector has been the fast-expanding number of new households across the continent, despite only modest population gains. The explanation for this apparent contradiction is that demographic trends have led to growing percentages of people living alone or solely with a spouse or other roommate. According to Eurostat, Europe's population increased by 5 percent between 1980 and 1995, but during that same period the number of households increased by 19 percent, bringing average household size down to 2.5 persons. The average household size in most countries fell by 10 to 15 percent, but in Iceland, Luxembourg, Sweden, and the United Kingdom it remained nearly constant. This drift toward smaller households puts added pressure on the environment, for small households consume more per capita than large ones. For example, smaller households result in higher rates of car ownership and lower rates of car occupancy; both of these trends contribute to rising rates of environmentally harmful automobile emissions and the loss of natural areas to new roadways necessary to relieve traffic congestion (ibid.).

The European Environmental Agency believes that the trend toward smaller households is likely to continue, with the percentage of single-person households in the EU jumping from the late-1990s figure of 30 percent to 36 percent by 2015. In the meantime, the proliferation of households occupied by smaller numbers of people has not produced a decrease in the average physical size of households. In fact, the average size of a European household increased from eighty-three cubic meters in 1985 to eighty-seven cubic meters in 1997 (Eurostat, http://europe.eu.int/com/eurostat; EEA, *Environmental Signals 2001,* 2000).

Material Wealth Drives Growth in Consumption

The financial prosperity enjoyed by Europeans also remains a double-edged sword for the environment, especially in the industrially advanced EU states. Financial wealth translates into increased comfort, better medical care and nutrition, greater educational opportunities, and numerous other "quality of life" benefits, but high levels of consumerism also create additional pressure on limited natural resources. "The economies of the EU Member States have been creating more material welfare for their inhabitants in the last decade," acknowledged the European Environment Agency. "But economic growth is so large that production and consumption will in general demand more natural resources and generate more pollution than before. The end use of consumer goods and services not only requires the materials and energy incorporated in the product or services itself, but also the materials and energy used in earlier stages of the production process." As a result, the EEA warns that the environmental impact from continued robust economic growth "is likely to erode gains from environmental policy initiatives and increase the difficulty in achieving sustainability" (EEA, *Environment in the European Union at the Turn of the Century,* 1999).

According to various studies, European household expenditures have undergone a gradual but nonetheless significant shift over the past few decades, with ever-higher percentages of income going to discretionary (that is, nonessential) expenditures such as restaurant meals, luxury goods, tourism, and recreation. For example, Eurostat reports that between 1980 and 1997, spending on housing increased by 47 percent, but spending on recreational equipment and activities jumped by 73 percent (Eurostat, *Consumers in Europe,* 2001). Moreover, the EEA notes that "as part of the 'new consumerism,' a marked increase in expenditure on recreation includes the growth in private car use and tourism. The increase in second homes for holidays, often in environmentally sensitive areas such as lakesides, seashores, and mountains, can add significantly to the environmental impact of a household" (EEA, *Environmental Signals 2001,* 2001).

During the 1990s the European Union and individual countries introduced a variety of programs to try to better align consumer behavior with environmental sustainability goals. For example, several states have levied special environmental charges on households that exceed specified levels of resource use. Other countries have launched education campaigns designed to give people more information about the environmental impact of products in the hopes that they will make more environmentally informed purchasing choices. In some cases, this "ecolabeling" seems to have had a tangible effect on buyer preferences. In Sweden, for instance, energy efficiency labeling of major appliances is credited as a factor in the dramatic increase in sales of refrigerators, freezers, and washing machines with high efficiency ratings during the late 1990s (Naturvårdsverket, "Ecolabelling Reduces Impacts," 2000). Still, many environmentalists, scientists, and officials within the EU have called on the member states to place greater emphasis on achieving specific conservation targets in the household sector (among other areas) in order to reduce its environmental impact in the coming years.

Most Europeans Live in Urban Environments

Approximately 75 percent of Western Europe's population currently resides in metropolitan areas, where most economy activity from tourism to manufacturing is concentrated. In Central and Eastern Europe the percentage is not quite so high, but the majority of the people in those regions also live in cities. Many of these cities are beloved for their rich histories and continued vibrance, but they are suffering on a host of environmental fronts. High levels of smog and other air pollution, excessive noise, vanishing "green spaces," traffic congestion, water contamination, waste disposal problems, and unsustainable withdrawals of freshwater resources typify many European metropolitan areas. Gains have been made in some of these areas in recent years. For example, air quality in urban environments improved considerably during the 1990s because of reductions in the lead content of gasoline. But other environmental problems will be difficult to remedy. So-called noise pollution, for example, is emerging as a quality of life issue for more and more Europeans. The European Environment Agency estimates that more than 30 percent of the people living in EU states live in dwellings with significant exposure to road, train, and aviation noise (EEA, *Environment in the European Union at the Turn of the Century,* 1999).

Europe's urban centers have also become the focus of a great deal of environmental analysis and policy-making because of their growing impact on landscapes and natural resources halfway around the world. Indeed, they—

and other cities like them on other continents—are acknowledged as a major influence on a broad spectrum of global environmental issues, including habitat and species preservation, deforestation, energy exploration, and climate change. After all, Europe's cities consume large volumes of food, timber, oil, natural gas, and other resources gathered from around the world.

This level of consumption, sometimes referred to as a city's "ecological footprint," illustrates just how interdependent the world has become in this era of global commerce. "London's footprint is 120 times the size of the city, drawing on resources from the wheat prairies of Kansas, the tea gardens of Assam, and the copper mines of Zambia among other places," reported the *AAAS Atlas of Population and the Environment.* "The critical question for cities is whether the wealth they generate can justify their large ecological footprint, and whether development policies can reduce that footprint. . . .A well-run urban sector can ensure national prosperity; a badly run sector can become a drag on the whole country." Indeed, analysts point out that some European cities actually use their high population densities to their advantage, maintaining extensive mass transit systems that reduce pollution from automobile emissions, or investing in ambitious waste-management programs that incorporate recycling and other environmentally sensitive practices (Satterthwaite, *An Urbanizing World,* 1996).

But as European scientists and government authorities admit, most of the footprints being left by the continent's urban populations are getting larger, not smaller. "Dramatic changes in land use patterns are having a particular impact," observed the European Environmental Agency. "Although more than 70 percent of Europeans live in urban areas, there has been a remarkable tendency since the 1950s for a dispersal and sprawling of urban settlements—by building more roads and other infrastructures, converting land permanently from other uses, sealing soils, opening up areas to tourism—causing new 'hot-spots' to emerge" (EEA, *Environment in the European Union at the Turn of the Century,* 1999). In Lyons, France, for instance, the metropolitan area holds 2.5 million people, but fewer than 10 percent of the residents live in the city's core. Similar demographic trends throughout Europe have led observers to conclude that "just as in the United States, Europe's middle class has moved to the suburbs—where they shop in malls, live in secluded subdivisions, and drive on traffic-clogged freeways" (Marshall, "Eurosprawl," 1995).

Of course, lightly populated regions may also suffer terrible environmental damage as a result of human consumption patterns. "Where land is not in short supply it may be wasted and degraded as if it were an essentially infinite resource. The oilfields of western Siberia are a spectacular example of a wetland landscape that, while almost uninhabited, is highly degraded—fragmented and polluted by roads, powerlines, pipelines, survey tracks, well flares, and waste sumps" (Harrison and Pearce, *AAAS Atlas of Population and Environment,* 2001).

Land-use planning does vary considerably from nation to nation within Europe. Indeed, land management philosophies often differ in significant respects from region to region within individual countries. In Germany, for instance, some *Länder* (states) are more restrictive than others (Nivola, "Are Europe's Cities Better?" 1999). And some European policies that are not conservationist in nature at first glance have nonetheless helped curb development pressure in outlying areas. For example, Europe's generous agricultural subsidies to farmers have kept large areas of farmland out of the hands of developers. "Per hectare of farmland, agricultural subventions are 12 times more generous in France than in the United States, a divergence that surely helps explain why small farms still surround Paris but not New York City" (ibid.).

These factors have enabled some European nations to exercise greater control over sprawl than the United States and some other countries. But as one commentator noted, "[C]ritics who assume that land regulators in the United States are chronically permissive, whereas Europe's growth managers are always scrupulous and 'smart,' ought to contemplate, say, the unsightly new suburbs stretching across the northwestern plain of Florence toward Prato, and then visit Long Island's East End, where it is practically impossible to obtain a building permit along many miles of pristine coastline" (ibid.).

Indeed, even in European states where meaningful land management restrictions are in place, urban sprawl and its myriad manifestations—conversion of natural and seminatural areas to industrial parks and subdivisions, feverish construction of roadways and other elements of transportation infrastructure, and so forth—are recognized as a significant threat to the environment. That is especially true in states that are under perpetual pressure to build new roads, hotels, resorts, and other facilities to accommodate ever-growing throngs of tourists. "Today, most of the EU countries have at least 80 percent of their territory given over to 'productive' uses like agriculture, forestry, urban centres, transport and industry, leaving limited margin for further uses; before the next 10 years is out, the length of motorways is proposed to be extended by more than 12,000 kilometers. And a 5 percent increase in urban population will, according to present trends, require at least an equal increase in the take of urban land. This whole issue is an increasingly important one—the more so since existing EU, national and regional policies on land use tend to encourage these problems—and it needs more attention from policy-makers" (EEA, *Environment in the European Union at the Turn of the Century,* 1999).

One encouraging sign in the battle to establish sustainable models of urban growth in Europe has been the enduring interest in the Agenda 21 movement. Agenda 21 is an environmental commitment that was adopted by 178 countries at the UN Conference on Environment and Development (UNCED, also known as the Earth Summit) in June 1992 in Rio de Janeiro, Brazil. It is essentially a formal statement of intention to foster forms of development that reflect a recognition that economic growth, social equity, and environmental health are all closely intertwined. Since its unveiling, many European cities have implemented "Local" Agenda 21 (LA21) policies and regulations. Indeed, grassroots environmental groups and local governments have emerged as some of the strongest voices urging greater environmental sustainability. In fact, more than 1,200 local authorities hailing from thirty-six European countries are active participants in the Aalborg Charter of European Cities and Towns towards Sustainability, a campaign specifically designed to promote the objectives of the Agenda 21 process (Lafferty, *Sustainable Communities in Europe,* 2001) (see sidebar, page 14).

Progress toward environmental sustainability at the local and regional level varies across Europe. Such initiatives remain in their infancy in some Central and Eastern European nations, as well as in some EU states that continue to maintain policies that make sustainability more difficult to attain. For example, weak land use planning and regulation in Italy has made environmentally destructive development difficult to control. Many nations, however, have embraced the Agenda 21 process. In Sweden, all 288 municipalities were given free rein to develop Agenda 21 plans deemed appropriate for their own situations. In the meantime, the Swedish government formed a special Commission on Sustainable Development to help municipalities make their sustainability projects a reality. By the late 1990s, every municipality had delivered proposals for new recycling, wastewater treatment, traffic reduction, consumer education, and other sustainability programs, while the Commission on Sustainable Development had helped prompt changes in broad policy areas at the national level, including business and consumer policy, energy and transport, forestry and agriculture, urban planning and building, the educational system, research and development, and architecture and design (Larsson, "Making Agenda 21 Work at the Municipal Level," 1999). "Swedish experiences suggest that one of the most important measures to integrate social, economic, and ecological dimensions in the spirit of Agenda 21 is to let people and authorities at the municipal level come forward with their wishes and proposals, and take part in decision-making and implementation, bringing together responsible actors at the local and national levels" (ibid.).

This sort of locally driven activity has propelled the creation and implementation of sustainability programs around the continent. The European Commission also has provided funding for local sustainability campaigns, and sustainability was a major focus of the EU's Fifth Environment Programme. In June 2001 the European Union formally agreed to develop a common, cooperative program to promote sustainable urban development throughout all member states in accordance with Agenda 21 principles.

Waste Management in Europe

The population of Europe generates about four billion tons of solid waste each year, about five tons per person. In the mid-1990s agriculture accounted for more solid waste in European members of the Organization of Economic Co-operation and Development—OECD (twenty-three European nations in Western and Central Europe, including all EU states) than any other sector (37 percent), followed by mining (33 percent), manufacturing (19 percent), municipal (7 percent), and energy (3 percent) (EEA, *Europe's Environment,* 1998). In many of these nations, waste quantities from the manufacturing sector appear to be holding steady or falling, but waste generated in other sectors is increasing. These increases have been attributed both to economic expansion and improved reporting and monitoring of waste generation and treatment. "Waste generation in the EU continues to increase and remains closely linked to economic growth," summarized the EEA. "In many countries, large amounts of biodegradable waste are still being landfilled and the continuing increase in quantities of waste produced is making it difficult to reach targets to reduce this. Improvements in wastewater treatment are resulting in growing volumes of sewage sludge for disposal and concern about the contaminants, such as heavy metals, that this may contain. . . . A relatively new and growing concern is the quantities of waste that arise from attempts to solve other environmental problems such as air and water pollution—such as acid wastes from the cleaning of flue gases and sewage sludge from wastewater purification" (EEA, *Environmental Signals 2001,* 2001).

Rising levels of waste are even more problematic in Eastern Europe. According to the Regional Environmental Center for Central and Eastern Europe, ten countries—Bulgaria, the Czech Republic, Estonia, Hungary, Latvia, Lithuania, Poland, Romania, Slovenia, and the Slovak Republic—produce twice the amount of waste as OECD member countries on the average, depositing most of the material in landfills.

Reducing Municipal Waste

One focus of Western Europe's efforts to institute environmentally sustainable ways of living has been in the realm of municipal waste, with particular emphasis on reducing the total volume of waste and safely treating the waste that is produced. According to Eurostat, Norway and the EU member states alone produced approximately 197 million tons of biodegradable municipal waste (BMW) in 1995, two-thirds of which went into landfills (ibid.). But Western Europe has made some notable gains in recycling in the last two decades. According to the Organization for Economic Co-operation and Development, the average recycling rate for paper and glass products rose in striking fashion

The Aalborg Charter: European Cities and Towns Working toward Sustainability

The Charter of European Cities and Towns Toward Sustainability (commonly known as the Aalborg Charter) is one of the continent's most important efforts toward attaining environmental sustainability. First launched in May 1994 in Aalborg, Denmark, at its inception the charter was signed by representatives of more than 120 European cities, towns, and counties. Since that time, this campaign to institute environmentally sustainable operating and management practices at the local and regional level has expanded dramatically. By 2001, Aalborg Charter participants included 1,200 local authorities from thirty-six European nations.

The charter signed in Aalborg in 1994 consisted of three sections. The first section was a declaration of civic responsibility to promote sustainable development. The second and third sections provide brief summary of the planned activities associated with the charter. Following is the text of the first part of the Aalborg Charter, in which signatories explain their reasons for joining the campaign:

1.1 The Role of European Cities and Towns

We, European cities and towns, signatories of this Charter, state that in the course of history, our towns have existed within and outlasted empires, nation states, and regimes and have survived as centres of social life, carriers of our economies, and guardians of culture, heritage and tradition. Along with families and neighbourhoods, towns have been the basic elements of our societies and states. Towns have been the centres of industry, craft, trade, education and government.

We understand that our present urban lifestyle, in particular our patterns of division of labour and functions, land-use, transport, industrial production, agriculture, consumption, and leisure activities, and hence our standard of living, make us essentially responsible for many environmental problems humankind is facing. This is particularly relevant as 80 percent of Europe's population live in urban areas.

We have learnt that present levels of resource consumption in the industrialised countries cannot be achieved by all people currently living, much less by future generations, without destroying the natural capital.

We are convinced that sustainable human life on this globe cannot be achieved without sustainable local communities. Local government is close to where environmental problems are perceived and closest to the citizens and shares responsibility with governments at all levels for the well-being of humankind and nature. Therefore, cities and towns are key players in the process of changing lifestyles, production, consumption and spatial patterns.

(continues)

1.2 The Notion and Principles of Sustainability

We, cities and towns, understand that the idea of sustainable development helps us to base our standard of living on the carrying capacity of nature. We seek to achieve social justice, sustainable economies, and environmental sustainability. Social justice will necessarily have to be based on economic sustainability and equity, which require environmental sustainability.

Environmental sustainability means maintaining the natural capital. It demands from us that the rate at which we consume renewable material, water and energy resources does not exceed the rate at which the natural systems can replenish them, and that the rate at which we consume non-renewable resources does not exceed the rate at which sustainable renewable resources are replaced. Environmental sustainability also means that the rate of emitted pollutants does not exceed the capacity of the air, water, and soil to absorb and process them.

Furthermore, environmental sustainability entails the maintenance of biodiversity; human health; as well as air, water, and soil qualities at standards sufficient to sustain human life and wellbeing, as well as animal and plant life, for all time.

1.3 Local Strategies Towards Sustainability

We are convinced that the city or town is both the largest unit capable of initially addressing the many urban architectural, social, economic, political, natural resource and environmental imbalances damaging our modern world and the smallest scale at which problems can be meaningfully resolved in an integrated, holistic and sustainable fashion. As each city is different, we have to find our individual ways towards sustainability. We shall integrate the principles of sustainability in all our policies and make the respective strengths of our cities and towns the basis of locally appropriate strategies.

1.4 Sustainability as a Creative, Local, Balance-Seeking Process

We, cities and towns, recognise that sustainability is neither a vision nor an unchanging state, but a creative, local, balance-seeking process extending into all areas of local decision-making. It provides ongoing feedback in the management of the town or city on which activities are driving the urban ecosystem towards balance and which are driving it away. By building the management of a city around the information collected through such a process, the city is understood to work as an organic whole and the effects of all significant activities are made manifest. Through such a process the city and its citizens may make informed choices. Through a management process rooted in sustainability, decisions may be made which not only represent the interests of current stakeholders, but also of future generations.

(continues)

1.5 Resolving Problems by Negotiating Outwards

We, cities and towns, recognise that a town or city can not permit itself to export problems into the larger environment or to the future. Therefore, any problems or imbalances within the city are either brought towards balance at their own level or absorbed by some larger entity at the regional or national level. This is the principle of resolving problems by negotiating outwards. The implementation of this principle will give each city or town great freedom to define the nature of its activities.

1.6 Urban Economy Towards Sustainability

We, cities and towns, understand that the limiting factor for economic development of our cities and towns has become natural capital, such as atmosphere, soil, water and forests. We must therefore invest in this capital. In order of priority this requires

1. investments in conserving the remaining natural capital, such as groundwater stocks, soil, habitats for rare species;
2. encouraging the growth of natural capital by reducing our level of current exploitation, such as of non-renewable energy;
3. investments to relieve pressure on natural capital stocks by expanding cultivated natural capital (such as parks for inner-city recreation to relieve pressure on natural forests); and
4. increasing the end-use efficiency of products, such as energy-efficient buildings, environmentally friendly urban transport.

1.7 Social Equity for Urban Sustainability

We, cities and towns, are aware that the poor are worst affected by environmental problems (such as noise and air pollution from traffic, lack of amenities, unhealthy housing, lack of open space) and are least able to solve them. Inequitable distribution of wealth both causes unsustainable behaviour and makes it harder to change. We intend to integrate people's basic social needs as well as healthcare, employment and housing programmes with environmental protection. We wish to learn from initial experiences of sustainable lifestyles, so that we can work towards improving the quality of citizens' lifestyles rather than simply maximising consumption. We will try to create jobs which contribute to the sustainability of the community and thereby reduce unemployment. When seeking to attract or create jobs we will assess the effects of any business opportunity in terms of sustainability in order to encourage the creation of long-term jobs and long-life products in accordance with the principles of sustainability.

1.8 Sustainable Land-Use Patterns

We, cities and towns, recognise the importance of effective land-use and development planning policies by our local authorities which embrace the strategic environmental assessment of

(continues)

all plans. We should take advantage of the scope for providing efficient public transport and energy which higher densities offer, while maintaining the human scale of development. In both undertaking urban renewal programmes in inner urban areas and in planning new suburbs we seek a mix of functions so as to reduce the need for mobility. Notions of equitable regional interdependency should enable us to balance the flows between city and countryside and prevent cities from merely exploiting the resources of surrounding areas.

1.9 Sustainable Urban Mobility Patterns

We, cities and towns, shall strive to improve accessibility and sustain social welfare and urban lifestyles with less transport. We know that it is imperative for a sustainable city to reduce enforced mobility and stop promoting and supporting the unnecessary use of motorised vehicles. We shall give priority to ecologically sound means of transport (in particular walking, cycling, public transport) and make a combination of these means the centre of our planning efforts. Motorised individual means of urban transport ought to have the subsidiary function of facilitating access to local services and maintaining the economic activity of the city.

1.10 Responsibility for the Global Climate

We, cities and towns, understand that the significant risks posed by global warming to the natural and built environments and to future human generations require a response sufficient to stabilize and then to reduce emissions of greenhouse gases into the atmosphere as soon as possible. It is equally important to protect global biomass resources, such as forests and phytoplankton, which play an essential role in the earth's carbon cycle. The abatement of fossil fuel emissions will require policies and initiatives based on a thorough understanding of the alternatives and of the urban environment as an energy system. The only sustainable alternatives are renewable energy sources.

1.11 Prevention of Ecosystems Toxification

We, cities and towns, are aware that more and more toxic and harmful substances are released into the air, water, soil, food, and are thereby becoming a growing threat to human health and the ecosystems. We will undertake every effort to see that further pollution is stopped and prevented at source.

1.12 Local Self-Governance as a Pre-Condition

We, cities and towns, are confident that we have the strength, the knowledge and the creative potential to develop sustainable ways of living and to design and manage our cities towards sustainability. As democratically elected representatives of our local communities we are ready to take responsibility for the task of

(continues)

reorganising our cities and towns for sustainability. The extent to which cities and towns are able to rise to this challenge depends upon their being given rights to local self-governance, according to the principle of subsidiarity. It is essential that sufficient powers are left at the local level and that local authorities are given a solid financial base.

1.13 Citizens as Key Actors and the Involvement of the Community

We, cities and towns, pledge to meet the mandate given by Agenda 21, the key document approved at the Earth Summit in Rio de Janeiro, to work with all sectors of our communities—citizens, businesses, interest groups—when developing our Local Agenda 21 plans. We recognize the call in the European Union's Fifth Environmental Action Programme "Towards Sustainability" for the responsibility for the implementation of the programme to be shared among all sectors of the community. Therefore, we will base our work on cooperation between all actors involved. We shall ensure that all citizens and interested groups have access to information and are able to participate in local decision-making processes. We will seek opportunities for education and training for sustainability, not only for the general population, but for both elected representatives and officials in local government.

1.14 Instruments and Tools for Urban Management Towards Sustainability

We, cities and towns, pledge to use the political and technical instruments and tools available for an ecosystem

(continues)

between 1980 and 1995. Several countries have reached recycling rates of 60 percent for glass and 40 percent for paper, and a number have even realized recycling rates of 80 percent for glass and 70 percent for paper.

The jump in recycling rates is credited in large part to the EU Packaging and Packaging Wastes Directive. This legislation, designed to harmonize recycling and recovery standards in the EU, directed all member states to recover at least 50 percent of their packaging waste (by weight) and recycle 25 to 45 percent of it by the year 2001. Spurred on by this directive, Germany increased its recovery rate from 43.5 percent to 70.6 percent and boosted its use of recycled material from 48.6 percent of fiber input in 1990 to 60.3 percent in 1996 ("Europe Generates Avalanche of Paper," *Paperboard Packaging,* 1997). Other new recycling rules continue to be introduced by the European Union as well. In 2002, for instance, the EU implemented a series of directives aimed at reducing the amount of waste deposited into landfills. One directive requires that insulation foam, which contains toxic chlorofluorocarbons (CFCs), be removed from reapproach to urban management. We shall take advantage of a wide range of instruments including those for collecting and processing environmental data; environmental planning; regulatory, economic, and communication instruments such as directives, taxes and fees; and mechanisms for awareness raising including public participation. We seek to establish new environmental budgeting systems which allow for the management of our natural resources as economically as our artificial resource, "money."

We know that we must base our policy-making and controlling efforts, in particular our environmental monitoring, auditing, impact assessment, accounting, balancing and reporting systems, on different types of indicators, including those of urban environmental quality, urban flows, urban patterns, and, most importantly, indicators of an urban systems sustainability.

We, cities and towns, recognise that a whole range of policies and activities yielding positive ecological consequences have already been successfully applied in many cities through Europe. However, while these instruments are valuable tools for reducing the pace and pressure of unsustainability, they do not in and of themselves reverse society's unsustainable direction. Still, with this strong existing ecological base, the cities are in an excellent position to take the threshold step of integrating these policies and activities into the governance process for managing local urban economies through a comprehensive sustainability process. In this process we are called on to develop our own strategies, try them out in practice and share our experiences.

frigerators and freezers prior to discarding. Other recycling directives target scrapped automobiles, computers, and mobile phones.

European leaders are mulling further integration of waste reduction goals into other policy areas as well. One initiative that has been introduced with some success in several countries has been a special "landfill tax" levied against those who choose that disposal method. In some countries, including Austria, Sweden, and Denmark, such taxes have increased rates of recycling and incineration by making it less economically advantageous to use landfills. Subsequent reductions in landfill use have benefited the environment in a number of ways, from reducing greenhouse gas emissions produced by landfill decomposition to sparing land that would otherwise have to be converted for storage of refuse.

Finally, the nations of Europe are grappling with growing concerns about safe treatment and disposal of hazardous waste. This issue is a serious one across the length and breadth of the continent, from Germany and France,

A trash collector dumps ten tons of waste, about a year's worth of garbage for the average family. MARTYN GODDARD/CORBIS

which together accounted for 38 percent of the 42 million tons of hazardous waste produced annually by OECD Europe countries in the mid-1990s, to Russia, which generated about two-thirds of the 30 million tons of hazardous waste produced each year in Eastern Europe during the early 1990s (EEA, *Europe's Environment,* 1998). Today, the EEA estimates that there are more than 1.5 million industrial and waste disposal sites in EU states alone that could be poisoning the land. About 300,000 of these sites have already been identified as definitely or potentially contaminated, but progress in addressing this problem has been slow. Analysts agree that cleaning up contaminated sites will be a tremendously expensive proposition, especially for Central and Eastern European nations with limited financial resources.

Roadways Expand as Mass Transit Struggles

For years, Europe's extensive mass transit system enabled it to prosper without resorting to endless networks of highways and other roadways. This state of affairs reduced pressure on the environment in a host of ways. Heavy use of these systems enabled governments to preserve natural and seminatural areas that otherwise would have been sacrificed to road construction. Mass transit also decreased European reliance on the automobile, which generates environmentally destructive emissions from the burning of gasoline. This in turn made Europe less reliant on oil exploration and drilling—whether carried out on European soil or outside its borders—than many other regions of the world.

In recent years, however, a smaller percentage of Europeans have been utilizing trains, buses, and ferries, the principal transport modes of its mass transit systems. Despite high gasoline prices, travel by automobile has become less expensive relative to bus and train transport than in past decades throughout much of Europe. This trend, coupled with increased sprawl, spiraling rates of tourism, and dissatisfaction with mass transit service, has triggered parallel increases in private car ownership and road construction activity in Europe. These changes have serious ramifications for the environment:

> The rapid increase in private transport and resource-intensive consumption are major threats to the urban environment and, consequently, to human health and welfare. In many cities, cars now provide over 80 percent of mechanized transport. Forecasts of transport growth in Western Europe indicate that, for a "business as usual" scenario, road transport demands for passengers and freight could nearly double between 1990 and 2010, with the number of cars increasing by 25–30 percent and annual kilometers per car increasing by 25 percent. The current growth in urban mobility and car ownership in Central and Eastern Europe is expected to accelerate during the next decade, with corresponding increases in energy consumption and transport-related emissions. (ibid.)

Another factor driving the expansion of Europe's system of roadways is tourism. According to the EEA, more than 60 percent of total tourist movement (domestic and international) on the continent is by motorway, including almost 40 percent of international trips. "Car travel for tourism has advantages such as lower costs and a high degree of freedom. In contrast, public transport is expensive, particularly for families, and does not provide door-to-door service,

Figure 1.2 Growth in Number of Vehicles in Europe, 1980–1996

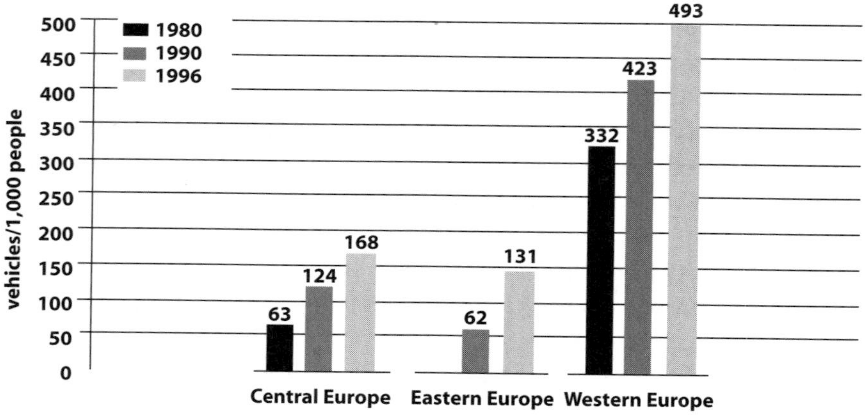

SOURCE: Compiled by UNEP GRID Geneva from International Road Federation 1997.

a particular problem with respect to baggage handling. The attractiveness of public transport for tourism traveling is further reduced by inadequate access, especially to remote and tourist areas, and insufficiently frequent operation, especially during peak tourist seasons" (EEA, *Environmental Signals 2001,* 2001).

These trends clearly require the attention of European authorities, who hope to reinvigorate the continent's declining mass transit systems. Certainly, the infrastructure is already in place. Indeed, one saving grace of the sprawl problems confronting many countries is that at least new suburbs retain significant transportation linkages to city centers, unlike many metropolitan areas in North America. These existing linkages—bus lines, train or subway systems, bike lanes—are pivotal in regional schemes to increase mass transit use. But in recent decades, mass transit systems have received far less funding for upkeep and expansion than motorways. According to Eurostat, Western Europe's network of roadways grew by more than 50 percent from 1970 to 1998, swallowing up an estimated 10 hectares of land every day during the last eight years of that period. Conventional railway and inland waterway networks, on the other hand, decreased in size by about 9 percent from 1970 to 1998 (ibid.). Not surprisingly, this disparity in funding has been cited as a major reason for the European public's growing disenchantment with the quality and reliability of mass transit service.

There are indications, however, that mass transit systems are coming back into favor again. Municipal authorities and environmentalists alike have cited healthy bus, rail, and inland water transportation systems as one of the key elements of long-term sustainability efforts. Indeed, establishing "sustainable urban mobility patterns" is one of the centerpieces of sustainability campaigns like the Aalborg Charter: "We know that it is imperative for a sustainable city to reduce enforced mobility and stop promoting and supporting the unnecessary use of motorised vehicles. We shall give priority to ecologically sound means of transport (in particular walking, cycling, public transport) and make a combination of these means the centre of our planning efforts" (see charter document, page 14). One high-profile effort to counter the exodus of Europeans and overseas tourists from the continent's rail and bus systems has been the trans-European Transport Network (TEN), a high-speed rail system that is expected to include 24,000 kilometers of track connecting European urban centers by 2010. Proponents of TEN hope that the high-speed line will attract enough travelers to slow the rate of motorway construction, and that its example will contribute to a resurgence in mass transit investment.

In Central and Eastern Europe, meanwhile, road networks are far less extensive than in the West. These nations historically relied on low-cost railroad lines for the bulk of their transportation requirements, and their political and economic structures made private car ownership a rarity. Russia, for instance, is the world's largest country in terms of land mass, but it ranks only sixth in the size of its road system, and one out of five of its 600,000 miles of roads is unpaved. Rates of private car ownership increased in most of these countries during the 1990s as economic changes took hold. But analysts believe that with appropriate modernization, these existing rail lines can serve as the foundation for sustainable transportation systems throughout the region.

Tourism Brings Economic Prosperity and Environmental Stress

One of the greatest sources of pressure on Europe's natural resources is tourism. Wildly popular with travelers, Europe accounts for 60 percent of all international tourist arrivals (373 million tourists in 1998) and boasts four of the world's five leading countries for tourism, with France alone accounting for almost 11 percent of global tourist arrivals (Spain is third with 7 percent, Italy is fourth with 5.5 percent, and the United Kingdom is fifth with about 4 percent). On a regional basis, the Mediterranean is the most popular tourism destination in the world, accounting for 30 percent of international arrivals and 25 percent of receipts from international tourism. And the tremendous popularity of the Mediterranean countries shows no signs of slowing; according to the World Tourism Organization, the number of tourists annually visiting the region is expected to increase from 260 million in 1990 to 665 million by 2025 (World Tourism Organization, *Compendium of Tourism Statistics,* 2000; World Tourism Organization, *Tourism Highlights 2000,* 2000).

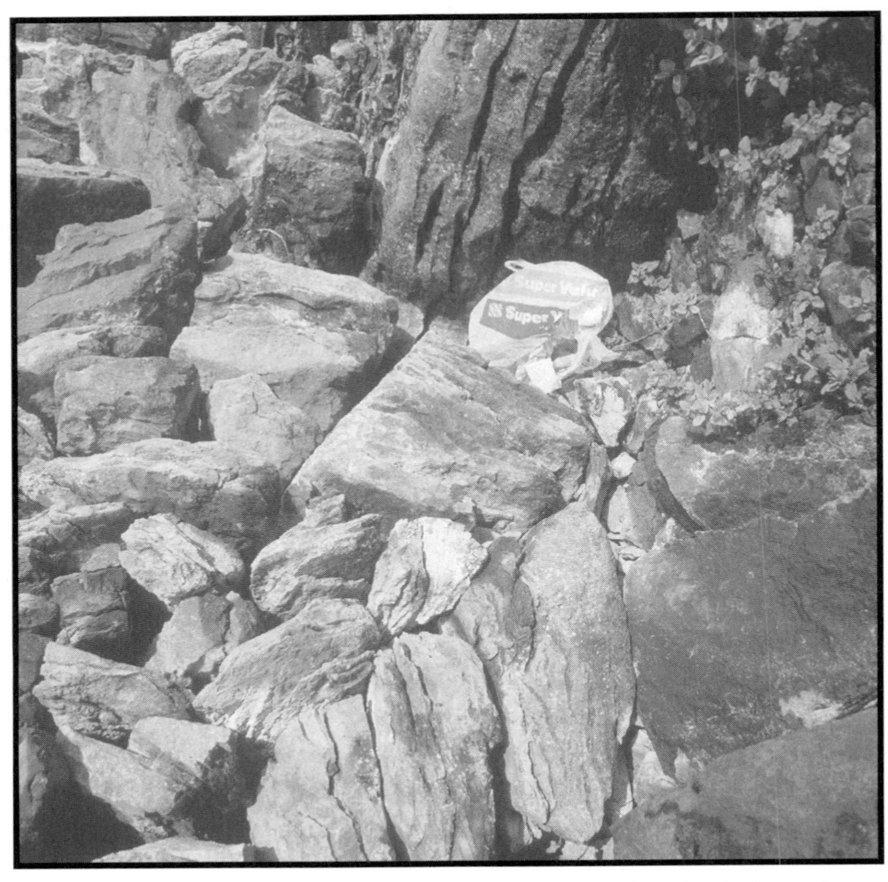

A discarded plastic bag litters a dry stone wall at the site of the Burren rock formations in County Clare, Ireland. IAN HARWOOD; ECOSCENE/CORBIS

Irish Tax on Plastic Bags Elicits Praise and Anger

In March 2002 the Republic of Ireland instituted a small surcharge on all plastic bags used by retail outlets in an effort to address the growing blight of windblown, discarded bags littering the Irish countryside. The surcharge—9 pence, or 15 cents per bag—angered some Irish citizens, who characterized it as an unfair drain on their incomes. But the introduction of this special tax, receipts of which will be used to fund environmental protection projects, has been lauded by environmental groups. They point out that prior to the surcharge, 1 to 1.2 billion plastic bags were doled out to Ireland's population of 3.8 million every year (about 325 bags per person). Most of these bags ended up strewn along roadways and in hedgerows and woodlands, or in local landfills. Environmentalists contend that the levy will address the root of this problem by reducing the number of bags given away to the country's shoppers.

The measure has also caused consternation in some business sectors, but many companies and associations have expressed cautious support for the measure. The Irish Business and Employers Confederation (IBEC), for example, acknowledged concerns that the plastic bag levy might be a possible precursor to other environmental taxes. But it also admitted that the surcharge addresses a growing problem, and that it was instituted only after extended consultation with Irish retailers. Tesco Ireland, one of the country's leading supermarket chains, also has publicly praised the measure. "Customers are telling us they broadly welcome the introduction of the levy," said one spokesman for the chain. "We have seen a marked change in customers' behaviour in anticipation of the new levy, reflected in the significant increase in sales of our reusable bags" (BBC News Online March 4, 2002). Indeed, supporters of the new tax have observed that many consumers are evading the surcharge altogether simply by using reusable bags. Ireland's leading supermarket chains anticipate that this turn to sturdier, reusable bags will result in a 40 to 50 percent reduction in the number of plastic bags they hand out by the fall of 2002.

Sources:

BBC News Online. 2002. "Shoppers Face Plastic Bag Tax." March 4. http://news.bbc.co.uk.

Roddy, Michael. 2002. "Irish See Red over Plastic Bag Tax." Reuters News Service, March 3. http://www.planetark.org .

Tourism is thus extremely important to the economy of every nation in Western Europe. Indeed, tourism already accounts for approximately nine million jobs in the EU—6 percent of total employment—and the number of jobs directly related to tourism is expected to more than double by 2010. Tourism also generates up to 12 percent of Gross Domestic Product in EU states (World Tourism Organization, *Compendium of Tourism Statistics*, 2000; EEA, *Environmental Signals 2001,* 2001).

But while the economic benefits of tourism are undeniable, the accompanying drain on regional resources is a major problem that defies easy solutions. Ever-growing levels of tourism inevitably lead to increased pressure to convert previously undisturbed landscapes—which often serve as essential habitat for local flora and fauna—to human use. Tourism also accounts for fully half of the energy used in passenger transport, and various elements of tourism infrastructure—resorts, hotels, and the like—significantly increase the amount of greenhouse gases generated in Europe. In France, for example,

Figure 1.3 Total International Inbound Tourism in Europe

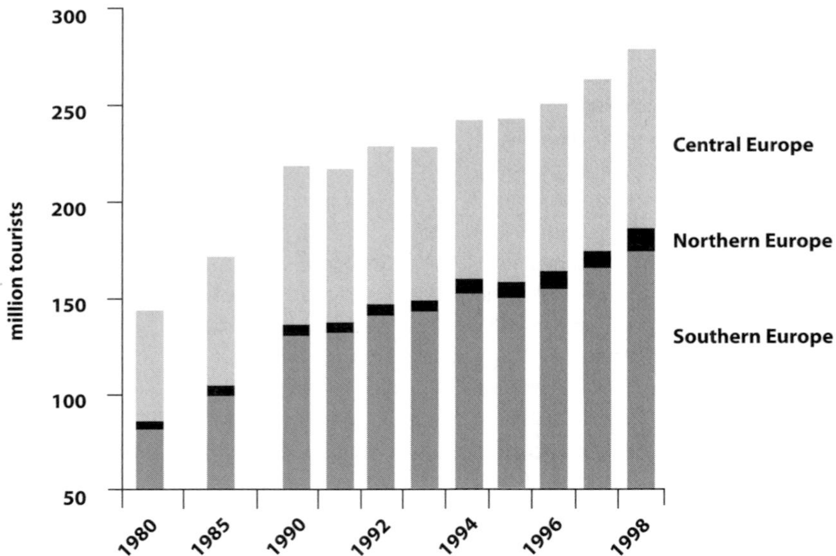

SOURCE: World Tourism Organization

as much as 7 percent of the country's greenhouse gas emissions are attributed to tourism, in large part because 80 percent of domestic tourist travel is by private automobile. Tourist attractions such as swimming pools and golf courses also put extreme pressure on limited freshwater resources, especially in the Mediterranean. And in some areas, hordes of tourists generate truly prodigious amounts of refuse. In France, the world's leading tourist destination, annual waste generation per capita at coastal holiday resorts in France is 100 kilograms higher than the national average (EEA, *Environmental Signals 2001*, 2001).

Some communities, however, are actively working to effectively manage tourism so as to minimize its impact on the environment. Steps taken in this regard include establishment of nature conservation areas, restrictions on building construction and other forms of development, water conservation and recycling programs, and imposition of special fees to raise funds for environmental protection initiatives. Many of these efforts are being undertaken within the framework of Europe's Agenda 21 program, which seeks to shape economic growth in environmentally sustainable ways.

Sources:

Commission of the European Communities. 1999. *Agriculture, Environment, Rural Development: Facts and Figures—A Challenge for Agriculture.* Luxembourg: European Commission.

Department of Energy, United Kingdom. 1995. *Making Waste Work.* London: Department of Energy.

Ellul, Anthony. 2000. "Tourism and the Environment in European Countries." *Nature and Environment*, No. 116. Strasbourg: Council of Europe.

ENERDATA/Odyssee. 1999. *Energy Efficiency in the European Union 1990–1998.*

"Europe Generates Avalanche of Paper." 1997. *Paperboard Packaging* 82 (December).

European Commission. 1999. *Facts and Figures on the Europeans on Holidays, 1990–1998.* Luxembourg: European Commission.

———. 2000. *Transport in Figures: Statistical Pocketbook.* Luxembourg: DE TREN, Eurostat.

European Council. 1999. *Strategy on the Integration of Environment and Sustainable Development into the Transport Policy.* Strasbourg, France: European Council.

European Environment Agency. 1998. *Europe's Environment: The Second Assessment.* Oxford, UK: Elsevier Science.

———. 1999. *Environment in the European Union at the Turn of the Century.* Copenhagen: EEA.

———. 2000. *Household and Municipal Waste: Comparability of Data in EEA Member Countries.* Copenhagen: EEA.

———. 2001. *Biodegradable Municipal Waste Management in Europe: Strategies and Instruments.* Copenhagen: EEA.

———. 2001. *Environmental Signals 2001.* Oxford, UK: Elsevier Science.

Eurostat. 2001. *Consumers in Europe: Facts and Figures.* Luxembourg: Eurostat.

———. 2001. *Transport and Environment: Statistics for the Transport and Environment Reporting Mechanism (TERM) for the European Union.* Luxembourg: Eurostat.

Eurostat and Organization for Economic Co-operation and Development. 2000. *Waste Generated in Europe.* Luxembourg: Eurostat and OECD.

Harrison, Paul, Fred Pearce, and the American Association for the Advancement of Science. 2001. *AAAS Atlas of Population and the Environment.* Berkeley: University of California Press.

International Organization for Migration. 1998. *Report on Migration of Population in CIS Countries,* Geneva: IOM.

Jongman, Rob H. G., ed. 1996. *Ecological and Landscape Consequences of Land Use Change in Europe.* Proceedings of the ECNC Seminar on Land Use Change and Its Ecological Consequences, February 16–18, 1995. Tilburg, the Netherlands: European Centre for Nature Conservation.

Lafferty, William M. 2001. *Sustainable Communities in Europe.* London: Earthscan.

Larsson, Kjell. 1999. "Making Agenda 21 Work at the Municipal Level: The Swedish Experience." *UN Chronicle* 36 (spring).

Marshall, Alex. 1995. "Eurosprawl." *Metropolis* (January–February).

Naturvårdsverket. 2000. "Ecolabelling Reduces Impacts." *Enviroreport* 2000.

Nivola, Pietro S. 1999. "Are Europe's Cities Better?" *Public Interest* 137 (fall).

Norsworthy, L. Alexander, ed. 2000. *Rural Development, Natural Resources and the Environment: Lessons of Experience in Eastern Europe and Central Asia.* Washington, DC: World Bank.

O'Riordan, Timothy, and Heather Voisey. 1998. *The Transition to Sustainability: The Politics of Agenda 21 in Europe.* London: Earthscan.

Organization for Economic Co-operation and Development. 1999. *Towards More Sustainable Household Consumption Patterns—Indicators to Measure Progress.* Paris: OECD.

———. 2000. *Tourism and Travel Patterns: Tourism and Travel Trends and Environmental Impacts.* Paris: OECD.

———. 2001. *OECD Environmental Outlook.* Paris: OECD.

Palin, Ray, and Kevin Whiting. 1998. "All Fired Up." *Chemistry and Industry* (November 16).

Satterthwaite, Ann. 1996. *An Urbanizing World: Global Report on Human Settlements, 1996.* Oxford: UN Centre for Human Settlements.

UN Environment Programme. 2000. *Global Environment Outlook 2000.* London: Earthscan.

World Tourism Organization. 2000. *Compendium of Tourism Statistics, 1994–1998.* Madrid, Spain: WTO.

———. 2000. *Tourism Highlights 2000.* Madrid, Spain: WTO.

Biodiversity

The European continent is home to an estimated 230,000 species of animals and plants, spread over 10,000 distinct habitat types, from the heathlands of Spain to the mountains of the Caucasus (Delbaere, *Facts and Figures on Europe's Biodiversity 1998–1999,* 1998). This rich level of biodiversity—generally defined as the variety of life forms found in a given region (whether an ecosystem, nation, continent, or other defined region) but also including genetic diversity within species—exists even though Europe's natural landscapes have been dramatically altered over the centuries by logging, farming, and the establishment of population centers ranging from small villages to internationally famous cities. Today numerous important habitat areas continue to be converted for agricultural operations, urban development, and other human uses. The viability of wilderness habitat is also threatened by exploitation of forest and water resources, ecosystem infiltration by alien species, and emissions of toxic pollutants into the air and water. These modifications to the natural environment are especially pronounced in the continent's western and northern reaches, and they are difficult to halt because they are so thoroughly integrated into the economic fabric of the continent. "In the European countries a sharp degradation of biodiversity and landscape diversity is the result of common and 'normal' economic activities," observed one analyst. "Producers and consumers do not take into account the negative effects of their economic activities on biodiversity and landscape diversity" (Van der Straaten, "Economic Processes, Land Use Changes and Biodiversity," 1996).

All of these environmental changes have had grim consequences for Europe's flora and fauna. Numerous wild species have experienced dramatic population declines in recent decades, and recent conservation efforts at the national and international levels have only slowed—not stemmed—the tide. "The threat to Europe's wild species continues to be severe and the number of species in decline is growing," admitted the European Environment Agency

(EEA). "In many countries, up to half of the known vertebrate species are under threat. . . .More than one-third of the bird species in Europe are in decline, most severely in north-western and central Europe" (EEA, *Europe's Environment,* 1998). Scientists also believe that climate change could exacerbate pressure on the continent's plants and animals in coming years, impacting species and their habitats in a host of unpredictable ways.

This trend toward ever-increasing levels of habitat degradation, with its associated toll on biodiversity, is one of the greatest environmental threats facing Europe—and the rest of the world—at the dawn of this new century. "While all the changes in the environment having to do with pollution, ozone depletion, and global warming are vitally important, they can be reversed—while on the other hand species extinction, the loss of biodiversity, cannot be reversed," remarked Harvard biologist Edward O. Wilson. "We are not deliberately trying to wipe out Creation, but we are, by general agreement among experts on biodiversity, heading toward extinction of as many as 20 percent of species in the next 30 years. . . .The average life span of a species before humanity came along was between half a million years in mammals and, in some groups like the insects, 10 million years. To wipe out species at the rate we are now inflicting has been to increase the extinction rate by between a hundred and a thousand times. By impoverishing the planet of life forms, we also reduce the productivity and stability of natural ecosystems" (Christen, "Why Biodiversity Matters," 2001).

In recognition of the imperiled state of much of Europe's flora and fauna, conservationists, scientists, lawmakers, and planners have all sought to incorporate habitat preservation, species protection, and other environmental objectives into sectoral policies. "Policies of nations and of the European Union are officially aimed at reaching a sustainable development in a few decades. However, vested interests that have benefited from an unsustainable development are not willing to give up their comfortable position without political struggle (Van der Straaten, "Economic Processes, Land Use Changes and Biodiversity," 1996).

Most Types of Habitat in Decline

During the course of European history, most of the continent's natural areas have been swept away or fundamentally altered in order to meet the needs and aspirations of its peoples. As a result, few regions of Europe, which was once blanketed in wilderness, remain unmarked by human activity. Today, as Europe's population continues to grow, many cities are laboring mightily to provide for citizens and visitors. New housing projects, commercial developments, roadways, and high-speed rail lines all are being built to accommodate the crush of people, but in many instances at a high environmental price. Indeed, most countries in the European Union have turned over at least 80 percent of their territory to uses such as agriculture, forestry, transportation, and industry (EEA, *Environment in the European Union at the Turn of the Century,* 1999).

As natural spaces are sacrificed to residential, commercial, and agricultural development, humans experience diminished air and water quality, increased noise and light disturbance, and loss of green space, while native flora and fauna reel from habitat fragmentation and destruction, often on a major scale. "Almost all parts of Europe are directly affected by human land use, which has wiped away large parts of Europe's natural heritage," stated an analysis by the European Centre for Nature Conservation. "Extremely valuable habitats, such as the European coast and the Alpine region, have become the most threatened habitats of their kind in the world. The species-rich semi-natural grasslands have decreased dramatically in area, clinging on in only a few regions. The natural European forests have nearly all disappeared. Most cultural and natural landscapes are under some kind of pressure from human activities. Birds and butterflies find it more and more difficult to survive in Europe" (Delbaere, *Facts and Figures on Europe's Biodiversity 1998–1999,* 1998).

Forests

Few habitat types have seen as precipitous a decline as Europe's forests. Cleared for farming, mining, human settlement, and the construction of everything from schooners to tables, only 2 percent of Europe's forests (excluding those in Russia) remain in a natural state. Moreover, less than 10 percent of the forestland that remains in Western Europe (excluding Russia) is classified as being in an even seminatural state. In fact, the continent's intact forestlands are confined almost entirely to Central and Eastern Europe, where animal and plant species in the Baltic States and elsewhere have benefited enormously from the (thus far) limited economic and technological resources of regional timber and energy interests (EEA, *Europe's Environment,* 1998).

Nonetheless, the overall status of Europe's forests is very poor. "Some forest habitats with a recognized high biodiversity value, such as original European riverine or swamp forests, have been all but totally destroyed, while the biological value of the other 98 percent has largely been diminished. Forest managers have tended to tidy up their forests by removing dead and hollow trees, fallen branches and the like. In doing so, they condemn many wood-dwelling species to homelessness. Less than 2 percent of European forests are fully protected, and these are inadequately distributed from a geographical and ecological point of view" (Delbaere, *Facts and Figures on Europe's Biodiversity 1998–1999,* 1998). In addition, those forests that do remain in natural or seminatural states tend to be small and isolated from one another, separated by cities, towns, resource extraction activities (logging, mining, drilling), agricultural operations, and the roads and rail lines that stitch them all together. According to one study, 95 percent of Europe's protected forest areas are found as fragments of less than 1,000 hectares, with 90 percent (forty-five of fifty) of the largest protected forest areas concentrated in the Russian Federation and Northern Europe (WCMC, *European Forests and Protected Areas,* 2000).

Still, in some respects, the condition of Europe's forests is improving, albeit incrementally. The continent experienced a modest recovery in total forest cover in the twentieth century, fueled by tree plantation operations, expansion of the continent's system of protected areas, and increased recognition of the importance of sustainable forest management. In fact, environmental considerations are an increasingly integral part of timber management, and certification programs designed to ensure consumers that timber was harvested in environmentally sound fashion have grown in popularity, especially in Western Europe. Many European nations have also taken other steps—both unilaterally and in concert with other countries—to limit the eradication of natural and seminatural forest areas that do remain.

But despite these welcome trends, Europe's forests remain a shadow of their former selves in terms of size, health, and biodiversity. Scarred by infestations of destructive insects, human-induced forest fires, fragmentation, and acid rain and other forms of atmospheric pollution, most forests now sustain only a fraction of the species they once did. This paucity of biodiversity is especially pronounced on the continent's tree farms, which themselves are monocultural in nature. "Intensive forestry, as generally practiced in Western Europe, cannot provide the same biodiversity as natural forests. The use of fast-growing species, especially in the Nordic countries, has somewhat relieved the pressure on existing forests. But this has led to the loss of a vast number of species which used to inhabit indigenous forests but cannot survive in monoculture plantations. . . .All in all, there is little diversity in European forests today, with just a few species dominating" (UN Environment Programme, *Global Environment Outlook 2000,* 2000).

Coastal Dunes and Beaches

Many species-rich dune areas have also been lost, mainly along Europe's western shores. The problem is most prevalent in the heavily visited Mediterranean region, where an estimated 75 percent of dunes have been sacrificed to accommodate hotels, resorts, marinas, and other trappings of tourism-based economies. Europe as a whole lost an estimated 40 percent of its dune habitat during the twentieth century to forest plantations, housing and commercial developments, recreation, and tourism.

It appears unlikely that this massive loss of dune habitat has come to an end. The dwindling number of dunes and beaches that remain in natural or semi-

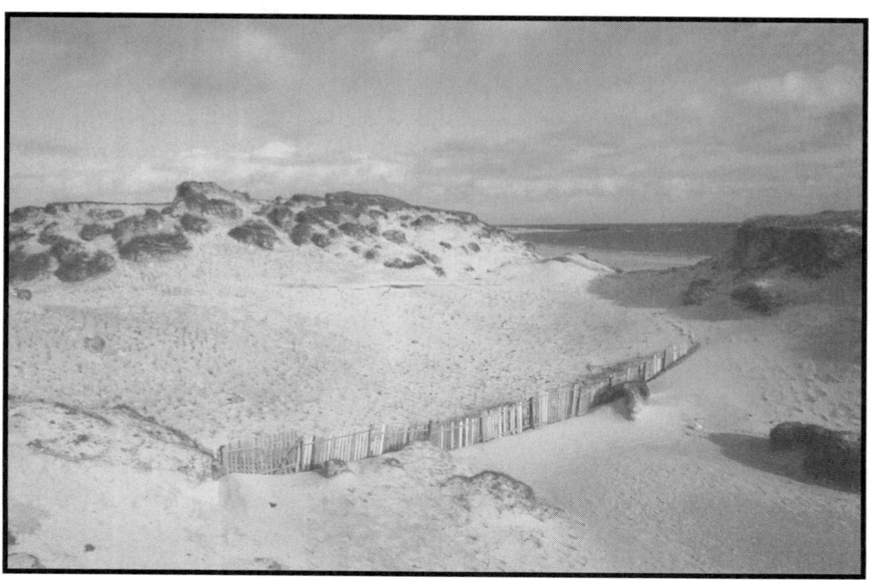

A fence surrounds an eroded dune on an island in the Outer Hebrides, Scotland, to enable regeneration.
ROGER TIDMAN/CORBIS

natural states are under imminent threat of development. Environmental groups and scientists say that the loss of these remaining pockets of habitat would almost certainly result in the extinction of species such as the *Phoenix theophrasti,* the only palm tree native to the Mediterranean basin. Reduced in range to a tiny corner of Crete and Turkey's Datca Peninsula, the tree is under imminent threat from tourism development (Mittermeier et al., *Hotspots,* 1999). Destruction of this and other habitat remnants would also constitute a severe blow to myriad other species of plants, birds, fish, and insects that depend on dune ecosystems for their survival. And as each of these species disappears, the complex ecosystem of which it was once a part unravels a little more.

Determined to ward off such scenarios, scientists, environmentalists, and sympathetic officials have mounted an energetic defense of Europe's dunes and beaches. In addition to establishing formal protection for those natural dune and beach areas that remain, they have undertaken significant dune restoration efforts in Spain and areas of northwestern Europe, convinced that such initiatives will prove essential in preserving these habitats and the creatures and plants therein. "The restoration capacity of dunes appears to be considerable owing to their dynamic character," observed one study undertaken by the European Centre for Nature Conservation (ECNC). "Removal of forest plantations, re-establishing dynamic dune formations and reversing pollution trends are among the successful restoration measures being taken" (Delbaere, *Facts and Figures on Europe's Biodiversity 1998–1999,* 1998).

Wetlands

Europe has also converted many of its wetlands for other uses, to the great detriment of migratory waterfowl, frogs and other amphibians, and numerous other species. Wetland drainage and filling has been most extensive in the continent's southern sector, where agricultural operations continue to expand, but losses have also been significant in Northwest and Central Europe. In addition, studies indicate that pollutants caused by water discharge and leaching and by runoff from pesticide-sprayed croplands, pastures, and urban areas have caused extensive damage to wetland biodiversity (ibid.). The introduction of alien species has also caused severe problems in some areas, altering ecosystems in profound ways and replacing some indigenous species entirely.

Fortunately, the nations of Europe have taken significant steps to address wetlands loss and degradation. By the late 1990s Europe had more than 560 designated Ramsar sites. These wetlands—formally recognized by the international treaty as natural resources of international importance—cover 140,000 square kilometers. Europe has also curbed its discharge of pollutants into the rivers and streams that replenish wetlands, in some instances making dramatic reductions in emissions. For example, total discharge of phosphorus from industrial facilities and urban wastewater sources dropped by more than 70 percent in several European countries between 1980 and 1995 (EEA, *Europe's Environment,* 1998). Restoration projects have also mitigated the impact of wetland loss in some localities.

Campaigns specifically targeted to protect particularly beloved or valued animals from extinction have also benefited wetlands preservation efforts in some countries. Poland, for instance, has long been justifiably proud of its large stork population. Only two of the world's nineteen species of stork breed in Europe. One is the reclusive and seldom seen black stork, but the other is the gregarious white stork, a staple of Polish folklore that relies on wetlands for survival. Alarmed by reports that the global population of white storks had declined by 20 percent or more between 1970 and 1990, bird conservationists pointed to Poland, where 40,000 breeding pairs live—one-quarter of the global population—as a key to arresting the decline. Polish environmental organizations such as ProNatura subsequently launched stork preservation initiatives, relying heavily on their country's longstanding affection for the bird (Polish law forbids killing or harassing storks or removing nests during nesting periods, and community beliefs are an even stronger deterrent to mistreatment). These preservation programs have both shored up stork numbers in Poland and protected wetland habitat that is essential for numerous other species. "Here [in Poland] storks mean wetlands, so saving them means saving frogs, toads, the corncrake—a short-billed, crane-like bird that loves to run in mud—and all the other animals you rarely see, or nobody cares about," explained one of ProNatura's founders (McConahay, "Save the Storks," 1999).

Grasslands and Heathlands

The famous heathlands of Europe's Atlantic coast region have been whittled away piece by piece over the past two centuries to make room for homes, farming operations, commercial development, and roadways. At the beginning of the nineteenth century, these open, mostly treeless expanses of low-growing shrubs and other vegetation covered an estimated 30,000 square kilometers of Europe. But conversion of these lands—initially created by the clearing of ancient forests and now suffused with historical and cultural significance—accelerated during the past two centuries, reducing the extent of heathlands to less than 4,000 square kilometers. This decline is a significant loss for European biodiversity, for heathlands provide rich habitat for reptiles, amphibians, birds, and a great many insects, including myriad species of dragonflies, beetles, bees, and wasps. But Europeans have gained a belated appreciation for the cultural and ecological significance of these landscapes, and efforts to protect the heathlands of Western Europe before the last remnants vanish have proliferated in recent years at both the national and regional levels. As a result, many of the remaining tracts now enjoy significant protection from development (Delbaere, *Facts and Figures on Europe's Biodiversity 1998–1999,* 1998).

Europe's grasslands are in much better shape, although some regions are faring better than others. In Northwestern Europe's lowlands, most seminatural grasslands are gone, paved or plowed under for other uses. In the continent's interior, however, millions of hectares remain relatively intact. This is a boon to many European species of flora and fauna, for grasslands provide valuable habitat. Some of the remaining grasslands in Northwestern Europe, for example, provide habitat for as many as 700 different plant species, including 200 mosses and lichens. In Germany's Black Forest, a single hectare was found to support 56 butterfly species and 131 species of bees (Van Dijk, "The Status of Semi-natural Grasslands in Europe," 1991; Delbaere, *Facts and Figures on Europe's Biodiversity 1998–1999,* 1998).

Europe is even losing many of its "small-scale landscapes"—hedgerows, ponds, woods, and other small natural areas that lie in suburbs and other developed areas but nonetheless support significant communities of creatures. In the United Kingdom, for instance, 53,000 miles of species-rich hedgerows were lost, mostly to agricultural operations (Government of the United Kingdom, *This Common Inheritance,* 1992). "Mechanized agriculture has reduced the rich patchwork quilt of woodlands, hedges, and small fields to an agro-industrial prairie largely devoid of wildlife," lamented one researcher (Zupancic-Vicar, "Parks for Life," 1997). Again, this problem is most severe in Europe's densely populated western region.

Europe's Imperiled Animals and Plants

Researchers acknowledge that gauging the exact status of Europe's flora and fauna is impossible at this time. Europe does not currently possess a comprehensive species monitoring and inventory tracking system, and data on some species (especially invertebrates) and habitats is incomplete. Information on regional biodiversity is particularly sparse in Central and Eastern Europe, where most countries have limited financial resources to allocate to scientific research. But despite the absence of important biodiversity information from some regions, scientists have documented the existence of more than 230,000 species in Europe, including birds (514 species), mammals (187), freshwater fish (358), reptiles (123), amphibians (62), invertebrates (200,000), and higher plants (12,500) (Delbaere, *Facts and Figures on Europe's Biodiversity 1998–1999*, 1998).

The nations of the former Soviet bloc are particularly rich in terms of biodiversity. For example, Russia and Ukraine contain the greatest total number of known mammal species in Europe, with 269 and 108, respectively. The Western European nations with the greatest mammal diversity are Greece (95) and France (93). Russia also houses the greatest number of bird species, with around 630, and the largest known species of fish, with 290. Yugoslavia has the greatest number of known reptile species, with 70, while the greatest variety of amphibians can be found in Russia and Italy, with 41 species each. Italy is Europe's leader in plant varieties, with about 5,600 distinct species within its borders (UN Development Programme et al., *World Resources 2000–2001,* 2000).

The quality of assessments is highly variable in all categories, but, overall, studies indicate that European biodiversity is in a state of decline, with species native to and geographically confined to Europe at particular risk (EEA, *Europe's Environment,* 1998). In fact, as the twentieth century came to a close, populations of numerous species in Europe had fallen to a point at which they merited listing on the Red List of Threatened Species maintained by the World Conservation Union (IUCN). Massive in size and rich in biodiversity—but bedeviled by decades of environmental degradation—Russia has a greater number of threatened species than any other nation of Europe or North Asia (where it is located on the Red List) except for Portugal. According to the 2000 Red List, the Russian Federation reported 129 threatened species (42 mammals, 38 birds, 6 reptiles, 14 fishes, and 29 other animal species), while neighboring Ukraine (also designated by the IUCN as

Butterfly Conservation in Europe

Of the 576 butterfly species known to occur in Europe, 69 (12 percent) are considered threatened. The major threats to Europe's butterflies are outlined in a 1997 report produced by the Dutch Butterfly Conservation and the British Butterfly Conservation. These organizations collected data from every European nation through a network of more than fifty butterfly experts.

The data show that the largest single threat to butterflies in Europe—affecting more than sixty species—is the conversion of habitat to agricultural use. For example, seminatural grasslands, most of which have been destroyed for farming and other uses, support large numbers of butterfly species. Other major threats include the fragmentation of habitat, the conversion of habitat to residential and industrial development, chemical pollution, and the afforestation of nonwoodland habitats. Each of these threats affects more than fifty species of butterflies. Threats affecting more than forty species include disturbance by human recreational activities, destruction of woodlands, climate change, and collection or taking.

Despite the many factors that have served to reduce butterfly populations in Europe, there is some hopeful news surrounding the reintroduction of one threatened species—the dusky large blue *maculinea nausithous.* A lovely creature with dark blue markings on the upper side of its wings, the species has suffered a 20 to 50 percent decrease in numbers throughout Europe. Improvement of land for agricultural use has been a major factor in the butterfly's decline, accounting for the disappearance of half of the former colonies.

The preferred habitat of the dusky large blue *maculinea nausithous* is marshy meadows. The female butterflies lay their eggs on the greater burner plant. The larvae eventually drop

Figure 2.1 Number of Threatened Butterfly Species in Europe and Severity of Individual Threats

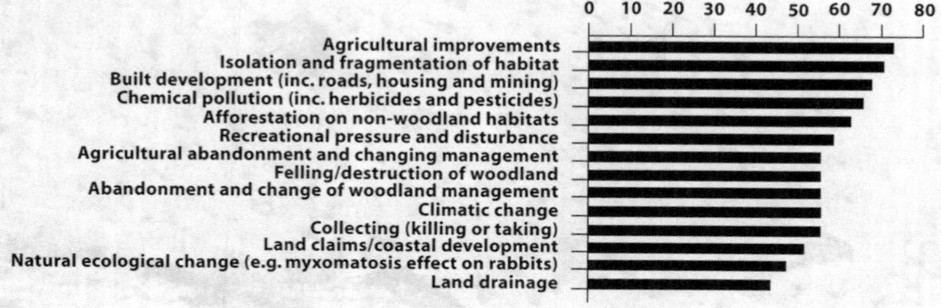

SOURCE: C. A. M. Van Swaay and M. S. Warren, *Red Data Book of European Butterflies.* Report no. Vs98.15. Wareham: De Vlinderstichting (Dutch Butterfly Conservation), Wageningen, and British Butterfly Conservation.

(continues)

to the ground, where they depend on the assistance of *Myrmica rubra* (red ants) for their survival. The ants—possibly reacting to a chemical signal that causes them to treat the larvae as their own offspring—carry the butterfly larvae into their nests, where the larvae feed on ant eggs. The adult butterflies typically emerge in July and have a life span of five to seven days. Because of the highly specialized conditions they favor, populations tend to remain fairly localized.

The dusky large blue *maculinea nausithous* disappeared from the Netherlands in 1972. Beginning in 1990, however, it has been successfully reintroduced through the Butterfly Protection Plan. Individuals taken from a stable population in southern Poland were placed in a nature reserve in the province of Noord-Brabant, and the population has shown a considerable increase in numbers since that time. In fact, the reintroduced butterflies have formed three subpopulations, including one located about 5 kilometers away from the original release site. Experts say that the success of this program gives the dusky large blue *maculinea nausithous* a strong chance of survival or possibly even expansion in parts of Europe.

Sources:

Delbaere, B. C. W., ed. 1998. *Facts and Figures on Europe's Biodiversity, 1998–1999.* Tilburg, Netherlands: European Centre for Nature Conservation.

Karsholt, O., and J. Razowsky, eds. 1996. *The Lepidoptera of Europe.* Stenstrup, Denmark: Apollo Books.

Van Dijk, G. 1991. "The Status of Semi-natural Grasslands in Europe." In P. D. Goriup, ed., *The Conservation of Lowland Dry Grassland Birds in Europe.* Peterborough, UK: Joint Nature Conservation Committee.

Van Swaay, C. A. M., and M. S. Warren. 1999. *Red Data Book of European Butterflies.* Strasbourg Cedex: Council of Europe.

North Asia) had 55 species on the list (17 mammals, 8 birds, 2 reptiles, 12 fishes, 15 other animal species, and 1 plant). Far to the West, Portugal had 131 species of threatened flora and fauna—including 67 species of molluscs—giving the nation the highest number of Red Listed species in all of Europe. Other countries with a high number of threatened species include Spain (100 species), France (99), and Italy (95) (World Conservation Union, *2000 IUCN Red List of Threatened Species,* 2000).

Not surprisingly, the aforementioned nations also rank high in threatened species by taxonomic group. Russia has more threatened mammal species

(42) than any other European or Eurasian nation, followed by Spain (24), France (18), Romania (17), and Portugal (17). Russia also has more threatened bird species than any other country, with 38. Other nations with significant numbers of endangered bird species include Bulgaria (10), Hungary (8), and Romania (8). Greece and Spain have the highest number of reptiles on the Red List, with six each, while Croatia has the undesirable distinction of having the most endangered species of fish, with 21. The nations with the greatest number of threatened plants on the list are Portugal (15 species), Spain (14), the United Kingdom (13), and Germany (12) (ibid.).

Even if one sets aside philosophical arguments about humankind's responsibility to be good stewards of the planet's environmental resources, researchers contend that it is in Europe's best interest to halt these downward trends and to nurture threatened species back to health. "Most species that become extinct over the coming decades will have no practical consequences for human livelihoods. This is not to say that extinctions do not sometimes have serious ramifications. . . .The loss of a species can change the composition, structure, and functioning of entire ecosystems. Moreover, scientists stress that it is difficult to know which species are essential for maintaining various ecosystem processes, and thus the loss of any species is risky" (Reid, "Biodiversity, Ecosystem Change, and International Development," 2001).

Mammals

There are currently an estimated 187 mammal species in Europe (excluding Russia, Belarus, Ukraine, and Moldova), not including cetaceans (whales and dolphins). Many mammal populations are in decline, but recent findings indicate that the continent's larger mammals are under particular pressure, especially in Western Europe, where habitat fragmentation is the rule rather than the exception. Bears have nearly vanished from France, Spain, and Italy, for example, and they are in steep decline in half a dozen other countries (see sidebar, page 40). Exotic species such as American mink, raccoon, and gray squirrel have also carved out places in regional ecosystems, often at the expense of native fauna. Current European species under imminent threat of global extinction include the Pardel lynx and Mediterranean monk seal. The latter once was distributed throughout the Mediterranean, the Black Sea, and the northwest coast of Africa. Today, about 400 surviving seals occupy isolated spits of land in Turkey, Greece, the Atlantic coast of Morocco, and a few other remote spots.

The decline of the Mediterranean monk seal symbolizes the general downturn in habitat quality in Europe. Researchers do note, however, that some native species, such as the northern bat and golden jackal, have actually expanded their range in recent years. Moreover, some mammal reintroduction programs have proven effective, especially when executed in concert with habitat restoration programs. In the Netherlands, beavers once again are constructing dams after an absence of decades. In Germany, lynx again prowl the deep forest. And the pawprints of brown bear can once again be found deep in Austria's mountains. The return of all three of these mammals to their former ranges is a direct result of reintroduction programs.

The Status of Large Carnivores in Europe

The large carnivores of Europe—which include such species as the brown bear, polar bear, gray wolf, snow leopard, lynx, and wolverine—are under increasing pressure from habitat loss, dwindling prey species, hunting, road traffic, and conflict with humans. As in other regions, these large carnivores play an important role in maintaining Europe's biodiversity. They help keep prey species healthy by weeding out sick and injured animals, for example, and they often act as indicators of the overall health of ecosystems. However, the presence of large carnivores arouses hostility in many rural areas, especially those that contain large numbers of livestock.

The status of European carnivores varies by species and area. Grey wolves, which were nearly eliminated from many parts of Europe in the late nineteenth century, began making a comeback in the late twentieth century. Protected under the Bern Convention since 1982, wolves have increased their population on the continent to between 8,400 and 18,000. Wolves are fairly numerous in Eastern Europe, and in parts of Scandinavia, the Balkans, and Italy. They are also expanding into Western Europe, thanks to legal protection and a more supportive political climate. Wolves do face some public resistance, however, especially among rural farmers. Conservation groups have attempted to address this problem by reimbursing farmers for the loss of livestock and encouraging the use of such nonlethal control means as watchdogs and electric fences.

Brown bears number 36,000 in Russia and 14,000 elsewhere in Europe, including 7,000 in Romania. Bear populations are stable or increasing in Austria, Slovakia, Macedonia, Albania, Norway, and Sweden. But Western Europe holds some of the world's most endangered bear populations. Some countries have small and isolated populations that are highly vulnerable to habitat destruction, loss of genetic diversity, and conflict with humans. For example, there are between 70 and

(continues)

Most wild mammal populations of Europe that remain undisturbed can be found in the Arctic or in lightly populated areas of Central and Eastern Europe. But even those remote regions are being infiltrated by pollution generated thousands of miles away. In Norway and Siberia, for example, persistent organic pollutants carried by waterways and air currents have accumulated in the fatty tissues of polar bears and other predators. Indeed, scientists attribute the late–1990s discovery of several hermaphrodite polar bear cubs to the cumulative impact of these pollutants (Kirby, "Europe's

90 bears in Spain and fewer than a dozen in France. Even the stable populations of Russia and Eastern Europe face increasing risks from poachers, since bear parts are highly valued for traditional medicine in some Asian countries.

Between 22,000 and 28,000 polar bears exist in the world. They are found throughout their original range, including territory controlled by Russia, Norway, and Greenland. Although populations have been stable in recent years, polar bears face significant risks in the future from climate change. Shrinking ice coverage in the Arctic region will reduce their ability to find food, and warmer temperatures may cause the collapse of maternal snow dens. A 2000 pact between the United States and Russia that restricts hunting of polar bears is expected to provide some aid to the species.

Several other species of large carnivores are critically endangered in Europe and Central Asia. For example, poaching and habitat loss have reduced the number of Siberian tigers in the wild to between 300 and 400—fewer than the number held in captivity. The World Wide Fund for Nature predicts that another European cat species, the Iberian lynx, will disappear within the next fifty years. "In the last four decades, its range has shrunk by a staggering 90 percent. From a species that recently ranged the entire [Iberian] peninsula, it is now reduced to populations numbering a dozen animals or fewer inhabiting scattered islands" (Goncalves). An estimated 300 to 800 animals remain in isolated pockets of Spain and Portugal, in territory that remains unprotected from proposed dams, roadways, and timber harvesting. Its imperiled status has led the World Conservation Union to label the creature as the most critically endangered cat species on the planet.

Conservation of large carnivores in Europe has been complicated in the past by the need to coordinate efforts across many nations. Conservationists recognized that "the challenge of conserving large carnivores is complex and dynamic, involving ecological,

(continues)

economic, institutional, political, and cultural factors and any attempt to solve this conservation issue must take this into account. Realistically, no single agency, organisation, or institution will be able to solve the carnivore constitution issue alone. No single plan or strategy can be completely comprehensive and correct as a guide for action, and continual monitoring is required" ("Large Carnivore Initiative for Europe mission statement," in Boitani 2000).

The development of the European Union, however, which relaxed national boundaries and allowed for more unified planning, created new opportunities for the management of carnivore populations on a continental scale. In 1995 a coalition of environmental groups, scientists, land managers, and governments from seventeen European nations took advantage of this situation by launching the Large Carnivore Initiative for Europe (LCIE). The initiative grew rapidly from its inception, with experts from more than two dozen countries now actively involved in the program. The main goal of the LCIE is to maintain and restore viable populations of large carnivores across Europe. The initiative builds on existing programs in order to avoid duplication of effort between nations and ensure the efficient use of resources. It also develops and implements programs to help large carnivores coexist with humans, including educational programs to increase public acceptance and habitat preservation efforts to shield vital breeding, hunting, and migratory territory.

Sources:

Boitani, Luigi. 2000. *Action Plan for the Conservation of Wolves in Europe.* Nature and Environment series No. 113. Strasbourg Cedex: Council of Europe, October.

Burke, Greg, et al. 1999. "Back on the Prowl: As the Wolf Returns to Old Haunts in Western Europe, Conservationists Preach Peaceful Coexistence while Farmers Reach for Their Guns." *Time International* (April 19).

Delbaere, Ben, ed. 1998. *Facts and Figures on Europe's Biodiversity: State and Trends 1998–1999.* Tilburg, the Netherlands: European Centre for Nature Conservation.

Goncalves, Eduardo. "Lynx on the Brink." *The Ecologist Website.* http://www.theecologist.co.uk/article.html?article=223.

Kirby, Alex. 1999. "Campaign for Europe's Carnivores." *BBC News Online.* November 11. http://news.bbc.co.uk/ 1/low/sci/tech/284106.stm.

———. 1999. "Europe's Bears Battle to Survive." *BBC News Online.* July 26. http://news.bbc.co.uk/1/low/sci/tech/404059.stm.

Swenson, J. E., et al. 1998. *Draft Action Plan for the Conservation of the Brown Bear in Europe.* Rome: Large Carnivore Initiative for Europe.

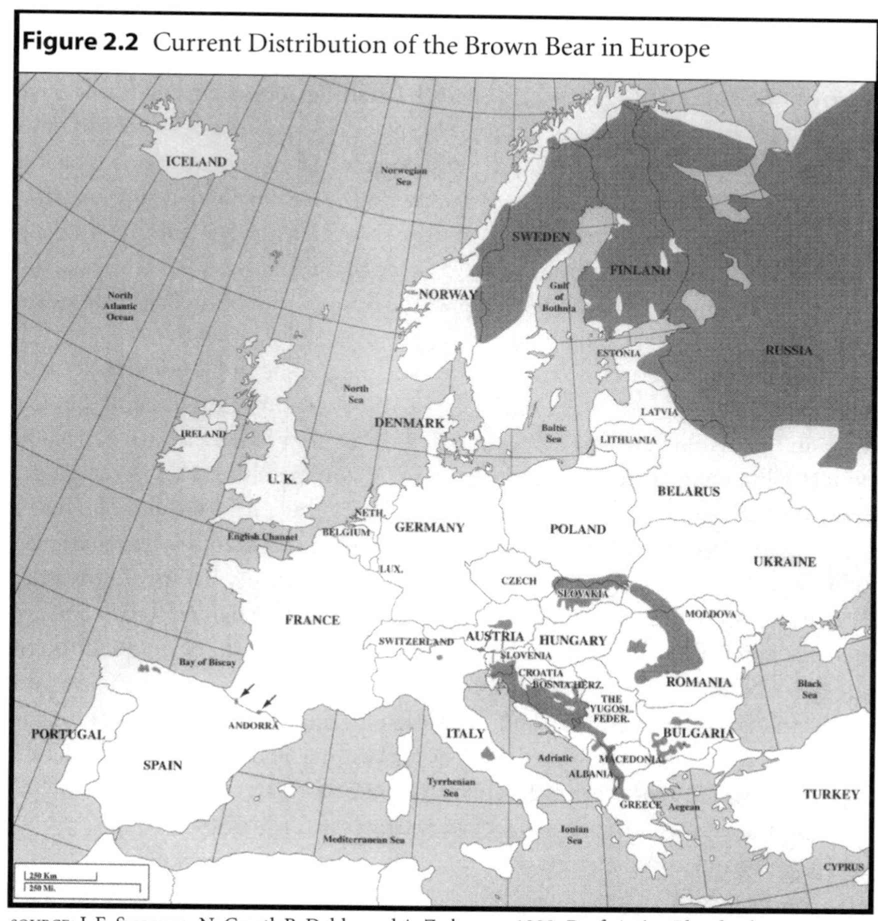

Figure 2.2 Current Distribution of the Brown Bear in Europe

SOURCE: J. E. Swenson, N. Gerstl, B. Dahle, and A. Zedrosser. 1998. *Draft Action Plan for the Conservation of the Brown Bear in Europe.* Rome: Large Carnivore Initiative for Europe.

Bears Battle to Survive," 1999). And in rural regions of Russia and other impoverished nations of the former Easternbloc, poaching of brown bear, wolf, and other large mammals is commonplace.

Birds

Many of Europe's 514 known bird species are suffering the effects of intensive habitat loss and modification. In fact, 195 species (38 percent of the continent's total) have been formally designated as Species of European Conservation Concern (SPECs) by BirdLife International, meaning that active conservation measures will have to be implemented to ensure their survival. Of that total, 26 species are classified as globally threatened, including the Spanish imperial eagle, the Dalmatian pelican, and the white-headed duck (Tucker and Heath, *Birds in Europe,* 1994; Collar et al., *Birds to Watch,* 1994).

Intensified agricultural activity has been blamed as the single greatest cause of falling bird populations. For example, irrigation measures implemented in the Iberian Peninsula between 1979 and 1989 resulted in the alteration of 10,000 square kilometers of steppe habitat, producing significant declines in the populations of stone curlews, little bustards, and great bustards. Other changes in farming practices, including field expansion, crop monocultures, increased use of inorganic fertilizers and pesticides that kill the insects upon which birds feed, and the loss of hedgerows and ditches that provide nesting habitat have triggered steep declines of species such as the partridge and the skylark. The population of the latter, for instance, fell by 50 percent in the United Kingdom, Germany, and the Netherlands between 1970 and 1990. All told, agricultural intensification has been cited as a major factor in 42 percent of Europe's SPECs (Tucker and Heath, *Birds in Europe,* 1994). The biggest blow to migratory waterfowl, meanwhile, has been drainage and conversion of wetlands along major migration routes.

Overhunting and poaching of birds is also a problem, particularly in some areas of Eastern Europe. Since the mid-1990s, for instance, Italian poachers have killed and smuggled tens of thousands of larks, blackbirds, and turtledoves out of Hungary, where they are protected, to Italy, where they are served as delicacies in restaurants. Bird populations in Romania and Serbia have also suffered significant setbacks from hunting activities.

Not all bird species are trending downward, however. Raptors in particular have made notable recoveries, boosted by species protection measures, habitat restoration programs, changes in forest management, and bans on DDT and other toxins destructive to avian populations. Scientists have also been encouraged by the success of species reintroduction programs such as the one that returned the lammergeier vulture to the Alps. The success of this and

Figure 2.3 Threats to European Bird Species That Are on the Decline

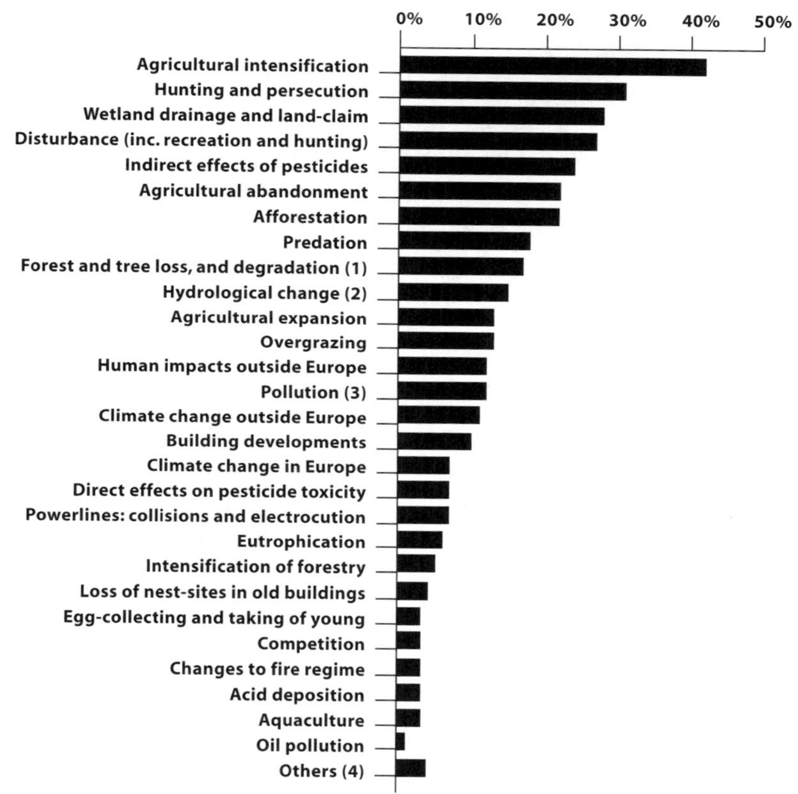

SOURCE: G. M. Tucker and M. F. Heath. 1994. *Birds in Europe: Their Conservation Status.* BirdLife Conservation Series no. 3. Cambridge: BirdLife International.

NOTE: Threats are only included if they are thought to have contributed to the decline of European populations over the period 1970 to 1990. (1) Clear cutting, unmanaged cutting, burning, grazing, loss of trees from orchards, farmland copses and hedgerows, etc. (2) Damming of rivers, water abstraction, flood control, canalization, etc. (3) Other than acid deposition, oil spills, pesticides and eutrophication. (4) Other: destruction of haystacks, hybridization, plant diseases, drowning in fishing nets and overfishing (each affecting only one species).

other initiatives has fed new reintroduction schemes, including a program that reintroduced golden eagles to the skies of Ireland in 2001, nearly a century after they were wiped out by hunters (Delbaere, *Facts and Figures on Europe's Biodiversity 1998–1999,* 1998).

Reptiles and Amphibians

Amphibian and reptile populations in Europe have been buffeted by habitat destruction, pesticide- and herbicide-laced streams and ponds, increases in ultraviolet radiation caused by human-induced changes in the atmosphere, and the introduction of alien species of fish. Scientists believe that 30 percent of the continent's amphibians and 45 percent of its reptiles are now threatened, with species in Southern Europe over-represented because many species of reptiles and amphibians are native only to that region (EEA, *Europe's Environment,* 1995).

Researchers say that much of the decline in Europe's reptile and amphibian populations can be halted through increased protection of wetlands, ponds, and other natural habitat. But in many regions of Europe, this presents a formidable challenge, because of the extent of protection that is necessary to safeguard species that require different habitat types during various stages of their life cycles (Delbaere, *Facts and Figures on Europe's Biodiversity 1998–1999,* 1998). In addition, countries must follow through on their stated commitments to protect the biodiversity of wild fauna and flora. In 2002, for example, the European Court of Justice found that Greece had yet to enact a legitimate program to protect vital breeding grounds of the Caretta sea turtle on Zakinthos Island, eight years after conservation policies should have been put in place according to European Commission legislation. Conservation groups and others characterized this failure as a significant violation of its obligations to other member states within the European Union.

Fish

An estimated 538 distinct species of fish navigate the rivers, streams, and lakes of Europe (excluding the former USSR) (Kottelat, "European Freshwater Fishes," 1997). But a number of these species are vulnerable. "Pollution from domestic, agricultural or industrial wastes may kill fish, favour more tolerant species or have unknown sublethal effects," stated the ECNC. "Land use changes in catchment areas alter the hydrology and ultimately fish habitats. Engineering schemes on lakes and rivers, including the construction of dams, may interfere with migration patterns and lead to species extinction. Unregulated commercial and sport fishing can lead to over-exploitation of stocks. Lastly, introduced non-native species may compete for resources, prey on or hybridize with native species, causing them to decline in numbers." For example, all eight species of sturgeon in Europe are in jeopardy, with one critically endangered, five endangered, and two vulnerable. These species have been affected by the full spectrum of human activities detrimental to fish, including dam construction, which has destroyed important spawning grounds; high levels of legal and illegal fishing during the spawning season; and discharges of harmful effluents into waterways (Delbaere, *Facts and Figures on Europe's Biodiversity 1998–1999,* 1998).

Many European waterways are subject to high discharges of industrial, municipal, and agricultural pollutants, especially in the continent's Central and Eastern reaches. This daily insult to rivers and lakes is also occasionally compounded by major spills of oil and other pollutants. In January 2000, for instance, a massive spill of cyanide and heavy metals from a gold mining operation in Romania destroyed all biological life in the Tisza, Hungary's second largest river. The toxic poisons eventually traveled 1,000 kilometers through Hungary and Yugoslavia, where they wreaked havoc on the Danube. The spill contaminated the drinking supplies of more than two million people and destroyed the regional fishing industry, but it also bludgeoned the region's fish and wildlife, killing millions of fish and poisoning otters, ospreys, and other wildlife dependent on the river for sustenance. "The Tisza has been killed," remarked Serbian environment minister Branislav Blazic. "Not even bacteria have survived. This is a total catastrophe" (Batha, "Death of a River," 2000).

Plants

Europe contains an estimated 12,500 higher plant species (EEA, *Europe's Environment,* 1995). Many of these plants are "endemic" species—that is, confined to a particular geographic region—with such species especially prevalent in areas of the Mediterranean basin, the mountains of Central and Southern Europe, and various islands. As with other species, loss or degradation of habitat is the biggest culprit in the decline of plant species. Common causes of habitat loss are agricultural operations and commercial forestry projects. Other significant threats to Europe's flora include water pollution, which is particularly injurious to water plants, and global climate change. "In a greenhouse-affected world, plant and animal communities will try to follow warm-temperature zones as these head northwards," noted one report by Conservation International (CI). "Those in northern Italy will have to try to migrate over the Alps and those in eastern Spain over the Pyrenees, while those in western Spain and Portugal will find themselves migrating into the Bay of Biscay" (Mittermeier et al., *Hotspots,* 1999).

European Biodiversity—Regional Trends

Mediterranean Basin

Europe's Mediterranean basin ranks as one of the continent's greatest storehouses of biodiversity. By one estimate the region includes 25,000 species of vascular plants, while the remainder of Europe has only 6,000. But the majority (13,000) of the basin's plant species are endemic, and many of these are "narrow endemics," confined to unusually small areas, making them particularly vulnerable to expanded farming operations, overgrazing by domestic stock, and urban sprawl. Indeed, these manifestations of human activity have combined to place as much as 50 percent of the region's flora at risk (Medail, "Hot Spots Analysis," 1997; Myers and Cowling, "Mediterranean Basin," in Mittermeier et al., *Hotspots,* 1999).

Indeed, few areas of the globe are under as much human pressure as the Mediterranean Sea and its surrounding watershed. The region includes twenty-one nations—including major industrialized nations such as France, Italy, Turkey, and Egypt—with a collective population of more than 400 million people. In addition, the basin is world renowned as a tourist destination, and its climate is ideal for growing a wide variety of crops. "The main agricultural threat [to the Mediterranean basin] lies with food demands from people in far-off lands. Consumers of northern Europe are becoming accustomed to strawberries and carnations right around the year, and during October–March they turn to warmer climates for supplies. Thus the speedy expansion of horticulture in many parts of the Basin; the market is already huge. . . . All unwittingly, citizens' savings in Britain and Germany may be going to support the growing of exotic fruits, vegetables and flowers in Mediterranean lands way beyond the horizon—and thus lending an unintended hand to the despoliation of one of the world's finest hotspots" (Myers and Cowling, "Mediterranean Basin," in Mittermeier et al., *Hotspots,* 1999).

Some important conservation efforts have been launched in recent years to protect the basin's remaining natural and seminatural habitats. The European Union has developed programs to enhance conservation cooperation between EU nations and countries located along the Mediterranean's southern and eastern shores, and individual states and conservation organizations have implemented numerous programs to study, restore, and protect vital habitat areas. But most observers agree that these defenses, as currently constituted, will be insufficient to preserve the region's remaining bastions of biodiversity.

Western Europe

Centuries of human activity have permanently transformed most of Western Europe, leaving few areas that remain hospitable to native plants and animals. Blanketed by cities, towns, villages, and their underlying infrastructure (farming operations, factories and retail establishments, roads and high-speed railway lines, airports and harbors), few areas of life-sustaining natural and seminatural habitat now exist. Flora and fauna are particularly stressed in Northwestern Europe, where the continent's economic development has been greatest. Few natural ecosystems remain in this sector, and the only species that are prospering in the region are those that have a high tolerance for human activity and its by-products.

In recent years, the European Union has moved to address some of the major factors in biodiversity loss. Habitat restoration policies have proliferated, and emissions of some toxic materials into the air and water have decreased markedly. But critics in the scientific and environmental communities contend that habitat and biodiversity considerations are still insufficiently integrated into other policy areas (EEA, *Europe's Environment,* 1998).

Central and Eastern Europe

Unlike Western Europe, large, relatively intact wilderness ecosystems still exist in Central and Eastern Europe. The continued presence of these habitat areas has been attributed to comparatively light human populations and the historical concentration of factories in industrial centers; the latter phenomenon caused severe environmental degradation at the local level, but often spared remote wilderness areas (Nowicki, *The Green Backbone of Central and Eastern Europe,* 1998). In the wake of the political turmoil of the late 1980s and early 1990s, however, funding for increased agricultural and industrial activity became more readily available. As a result, economic development has surged in the post-Communist states. "Changes in farm structure—privatization and an increase in scale—have a considerable impact on biological and landscape diversity," commented the European Centre for Nature Conservation. "In these regions nature may meet the same fate as in Northwestern Europe if no additional measures are taken to integrate nature conservation considerations into economic and physical planning policies" (Delbaere, *Facts and Figures on Europe's Biodiversity 1998–1999,*1998). But as the twentieth century came to a close, programs designed to protect wildlife habitat and conserve biodiversity remained severely underfunded. Indeed, the conservation of biodiversity is not a priority with most governments in this area, as lawmakers and governments remain primarily focused on developing their economies to compete with Western Europe.

The Caucasus

Regarded as a boundary between Europe and Asia, the Caucasus region is a 500,000-square-kilometer expanse of Georgia, Azerbaijan, Armenia, Turkey, and southwest Russia containing some of the last bastions of wilderness in Europe. The mountain ranges of the region are so formidable that many high-altitude areas remain in pristine condition, and about 14,000 square kilometers of the Caucasus have been set aside in dozens of nature and hunting reserves, two biosphere reserves, and one national park (Sevan, in Armenia). But valleys and other low-altitude areas of the Caucasus are in a sorry state, scarred by years of environmentally insensitive timber-cutting, mining, and agricultural development that ravaged forest habitats, compromised freshwater ecosystems, and drained wetlands utilized by migratory birds. Moreover, Conservation International—which named the Caucasus one of twenty-five international biodiversity hotspots in 1999—reports that pressure on the environment has worsened significantly since 1992, when the collapse of Communism convulsed the governments, societies, and economies of the region. Illegal forest cutting and overgrazing destroyed some previously intact natural areas, and many poor residents turned to poaching to provide for their families. In fact, poaching became so widespread during the 1990s that it was cited as a major factor in the decline of already threatened species such as the leopard, brown bear, wolf, tur, Caucasian red deer, and Caucasus peregrine falcon. "As a result of the combined impacts of habitat destruction and modification and poaching, about 80 animal species from the Caucasus have now been placed on the IUCN Red List" (Zazanashvili et al., "Caucasus," in Mittermeier et al., *Hotspots,* 1999).

According to CI, the socioeconomic crisis in the region has even brought about "an increase in poaching, illegal forest cutting, mowing, and grazing in protected areas. At the same time, the wages of protected area staff have decreased, and with them, at least some of their motivation. All of this calls into question the future of protected areas in this critical hotspot." But while all of these trends are troubling, the outlook for the region's flora and fauna is not entirely without hope. A variety of governmental and nongovernmental organizations at the national and international levels are laboring to implement new nature conservation programs, and Georgia is planning to establish several new national parks in the region. Georgia's efforts have not gone unnoticed by scientists and environmentalists interested in preserving the remaining wild areas of the Caucasus. Indeed, they cite the country's parks initiative as a model for other regional governments. "A major part of the territories in the Caucasus are still under state ownership," noted one CI analysis. "Although the regime is now in a transition period from a socialist regime to a market economy, new parks and reserves can still be created by the State with relatively little difficulty, something that will change dramatically when land is privately owned." But analysts note that any effective network of protected areas will have to shield a wide variety of ecosystems from development, from regional rivers supporting rare and endemic species of fish to transboundary areas that contain leopard, brown bear, lynx, Asian wild sheep, and other threatened species (ibid.).

Conserving Europe's Natural Heritage

Since the 1970s, the nations of Western Europe have shown a heightened awareness of the importance of biodiversity issues and the fragility of the ecosystems upon which various species of flora and fauna depend. This awareness has manifested itself in a range of important ways. Many countries have passed new laws protecting species and habitats within their borders or funded new research initiatives to improve our understanding of various species and their needs. The role of national parks, preserves, and other protected areas in maintaining biodiversity and habitat has been widely acknowledged as well, leading to heightened efforts to designate new parks and limit human footprints on existing parks. "Protected areas are certainly not the only way of conserving nature and landscapes. However, they are the pinnacle of conservation efforts, acting as models for others to follow in the wider countryside. They are particularly important in maintaining biodiversity and the best way—in most cases the only way—of conserving the jewels of Europe's natural heritage. . . .Protected areas also enrich the quality of human life, in particular as places of recreation. They offer opportunities for inspiration, scope for peaceful enjoyment, and a place for understanding and learning. Above all, they are a source of mental, physical and spiritual renewal" (Zupancic-Vicar, "Parks for Life," 1997).

Today, much of Europe fully participates in important international biodiversity conservation efforts such as the Ramsar Convention for Wetlands, the UNESCO World Heritage Convention, the Bonn and Bern Conventions, the Convention on Biological Diversity, and the European Community Birds and Habitats Directives. The latter mandates, passed in 1979 and 1992, respectively, are the most vital habitat conservation measures currently in play in Europe. They establish a common framework for the European Union to protect flora and fauna and their habitats through the creation of an EU-wide ecological network called Natura 2000. This network of special protected areas—connected to one another via migratory corridors and buffered from incompatible land uses on adjacent land—is seen as one of Europe's best hopes of preserving its rich legacy of animals, birds, and plants. But creation of the network has been slowed by bureaucratic wrangling, land acquisition issues, and other implementation problems; completion of the Natura 2000 plan appears to be some years distant.

In some ways, the Natura 2000 initiative seems emblematic of many of Europe's biodiversity conservation programs and policies. On the one hand, the ECNC notes that these efforts "have succeeded in conserving considerable land and sea areas and safeguarding a number of species and habitats," but the organization adds that "implementation is often difficult and slow; the general decline has not been halted."

Moreover, since the early 1990s European biodiversity has come under still greater pressure from Central and Eastern European nations eager to develop their economies and improve their citizens' standard of living. The European Union has crafted legislation designed to help these "accession" countries make the transition to market economies without ruining their environmental assets, but even though "by far the greatest direct financial contribution to European biological and landscape diversity conservation comes from the EU" (Delbaere, *Facts and Figures on Europe's Biodiversity 1998–1999,* 1998), the nations that compose the EU do not have unblemished records in the realm of biodiversity protection or other environmental matters. "Not all Western European standards and policies are environmentally beneficial, and some management policies in eastern countries were environmentally beneficial. For example, forestry and farming systems in the Baltic states were comparatively sustainable throughout the communist era and maintained much higher levels of biodiversity than western systems; . . . [t]he accession countries need to find an acceptable balance between adapting to Western European policy and maintaining existing policies where these are environmentally beneficial" (UN Environment Programme, *Global Environment Outlook 2000,* 2000).

The rest of Europe, meanwhile, will need to devote even more of its attention and resources to biodiversity conservation if it hopes to avoid waves of species extinctions in the coming decades. Indeed, researchers and environmentalists contend that it is essential that governments fund more programs such as Britain's National Biodiversity Network, which will help organizations collect and share information about wild species throughout Great Britain. "There is as yet no coherent and efficient European policy for nature and biodiversity conservation, and the requirements of their conservation are neither adequately incorporated into sectoral policies nor are they part of the day-to-day decisions made by all those who use the land. . . . Without hard data on the state of Europe's nature and its relevance for European economy and society it will be difficult to convince policy makers, and the economy and financial sectors, of the pressing need to conserve nature" (Delbaere, *Facts and Figures on Europe's Biodiversity 1998–1999,* 1998).

Sources:

Batha, Emma. 2000. "Death of a River." BBC News Online, February 15. http://news.bbc.co.uk/1/hi/world/europe/642880.stm.

Bethe, F. H., ed. 1997. *Land Use in Rural Europe: Processes and Effects on Nature and Landscape.* The Hague, Netherlands: Ministry of Housing, Spatial Planning and the Environment.

Biodiversity Conservation in Russia. 1997. Moscow: State Committee of Russian Federation for Environment Protection, Project GEF.

Birdlife International. 2000. *Threatened Birds of the World.* Barcelona and Cambridge, UK: Lynx Edicions and BirdLife International.

Christen, Kris. 2001. "Why Biodiversity Matters." *OECD Observer* 225/226 (summer).

Collar, N. J., M. J. Crosby, and A. J. Stattersfield. 1994. *Birds to Watch 2: The World List of Threatened Birds.* Cambridge: BirdLife International.

Convention on Biological Diversity. 2000. *Global Biodiversity Outlook 2001.* Montreal: Convention on Biological Diversity.

Delbaere, Ben, ed. 1998. *Facts and Figures on Europe's Biodiversity: State and Trends 1998–1999.* Tilburg, the Netherlands: European Centre for Nature Conservation.

European Environment Agency. 1995. *Europe's Environment: The Dobris Assessment.* Copenhagen: EEA.

———. 1998. *Europe's Environment: The Second Assessment.* Copenhagen: EEA.

———. 1999. *Environment in the European Union at the Turn of the Century.* Copenhagen: EEA.

———. 2000. *Environmental Signals 2001.* Oxford, UK: Elsevier Science.

Government of the United Kingdom. 1992. *This Common Inheritance.* London: HMSO.

Jongman, R. H. G. 1995. "Nature Conservation Planning in Europe: Developing Ecological Networks." *Landscape and Urban Planning* 32.

Kirby, Alex. 1999. "Europe's Bears Battle to Survive." BBC News Online, July 26. http://news.bbc.co.uk/1/low/sci/tech/404059.stm.

Kottelat, M. 1997. "European Freshwater Fishes." *Biologia* 52, Supplement 5.

Kronert, R. 1999. *Land-Use Changes and Their Environmental Impact in Rural Areas in Europe.* Cambridge: CRC Press-Parthenon Publishers.

Mackay, Richard. 2002. *Atlas of Endangered Species: Threatened Plants and Animals of the World.* London: Earthscan.

Maessen, Rob. 2000. "The Conservation and Sustainable Use of Nature and Biodiversity in Europe: A Regional Perspective." *European Nature* 5 (November).

McConahay, Mary J. 1999. "Save the Storks, Touch the People." *Choices* (Special Environmental Issue) (April).

Medail, F., and P. Quezel. 1997. "Hot Spots Analysis for Conservation of Plant Biodiversity in the Mediterranean Basin." *Annals of the Missouri Botanical Garden,* 84.

Mitchell-Jones, A. J., et al. 1998. *Atlas of European Mammals.* London: Academic Press.

Mittermeier, Russell A., Norman Myers, and Cristina Goettsch Mittermeier. 1999. *Hotspots: Earth's Biologically Richest and Most Endangered Terrestrial Ecoregions.* Washington, DC: CEMEX, Conservation International.

Nelson, James Gordon, and Rafal Serafin. 1997. *National Parks and Protected Areas: Keystones to Conservation and Sustainable Development.* Berlin: Springer-Verlag.

Nowicki, P., ed. 1998. *The Green Backbone of Central and Eastern Europe.* Tilburg, the Netherlands: European Centre for Nature Conservation.

Oldfield, S., et al. 1998. *The World List of Threatened Trees.* Cambridge: World Conservation Press.

Reid, Walter V. 2001. "Biodiversity, Ecosystem Change, and International Development." *Environment* 43 (April).

Saiko, Tatyana. 2001. *Environmental Crises: Geographical Case Studies in Post-Socialist Eurasia.* Harlow, UK: Pearson Education.

Stattersfield, A. J., et al. 1998. *Endemic Bird Areas of the World: Priorities for Biodiversity Conservation.* Cambridge: BirdLife International.

Tucker, Graham M., and M. F. Heath. 1994. *Birds in Europe: Their Conservation Status.* Cambridge: BirdLife International.

Tucker, Graham M., and Michael I. Evans. 1997. *Habitat for Birds in Europe: A Conservation Strategy for the Wider Environment.* Cambridge: BirdLife International.

UN Development Programme, UN Environment Programme, World Bank, and World Resources Institute. 2000. *World Resources 2000–2001: People and Ecosystems, The Fraying Web of Life.* Washington, DC: World Resources Institute.

UN Environment Programme. 2000. *Global Environment Outlook 2000.* London: Earthscan.

Van der Straaten, Jan. 1996. "Economic Processes, Land Use Changes and Biodiversity." In Rob H. G. Jongman, ed., *Ecological and Landscape Consequences of Land Use Change in Europe.* Proceedings of the ECNC Seminar on Land Use Change and Its Ecological Consequences, February 16–18, 1995. Tilburg, the Netherlands: European Centre for Nature Conservation.

Van Dijk, G. 1991. "The Status of Semi-natural Grasslands in Europe." In P. D. Goriup, ed., *The Conservation of Lowland Dry Grassland Birds in Europe.* Peterborough, UK: Joint Nature Conservation Committee.

VanDeveer, Stacy D. 2000. *Protecting Regional Seas: Developing Capacity and Fostering Environmental Cooperation in Europe.* Washington, DC: Woodrow Wilson Center.

Wascher, D. M., ed. 2000. *The Face of Europe: Policy Perspectives for European Landscapes.* Tilburg, the Netherlands: European Centre for Nature Conservation.

World Conservation Monitoring Centre (WCMC). 2000. *European Forests and Protected Areas: Gap Analysis.* Cambridge: WCMC.

World Conservation Union (IUCN). 1996. *1996 IUCN Red List of Threatened Animals.* Gland, Switzerland: IUCN.

———. 2000. *2000 IUCN Red List of Threatened Animals.* Gland, Switzerland: IUCN.

Zupancic-Vicar, Marija. 1997. "Parks for Life: An Action Plan for the Protected Areas of Europe." In R. Gerald Wright, ed., *National Parks and Protected Areas: Their Role in Environmental Protection.* Cambridge, MA: Blackwell Science.

Parks, Preserves, and Protected Areas

Europe's protected cultural landscapes are well known around the world for their historical and aesthetic value, but the continent also has set aside significant expanses of land for the conservation of its ecological riches. For example, Europe maintains almost 300 of the world's 850 national parks, more than any other continent. According to the World Commission on Protected Areas (WCPA), more than 12 percent of Europe's total land mass—an area equivalent to France, Belgium, and the Netherlands combined—enjoys varying levels of formal protection as defined by the World Conservation Union (IUCN).

Many of these protected areas harbor threatened species and their habitats, while others preserve scenic or culturally significant landscapes. Whatever the basis of their protected status, however, few of Europe's protected areas have escaped some degree of degradation from air and water pollution or erosion of environmental quality from tourism, manufacturing, farming, logging, mining, hunting, water extractions and diversions, military conflicts, and other human activities, either within their boundaries or in adjacent regions. For some agencies charged with protecting Europe's protected areas from these potential threats, the task may be made even more difficult by inadequate funding and support from legislators, communities within or adjacent to the protected region, and the general public. "Many of these protected landscapes are not well managed—many lack management plans and staff, many have been set up without the necessary government authority and there are still many cases where local people are not yet seen as vital allies in conservation," reports the WCPA. "There is a need for much improvement in our protected landscapes" (WCPA, http://wcpa.iucn.org.region/europe).

Europe's Protected Areas: System under Stress

Numerous European parks and reserves are managed with a strong emphasis on wilderness preservation and scientific research. These include wilderness areas and strict nature reserves (defined as Category I protected areas by the IUCN), national parks (Category II), and natural monuments and landmarks (Category III). Cultural landscapes (Category V areas) that seek to blend conservation goals with tourism, recreation, and other human activities also make up a considerable extent of Europe's conservation legacy: they account for 50 percent of the continent's total number of protected areas and 30 percent of the total protected land area in Europe (the remaining IUCN designation—Category IV—is given to wildlife sanctuaries and other nature reserves subject to active management of habitat and species). All but the smallest of the aforementioned parks and reserves are listed in the UN List of Protected Areas, the definitive listing of protected areas around the globe (ibid.).

In 1997 the UN List of Protected Areas included more than 3,000 protected areas in Europe, including 288 national parks that cover approximately 15.53 million hectares (38.46 million acres). In addition, the nations of Europe have provided some level of formal protection to more than 12,000 sites, including 250 marine protected areas (World Conservation Monitoring Centre, http:// www.wcmc.org.uk). Europe is well represented on the World Heritage List as well, with 24 of the 138 sites included on the global list because of their natural values (of these sites, five are in the Russian Federation and four are in the United Kingdom). Europe is home to eight World Heritage sites with major wetland and marine values, five World Heritage sites with major freshwater wetland values (World Conservation Union, *A Global Overview of Wetland and Marine Protected Areas*, 1997), and seven areas that have been designated World Heritage sites for the ecological value of their forests (ibid). Europe also contains 736 Ramsar Wetlands of International Importance (714 in continental Europe and the Russian Federation and 22 sites in other regions), about 60 percent of the global total.

It is not surprising, given the many countries contained within Europe, that it has more transboundary protected areas than any other continent. Transboundary protected areas—also sometimes called transfrontier nature reserves or peace parks—are park/preserve complexes in multiple countries that adjoin across political boundaries, thus creating a single de facto area of habitat and species conservation. In 1998 there were 136 transboundary protected areas established around the globe that met minimum size stipulations and other criteria set by the IUCN. Forty-five of these protected area complexes were in

Europe (Africa had the second greatest number of transboundary protected areas, with 34). Europe also had the most proposed transboundary complexes under consideration at the end of the 1990s, with 26 of the global total of 69. These transboundary parks range across the length and breadth of the continent, from the Eastern Carpathians International Biosphere Reserve, which includes protected areas at the junction of the Polish, Slovakian, and Ukrainian borders, to the Pyrenees Occidentales National Park/Ordessa y Monte Perdido National Park complex along the border of southern France and northern Spain (Zbicz, "Transboundary Cooperation in Conservation," 1999; Zbicz and Green, "Status of the World's Transfrontier Protected Areas," 1997).

Most of Europe's protected areas are smaller than 100,000 hectares. In 1999 only 212 of the designated parks and reserves dotting the continent were greater in size, with 43 percent of those parks (92 parks) located in Russia. In addition, Russia is the only country in Europe with any protected areas larger than one million hectares, with 12 such parks and reserves. Other countries housing a significant number of Europe's larger parks include France (29 parks larger than 100,000 hectares), Germany (26 parks), and the United Kingdom (15 parks) (World Conservation Monitoring Centre, http://www.wcmc.org.uk). The countries with the highest percentage of protected land in Europe are Denmark (more than 32 percent of land protected, the third-highest percentage in the world), Austria (28 percent), and Germany (27 percent).

At the close of the twentieth century, only 1.5 percent of the total land area in Europe was being managed as a strict nature reserve or wilderness area. But as the World Commission on Protected Areas notes, "[It] is a mistake to think that all of Europe is a managed landscape and that opportunities only exist for establishing protected landscapes and small nature reserves. Despite its small size and large population density, Europe does still have some areas of wilderness" (World Commission on Protected Areas, http://wcpa.iucn.org.region/europe). Indeed, analysts say that Central and Eastern European nations are particularly well positioned to establish new protected areas in ecologically sensitive areas as they proceed with the transition from public to private ownership of lands, for large expanses of their territories remain relatively untouched by human activity. Georgia and some other nations seized this opportunity during the 1990s, establishing a number of new national parks that offer Category II-level protection to entire watersheds and other ecosystems. In fact the total land area of new national parks established in Europe between 1990 and 1997 was almost as large as the total area of national parks established in the previous twenty years. Numerous other landscapes are being considered for national park protection as well, spurred on in large part by the mandates to establish the Natura 2000 protected area network in the European Union and the Emerald protected area network in non-EU European countries.

Local Opposition Scuttles National Parks in Germany

Germany has one of the largest systems of protected areas in all of Europe, but the national parks that compose the heart of the nation's extensive land conservation network are not universally popular with the German citizenry. In fact, during the late 1990s, two proposed additions to the country's national park system were defeated because of sustained opposition from communities situated near the proposed parks. This phenomenon of organized local opposition to the formation of new protected areas—also evident in the United States and other areas of the world—has prompted some nature conservation agencies and organizations in Germany to explore conservation strategies that actively solicit the input and participation of local populations in designating and managing protected areas. This strategic shift reflects a growing belief in some quarters that "linking protected areas with local economic livelihoods and social identity is essential for long-lasting conservation" (Stoll-Kleeman, "Reconciling Opposition to Protected Areas Management in Europe," 2001).

Significant organized opposition to the expansion of Germany's national park system first appeared in 1997, when a citizens' group called the Federal Association of Persons Concerned by National Parks was established. This organization united approximately forty German associations opposed to establishing new protected areas or expanding existing ones. The antipark association included a wide array of constituencies troubled by limitations on activities in protected areas, including farming groups, fishermen and hunters, forest owners and foresters, representatives of the tourism industry, private landowners, and representatives of communities in rural areas that would be affected by proposed parks. Around this same time, a citizen initiative based in Hesse successfully derailed an effort to designate nearby Kellerwald National Park as a protected area. Public demonstrations, vandalism, and willful disobedience of rules designed to safeguard protected habitat also beleaguered efforts to boost conservation protection for Brandenburg's Uckermark Lakes Nature Park and Bavaria's Bavarian Forest National Park in the late 1990s. Opponents of the designation of new protected areas claimed their greatest victory in 1999, however, when a local citizens' group embarked on a successful media and legal campaign to stop a proposal to establish the Elbe Lowlands National Parks in lower Saxony (ibid.).

In most communities that are hostile to the designation of new protected areas in Germany, a chief

(continues)

concern is that nature conservation regulations will impose unreasonable restrictions on personal and property rights, as well as controls that threaten, reduce, or eliminate personal rights. Misperceptions about the goals of nature conservation agencies and concerns about the economic impact of rules safeguarding protected areas further add to the acrimony that is present in some communities. "Local people's feelings toward nature conservation and governmental interference in their livelihoods and their mistrust of the nature conservation mission—deemed to be dictatorial, insensitive, and alienating—can undermine the agencies' conservation efforts. It is critical that agencies consider the importance of these factors, because almost all of Germany's nature conservation efforts are thwarted by local opposition, which is often supported by regional politicians and sometimes even by the courts" (ibid.).

These concerns about dilution of the primary objective of protected area designation—to safeguard wilderness and other natural areas—remain very strong within the scientific and conservation communities. But other members of these communities in Germany grant that disputes with local communities have undermined the state's ability to add to its protected areas system, and they contend that a more collaborative approach can still produce meaningful triumphs in nature conservation. "In the face of prolonged opposition to protected areas management, more participative and discursive processes of communication and understanding need to be put in place. It is vital to improve the communication by conservation agencies so as to ensure wider public acceptance of their legitimate objectives" (German Advisory Council on Global Change, *World in Transition*, 2000).

Sources:

Federal Agency for Nature Conservation, Germany. 2000. *Nature Data 1999.* Münster: Landwirtschaftsverlag.

German Advisory Council on Global Change. 2000. *World in Transition: Conservation and Sustainable Use of the Biosphere, Annual Report 1999.* New York: Springer.

Solberg, B., and S. Miina, eds. 1997. *Conflict Management and Public Participation in Land Management.* Proceedings No. 14. Joensuu, Finland: European Forest Institute.

Stoll-Kleeman, Susanne. 2001. "Opposition to the Designation of Protected Areas in Germany." *Journal of Environmental Planning and Management* 44, no. 1.

———. 2001. "Reconciling Opposition to Protected Areas Management in Europe: The German Experience." *Environment* 43 (June).

But analysts caution that without enacting meaningful conservation programs, the newly created areas will likely encounter the same problems as many of the continent's existing national parks. "The greatest needs in Central and Eastern European countries are, besides financial assistance, in mitigating the effects of land redistribution on protected areas, as well as the development of environmental legislation, and the support of partnerships and exchanges between East and West and the Central and East European countries" (Zupancic-Vicar, "Parks for Life: An Action Plan for the Protected Areas of Europe," in Nelson and Serafinin, *National Parks and Protected Areas,* 1997).

Successful conservation of important wildlife habitat in Eastern and Central Europe will also depend on meaningful restrictions on activities within and adjacent to proposed parks. "It is unlikely that protected areas will be able to conserve biodiversity if they are surrounded by degraded habitats that limit gene flow, alter nutrient and water cycles and produce regional and global climate change that may lead to the final disappearance of these 'island parks.' Protected areas need to be part of broader regional approaches to land management" (IV World Congress on National Parks and Protected Areas, "Parks for Life," 1992). In Europe's Mediterranean basin, for example, nearly 2 percent of the total land area is protected by more than 200 national parks, regional parks, natural monuments, and hunting reserves, and several countries are planning to add substantially to their protected area systems. "But due to the demands of agriculture and other activities that absorb large tracts of natural environment, many protected areas are too small to meet the imperatives of what the scientific community refers to as 'island biogeography.' Moreover, many protected areas suffer some effects (smog, acid rain, etc.) of pollution arising far outside their specific locations. Some of them are short of water after feeder rivers rising in distant watersheds have been diverted for industry, agriculture, and urban communities. All of these problems are likely to become more pronounced as human numbers and human demands keep on growing" (Myers and Cowling, "Mediterranean Basin," in Mittermeier et al., *Hotspots,* 1999).

These challenges are present to some degree or another in all areas of Europe, according to the World Commission on Protected Areas. "In most national parks in Europe IUCN management objectives of a Category II protected area are not yet achieved. There are still long-standing impacts on the parks, such as hunting, forestry, and water management. Many of the parks are also too small to combat threats from adjacent areas. And in 18 of the 33 European countries that contain national parks, Category II national parks cover less than 1 percent of the total country area."

In recognition of the long-term impossibility of conserving park ecosystems that are surrounded by severely compromised landscapes, park managers and administrators in Europe and elsewhere have made a

> concerted effort to look beyond park boundaries and work cooperatively with adjacent landowners and stakeholders. Yet, the well-being of park ecosystems continues to erode. Impacts on species, flows, and other ecosystem processes that extend beyond park boundaries inevitably affect the park ecosystem. With pervasive habitat destruction beyond park boundaries, the concepts of metapopulation and minimum viable population have become critical issues for the long-term conservation of species within parks. There is evidence of widespread general declines in songbirds, waterfowl, and amphibians. One can only speculate on the consequences to the park ecosystem of declines in entire classes of species such as these." (Jope and Dunstan, "Ecosystem-Based Management: Natural Processes and Systems Theory," in Wright, *National Parks and Protected Areas,* 1996)

Increasing numbers of park authorities have also embraced the idea of restoring abused landscapes adjacent to protected areas. "A national park, surrounded by farmland, pasture, or any sort of development, cannot pick up its boundaries and move when conditions no longer favor the array of organisms it was designed to protect. Restoration may help add habitat to existing parks and reserves" (Wolf, *On the Brink of Extinction,* 1987).

Diverse Philosophies of Protected Area Management in Europe

Land conservation philosophies and practices vary across Europe, influenced by cultural traditions, legal and political factors, population demographics, regional and national economic activity, and size and extent of species and habitat diversity. Indeed, the level and kind of protection afforded to parks, reserves, sanctuaries, monuments, and other protected areas differs considerably from country to country. These differences are most evident between the continent's eastern and western regions, where differences in political philosophy and associated socioeconomic development profoundly influenced habitat conservation attitudes during the twentieth century. Led by Sweden and Norway, the nations of Western Europe created nearly twice as many national parks as the countries of the Eastern bloc by the late 1980s, despite notable conservation efforts by countries such as Poland and Yugoslavia. Indeed, conservation achievements by the latter countries were the exception rather than the rule; the communist rulers of the former German Democratic Republic (GDR), for instance, failed to create a single national park during their long tenure (Denisiuk et al., "Experience in Cross-Border Cooperation for National Parks and Protected Areas in Central Europe," in Nelson, *National Parks and Protected Areas,* 1997).

In the years following the fall of communism, however, a flurry of new national parks and other protected areas were created in Central and Eastern Europe. Romania, for example, approved eleven national park projects within a few years of the overthrow of Nicolae Ceausescu's dictatorial regime. But these protected areas are unlike those of Western Europe in a number of ways. "Different legal regulations in the various countries of Central and Eastern Europe greatly influence their systems of nature conservation and their achievements in this field. This applies particularly to large protected areas. In the countries of Central Europe they are represented by national parks and landscape parks, while in Eastern Europe (Russia, Ukraine, Belarus) the main form of protection is large strictly managed reserves, so-called *zapovedniki.* They exist along with landscape parks and national parks which are considered to be categories of lesser importance" (ibid.).

Zapovedniki reserves are particularly numerous in the Russian Federation, and scientists and conservationists are engaged in an intense effort to protect them from development. Prior to dissolution, the Soviet Union included 24 national parks and 172 nature reserves that protected about 1.5 percent of its total land area. In addition, more than 1,950 nature sanctuaries dotted the country from Siberia to the Middle Asian and Caucasus Mountains, raising protected coverage to more than 4 percent of the USSR's total land area. Together, these protected areas—60 percent of which were in the European USSR—were recognized as vital habitat for a wide variety of flora and fauna (World Conservation Union, *1992 Protected Areas of the World,* 1991).

But the Soviet government's authority to designate protected areas also permitted it to suspend those protections whenever it desired. On numerous occasions the central authorities removed reserves from the protected area system for purposes of economic exploitation. A total of eighty-eight state nature reserves were removed by a "reform" in 1951, for instance, with subsequent surface area reduced from 12.5 million hectares to 1.5 million hectares. One decade later, sixteen of the country's existing eighty-five state reserves were removed ("Nature Conservation in the Soviet Union" 1991). In subsequent decades, authorities gradually increased the size of the system again by designating dozens of new reserves, but formal recognition still did not always translate into meaningful protection from human activity. "The protected areas system has been threatened over time by a number of activities such as oil prospecting, livestock grazing, over-fishing, uncontrolled tourism, illegal building schemes, and hunting by the privileged few" (Braden, "Wildlife Reserves in the USSR," 1986).

Despite such problems, when the Soviet Union collapsed in 1989, its protected area system was among the most extensive in the world. Most of this species- and habitat-rich system is still in place. In Russia, more than a hundred

View of Caucasus Mountains from Mount Elbrus, Russia. DEAN CONGER/CORBIS

vast zapovedniki covering almost 83 million acres—an area roughly the size of the U.S. national park system—are scattered across the countryside, from Eastern Europe to the Pacific Coast of Asia. This network includes numerous reserves devoted primarily to scientific research. Indeed, Russia has set aside more land for scientific research on biodiversity and other conservation issues than any other country, according to the World Conservation Union. Members of the international scientific and conservation communities are working hard to preserve these protected areas as Russia continues its political and economic journey away from communism. But significant threats loom, including development pressure and meager levels of funding that do not cover the costs of basic maintenance and protection, let alone wildlife studies and other research programs. In 2000, for example, government funding for all of Russia's nature reserves was only U.S.$5.2 million. In the same year, the U.S. National Park Service spent more than U.S.$5 million every two days to operate America's national parks (Strebeigh, "Across the Russian Wilds," 2001).

The nations of Western Europe have a more venerable record of nature conservation than their counterparts in Central and Eastern Europe, though systems in individual countries each have their own unique wrinkles. In countries such as Belgium, Spain, Sweden, and the United Kingdom, nature conservation is managed and directed primarily at the regional and local levels, which enjoy significant levels of autonomy in a wide range of policy areas. But

Table 3.1 Protected Areas in the Russian Federation, 1999

Protected Areas, 1999	*Russian Federation*	*Europe*
Protected Areas (number)	219	12,356
Area of Protected Areas {a} (000 ha)	52,907	109,297
Percent of Land Area in Protected Areas	3.1%	4.7%
Number of Protected Areas at Least:		
100,000 hectares in size	92	212
1 million hectares in size	12	12
Number of Marine Protected Areas	16	760

SOURCE: EarthTrends 2001, World Resources Institute.

whereas regional responsibility for landscape and species protection has been a reality in places like Spain and Sweden for years, the United Kingdom's movement toward decentralization accelerated during the 1990s, when the single agency responsible for nature conservation in the UK was divided into separate offices responsible for habitat and species issues in England, Scotland, and Wales. The 1999 creation of separate parliaments for Scotland and Wales served to further separate responsibility for nature conservation management, among other areas.

In the aftermath of these changes, Scotland formally opened its first ever national park in 2001—at Loch Lomond and the Trossachs—and it has proposed a second national park in the Cairngorm Mountains that would include remnants of the ancient Caledonian Forest. But although conservation organizations and scientists have applauded Scotland's initiative in establishing national parks, some have also expressed uneasiness about the amount of power allocated to local interests in determining park policies, citing concerns that ecologically damaging development may be the end result. Defenders of this decision, however, contend that a conservation philosophy that encourages meaningful management participation from communities in close proximity to protected areas is the best way to meet long-term habitat and species preservation goals.

In France, responsibility for designation and management of protected areas is also spread among various ministries and levels of government. The Ministry of the Environment retains central control over management of the country's national parks, but many other conservation issues—such as control of hunting and logging—are managed completely independently of the ministry, and the ministry has no management authority over the country's national nature reserves or its regional natural parks, both of which are directed at the regional level (Bromley, *Nature Conservation in Europe*, 1997).

Some observers believe that this dilution of responsibility for conservation issues has not served France well. Problems cited in France (as well as other countries with such arrangements) have included poor coordination of shared conservation goals, reduced responsiveness to pressing environmental issues, heightened levels of bureaucratic and research redundancies, and diminished emphasis on nature conservation goals. For instance, France had twenty-nine regional nature parks within its borders in the late 1990s. These parks are nearly three times as large as France's national parks on the average, but they are all Category V protected areas providing significantly less protection from human activities than do the country's national parks (most of which are Category II). Towns and villages—and associated industrial activity—all lie within regional nature parks, and large tracts of land within the park boundaries are privately owned. These regional nature parks provide important protection for cultural landscapes and natural areas alike, but they are designated, managed, and funded (with some state subsidies) at the regional level (ibid.). According to critics of this arrangement, park managers too often accommodate development activities at the expense of vulnerable species and habitats because of pressure from local communities that rely on tourism, recreation, and other activities for their livelihood. They charge that in such situations, projects designed to increase tourism and recreation—such as construction of new visitor facilities—often receive full funding at the expense of wildlife monitoring studies and other conservation activities. Conservationists believe that in some cases, these management choices have contributed to the decline of the very habitats and species the parks were created to protect.

> Denmark, by contrast, has pursued a course of increased centralization in dealing with nature conservation and other environmental matters, although local and regional authorities still play a significant role in addressing environmental issues. A long time regional leader in the conservation of wilderness areas and the integration of environmental issues into other policy areas such as agriculture and freshwater management, Denmark's stances on conservation issues have been held up as models throughout much of Western Europe. Today, Denmark has extended formal protection to about 10 percent of its total land. This total does not even include North East Greenland National Park, a massive 97-million-hectare park in Greenland, which is a self-governing part of the Danish monarchy. (Bromley, *Nature Conservation in Europe*, 1997)

In Belgium some types of protected areas, such as nature parks, are relatively scarce because of the state's complex regulatory environment and its "explicit linkages of [protected area] designations with rural socioeconomic development" (Bromley, *Nature Conservation in Europe*, 1997). But it does have a plethora of nature reserves within its boundaries. These protected areas include both privately owned and state-owned reserves. In the former case, private land can be formally recognized as a reserve if it meets certain habitat requirements and if the landowner agrees to restrictions on hunting, building, and other management activities that interfere with the natural development of the ecosystem. State-owned and authorized nature reserves, on the other hand, include both actively managed resources in which species reintroduction, habitat restoration, and other activities take place, and fully protected reserves in which natural processes are permitted to evolve with minimal interference (ibid.).

In Ireland less than 1 percent of the land is formally protected for the purposes of habitat or species conservation, even though much of Ireland's territory is lightly settled. The largest of its five national parks, Glenveagh, covers only 16,548 hectares, and the largest of its ten national nature reserves listed on the 1997 UN List of Protected Areas, Slieve Bloom Mountains, covers less than 2,230 hectares. But, in actuality, Ireland's low population density is actually a key reason why the nation has such a small area of protected land. The Irish people simply do not perceive establishment of protected areas as an urgent need, given the nation's predominantly rural character and its economy, which is dependent upon agriculture and forestry (ibid.).

Campaigns to Safeguard Europe's Endangered Areas

Most European nations are signatories to important biodiversity and habitat conservation agreements such as the Convention of Biological Diversity, the Convention on Wetlands of International Importance (RAMSAR), the Convention on International Trade with Endangered Species (CITES), and the Convention for the Protection of the World Cultural and Natural Heritage. A number of countries are also participating in Biosphere Reserve programs, which seek to safeguard natural environments in areas in which a moderate degree of human intrusion or exploitation has already taken place. Regional conservation agreements have also emerged as important tools in restoring ecological integrity to the Black Sea, the Rhine River, and numerous other areas that have suffered extensive environmental abuse over the years. And of course, individual states and conservation organizations have also launched programs to study, restore, and protect habitat areas within their own borders.

But while all of the above initiatives are worthwhile, the programs that have drawn the most attention from scientists, legislators, conservationists, busi-

The Barra River in Glenveagh National Park, Ireland MICHAEL ST. MAUR SHEIL/CORBIS

ness interests, and the European public have been campaigns to establish a Europe-wide system for the conservation of wilderness and natural areas.

The Parks for Life campaign was the first major manifestation of this growing interest in land and species conservation and protection. Launched in 1994 and revised three years later, Parks for Life was an action plan developed by the World Commission on Protected Areas after extensive consultation with governments, conservation groups, and park managers. It sought to provide guidance to governments across Europe on improving the size and effectiveness of their protected area networks while simultaneously heeding economic, social, and cultural factors particular to each nation. Since its introduction, the WCPA's Parks for Life campaign has broadened in scope, although its basic mandate—to "improve the way in which protected areas in Europe are established and managed"—has not wavered. "Over the years, Parks for Life has become a synonym for actions to ensure an effective, adequate and well-managed network of protected areas in Europe," stated the WCPA. "It has become a 'network of networks,' which includes protected areas themselves, international and national organizations, governmental and non-governmental organizations and individuals" (WCPA http://wcpa. iucn.org. region/europe).

Another important milestone in European land conservation was the 1996 adoption of the Pan-European Biological and Landscape Diversity Strategy

(PEBLDS). Designed to ensure consistent implementation of the Convention on Biological Diversity across all of Europe, this program called for the development of a comprehensive Pan-European Ecological Network that would include *core areas* for the conservation of ecosystems, habitats, species, and landscapes; *wildlife corridors* to facilitate migration of species between core areas; *restoration areas* devoted to repairing damaged habitats, ecosystems, and landscapes; and *buffer zones* that would cushion fragile habitats and landscapes and their associated biodiversity from heavy human activity (Council of Europe et al., *Pan-European Biological and Landscape Diversity Strategy,* 1996). Envisioned as a series of four five-year action plans, the PEBLDS focuses on addressing habitat conservation and restoration by integrating those issues into other policy areas. By doing so, the PEBLDS hopes to establish sustainable models of biological and landscape diversity for the whole continent of Europe within 20 years, thus safeguarding the last remaining wild rivers, wetlands, coasts and virgin forests in Europe. "The requirements of biological and landscape diversity will be integrated as far as practicable into relevant economic and social sectors. In particular, the agriculture, marine fisheries, forestry, and tourism sectors will put biological and landscape diversity at the heart of their activities, and strive to conserve and enhance nature and the landscape" (Delbaere, *Facts and Figures on Europe's Biodiversity,* 1998).

The backbone of PEBLDS and other European habitat and biodiversity protection efforts is the Natura 2000 ecological network. This initiative arose out of the European Community's Birds and Habitats Directives, passed in 1979 and 1992, respectively. Natura 2000 requires all member states of the EU to designate a series of wild and seminatural or managed habitats in accordance with established criteria and then institute effective protection measures for their conservation. In addition, Natura 2000 provides for these special protected areas to be connected via migratory corridors and buffered from incompatible land uses on adjacent land. It even provides member states with the flexibility to protect and enhance habitats outside the network in order to support and enhance areas formally listed with Natura 2000. "Therefore, habitats such as hedgerows, water courses, semi-natural woodland or scrub, which would not fall into the higher category necessary for inclusion in Natura 2000, could still be statutorily protected as an enhancement of the Network" (Bromley, *Nature Conservation in Europe,* 1997). A similar initiative, called the Emerald Network of Areas of Special Conservation Interest, is being developed for European nations that are not EU members.

Conservation groups and scientists see Natura 2000 as Europe's greatest hope for conserving its remaining wilderness areas and preserving its most endangered habitats and species. But development of the network has faltered in some countries. According to the World Commission on Protected Areas, some members of the EU had fallen far behind schedule in their development of a protected area list for integration into the Natura 2000 network. "The protected area coverage is very uneven," stated the WCPA. "Some countries have very well-developed systems including all the main types of protected areas, but others have protected area systems that are rather weak by international standards. In addition, these areas are faced with habitat fragmentation, isolation, human pressures, climate change, inadequate funding, weak management capacity and lack of political commitment" (WCPA http://wcpa.iucn.org.region/europe). In addition, some nations obligated to participate in Natura 2000 have become mired in disputes over compensation for landowners who contend that the value of their land has been diminished by protected area designation (Stoll-Kleeman, "Reconciling Opposition to Protected Areas Management in Europe," 2001) (see sidebar, page 58). These and other obstacles have triggered considerable frustration in conservation circles. World Wide Fund for Nature (WWF) Europe, for example, has bluntly blamed delays in the designation process on "lack of planning, resources, and commitment" in some EU states. Despite unhappiness with the halting progress of the program, however, WWF Europe and other organizations continue to characterize Natura 2000 as one of the continent's most exciting opportunities to preserve its rich ecological heritage for the benefit of future generations (WWF Europe, *Natura 2000,* 2000).

Sources:

Bennett, Graham, ed. 1994. *Concerning Europe's Natural Heritage: Towards a European Ecological Network.* London: Graham and Trotman.

Braden, Kathleen E. 1986. "Wildlife Reserves in the USSR," *Oryx* 20, no. 3.

Bromley, Peter. 1997. *Nature Conservation in Europe: Policy and Practice.* London: Spon.

Brunner, Robert. 1999. *Parks for Life: Transboundary Protected Areas in Europe.* Cambridge: IUCN.

Carr, Mark H. 2000. "Marine Protected Areas: Challenges and Opportunities for Understanding and Conserving Coastal Marine Ecosystems." *Environmental Conservation* (June).

Convention on Biological Diversity. 2000. *Global Biodiversity Outlook 2001.* Montreal: Convention on Biological Diversity.

Council of Europe, UN Environment Programme, and European Centre for Nature Conservation. 1996. *Pan-European Biological and Landscape Diversity Strategy—A Vision for Europe's Natural Heritage.* Amsterdam: Council of Europe, UNEP, and ECNC.

Delbaere, Ben, ed. 1998. *Facts and Figures on Europe's Biodiversity: State and Trends 1998–1999.* Tilburg, the Netherlands: European Centre for Nature Conservation.

Europarc Federation. 2000. *Parks for Life: Transboundary Protected Areas in Europe.* Grafenau, Germany: Europarc.

European Environment Agency. 1998. *Europe's Environment: The Second Assessment.* Oxford: Elsevier Science.

———. 1999. *Environment in the European Union at the Turn of the Century.* Luxembourg: EEA.

———. 2000. *Environmental Signals 2001.* Oxford: Elsevier Science.

IV World Congress on National Parks and Protected Areas. 1992. "Parks for Life." Report of the IV World Congress on National Parks and Protected Areas. Caracas, Venezuela: IV World Congress on National Parks and Protected Areas.

Harmelin, Jean-Georges. 2000. "Mediterranean Marine Protected Areas: Some Prominent Traits and Promising Trends." *Environmental Conservation* (June).

Maessen, Rob. 2000. "The Conservation and Sustainable Use of Nature and Biodiversity in Europe: A Regional Perspective." *European Nature* 5 (November).

Mittermeier, Russell A., Norman Myers, and Cristina Goettsch Mittermeier. 1999. *Hotspots: Earth's Biologically Richest and Most Endangered Terrestrial Ecoregions.* Washington, DC: CEMEX, Conservation International.

"Nature Conservation in the Soviet Union." 1991. In *Nature Conservation in Austria, Finland, Norway, Sweden, Switzerland, Bulgaria, Czechoslovakia, Hungary, Poland, Romania, Yugoslavia, and the Soviet Union.* Luxembourg: European Parliament Director-General for Research.

Nelson, James Gordon, and Rafal Serafin. 1997. *National Parks and Protected Areas: Keystones to Conservation and Sustainable Development.* Berlin: Springer-Verlag.

State Committee of Russian Federation for Environment Protection. 1997. *Biodiversity Conservation in Russia.* Moscow: State Committee of Russian Federation for Environment Protection, Project GEF.

Stoll-Kleeman, Susanne. 2001. "Reconciling Opposition to Protected Areas Management in Europe: The German Experience." *Environment* 43 (June).

Strebeigh, Fred. 2001. "Across the Russian Wilds." *Smithsonian* 33 (June).

Synge, H. 1998. *Parks for Life 97: Proceedings of the IUCN/WCPA European Regional Working Session on Protecting Europe's Natural Heritage.* Cambridge: IUCN.

UN Development Programme, UN Environment Programme, World Bank, and World Resources Institute. 2000. *World Resources 2000–2001: People and Ecosystems, The Fraying Web of Life.* Washington, DC: World Resources Institute.

Wascher, D. M., ed. 2000. *The Face of Europe: Policy Perspectives for European Landscapes.* Tilburg, the Netherlands: European Centre for Nature Conservation.

Wetlands International Ramsar Sites Database. http://www.wetlands.org/RDB/europe (accessed December 5, 2002).

Wolf, Edward C. 1987. *On the Brink of Extinction: Conserving the Diversity of Life.* Worldwatch Paper No. 78. Washington, DC: Worldwatch.

Wood, Brian. 2000. "Room for Nature? Conservation Management of the Isle of Rum, UK and Prospects for Large Protected Areas in Europe." *Biological Conservation* (June).

World Conservation Monitoring Centre and World Wildlife Fund. 2000. *European Forests and Protected Areas: Gap Analysis.* Cambridge: World Conservation Monitoring Centre and World Wildlife Fund.

World Conservation Union. 1991. *1992 Protected Areas of the World: A Review of National Systems.* Gland, Switzerland: IUCN.

———. 1997. *A Global Overview of Wetland and Marine Protected Areas on the World Heritage List.* Gland, Switzerland: World Conservation Union-IUCN and World Conservation Monitoring Centre, September.

———. 1998. *1997 United Nations List of Protected Areas.* Gland, Switzerland: IUCN.

World Conservation Union-IUCN and World Conservation Monitoring Centre. 1997. *A Global Overview of Forest Protected Areas on the World Heritage List.* Gland, Switzerland: World Conservation Union-IUCN and World Conservation Monitoring Centre, September.

World Wide Fund for Nature Europe. 2000. *Natura 2000: Opportunities and Obstacles.* Brussels: WWF Europe.

Wright, R. Gerald, ed. 1996. *National Parks and Protected Areas: Their Role in Environmental Protection.* Cambridge, MA: Blackwell Science.

Zbicz, Dorothy C. 1999. "Transboundary Cooperation in Conservation: A Global Survey of Factors Influencing Cooperation between Internationally Adjoining Protected Areas." Ph.D. dissertation, Duke University.

Zbicz, Dorothy C., and Michael J. B. Green. 1997. "Status of the World's Transfrontier Protected Areas." *PARKS* (October).

Forests

—Andrew Park

Despite a history of exploitation that stretches back to the dawn of agriculture, Europe still accounts for approximately 27 percent of the world's forests, and its woodlands still provide essential habitat for a wide range of flora and fauna. But while significant pockets of forestland still dot the continent, Europe's forest holdings are not what they once were. The UN Environment Programme (UNEP) estimates that 56 percent of Europe's original forests (over 4 million square kilometers) have been lost, and that development of European woodlands has been so extensive that less than 10 percent of the forestland that remains in Western Europe is classified as being in an even seminatural state (UN Environment Programme et al., *European Forests and Protected Areas,* 2000; European Environment Agency, *Europe's Environment,* 1998).

Most of the intact forestlands that still exist on the continent are confined to Central and Eastern Europe, where populations densities are lighter and economic resources more limited than in the West; and Russia, a nation that still boasts massive forest holdings from St. Petersburg to the Far East. With the exception of these large tracts of coniferous forests in Russia and other regions of the sparsely populated north, Europe's forests are fragmented, divided into numerous small wooded areas by urban development, road construction, and agricultural expansion (UN Environment Programme et al., *European Forests and Protected Areas,* 2000).

Today's European Forests Shaped by Ice Age and Exploitation

Today, the diversity of European languages and cultures is matched by the ecological diversity of the continent's forests. Europe has six distinct climatic zones that have fostered the development of a wide variety of forests, ranging from the wet boreal forests of Scandinavia and northern Russia to the cork oak and Aleppo pine forests of the dry Mediterranean region. In all, scientists recognize between twenty and sixty-six distinct European forest types, depending on the precision of the classification scheme that is used (Polunin and Walters, *A Guide to the Vegetation of Britain and Europe,* 1985).

The character of these forests, however, would be much different were it not for major climatic changes that occurred thousands of years in the past. About 12,000 years ago, at the end of the last Ice Age, Europe was covered by a wooded tundra of grasses, dwarf birch trees, junipers, and willows. The continental ice sheet, which extended as far south as London, obliterated previous forests and acted as a "filter" on the trees that would later colonize the expanding forests of Europe. Species such as Douglas fir, which can still be found in abundance along the Pacific Coast of North America, grew in Europe in prehistoric times but found no home there after the ice retreated.

The climate warmed in the wake of the retreating ice, allowing successive waves of trees to colonize the scarred landscape. Adapting to Europe's complex climate regimes, forests differentiated into distinct types with locally adapted tree species. The mild, wet conditions of Central and Western Europe allowed forests of beech, oak, and hornbeam to develop. In the colder climates of Scandinavia, Poland, and Eastern Europe, the landscape was occupied by extensive boreal forests dominated by Norway spruce, fir, and larch. Oak, yew, and birch woods occupied the wet Atlantic coasts of Europe. The Mediterranean Basin—the area occupied today by southern France, Spain, Italy, and Greece—were covered by forests of pine and oak trees that were adapted to survive drought and periodic forest fires (ibid.).

The virgin postglacial forests of the Mediterranean provided both the backdrop and raw material for the unfolding drama of Classical civilization. For thousands of years, wood was a strategic resource, required for subsistence, commerce, and the waging of war. Wood and charcoal were essential household fuels for 5,000 years. Wood fuel was also important in the development of metalworking, and large timbers were needed to construct buildings and the ships that ensured sea power. The effects of this early exploitation of the Mediterranean forest were disastrous. For example, during the early Christian era the harbor in Ravenna, Italy, became so filled with silt carried downstream from denuded upland areas that Ravenna was transformed into an inland town (Thirgood, *Man and the Mediterranean Forest,* 1981).

Deforestation continued into the last millennium, with population growth and ship building among the principal factors driving the process. From the sixteenth to the nineteenth centuries, a renewed frenzy of ship building fueled the expansion of European empires. By the middle of the nineteenth century, war ships were being made of iron. But demand for wood remained high, driven by the continent's rapidly industrializing economy and its burgeoning population.

As European economies made the transition from subsistence to industrial economies, the exploitation of forests for multiple products by rural peasants was supplanted by the raising of forest plantations to feed the timber industry. For a while the old and new economies coexisted. Even as new technology made the manufacture of paper from wood pulp possible during the late nineteenth century, for example, 50 percent of Germany's timber harvest was still used for home heating (Schulz, "The Development of Wood Utilization in the 19th, 20th and 21st Centuries," 1993). Also around this time, foresters of the German school began to reverse several centuries of forest loss through the use of high-yield conifer plantations. Between 1878 and 1913, more than 350,000 hectares of new plantations were established in Germany. These usually contained a single species of tree, most often a conifer such as Norway spruce. These plantations helped meet the demand for wood products and may have somewhat relieved pressure on natural forests that might otherwise have been harvested for paper-making or home construction. But the monocultural orientation of these tree farms is believed to have had a deleterious effect on regional biodiversity.

In the late nineteenth century, public concern about the ecological impact of Europe's enthusiastic exploitation of its forest resources became evident. As early as 1877, a British statute declared that the New Forest should be conserved for its "ancient and ornamental values" (Goriup et al., *The New Forest Woodlands*, 1999). At the same time, the back-to-nature forestry movement led by Karl Geyer promoted the replacement of single-species plantations with multiple-species stands that could support a greater range of birds and other wildlife. However, Europe's population increased from about 274 million in 1850 to 727 million in 1995, with concomitant increases in the demand for wood, expansion and industrialization of agriculture, and proliferation of roads and cities.

In the second half of the twentieth century, the area of Europe technically under forest cover actually increased, boosted by increased investment in tree plantations, expansion of the continent's system of protected natural areas, and afforestation of abandoned agricultural lands. Moreover, foresters in many European countries came to believe that sustainable rates of timber harvest had been formulated and put in place. But since the early 1980s, concerns about Europe's stewardship of its forest resources have grown. "Many forests have undergone a loss of authenticity, measured in terms of both their composition of species and of the natural ecological processes they harbour. Environmental benefits, including soil conservation and contribution to the stability of hydrological systems, have also declined. Tree health and the health of other forest species has also degenerated in some areas, partly because of air pollution. Along with these ecological issues, the emphasis on timber production has meant that some forests have declined in social worth, for example, in their capacity for nonwood products and their recreational and aesthetic value" (Institute for European Environmental Policy, *European Environmental Almanac,* 1995). In addition, unceasing development pressure continues to eat away at the extent and quality of Europe's forest resources. Between 1990 and 1996, for example, 25,000 hectares of land—including large swaths of forest—were appropriated for new roads in the European Union (European Environment Agency, *Are We Moving in the Right Direction?,* 2000).

Inevitably, such patterns of conversion have taken a cumulative toll on Europe's forested wilderness areas over the years. "Natural forests proper are very rare in present-day Europe," confirmed one researcher. "The majority of them are in the boreal coniferous zone of European Russia and in small areas of Finland, Sweden, and Norway. Only isolated remnants can be found in remote and mostly inaccessible mountain areas in Europe. All other European forests are man-made tree communities maintained by silvicultural and logging measures" (Kuusela, *Forest Resources in Europe,* 1994). Indeed, it was estimated by the late 1990s that less than 1 percent of the old-growth forests in Europe (excluding Russia) remained intact (Worldwatch Institute, *State of the World,* 1998).

European Forest Holdings by Region

Europe's total land area, including the Russian Federation, amounts to approximately 2.26 billion hectares (5.58 billion acres). Of this land mass, approximately 1.039 billion hectares (2.57 billion acres)—46 percent of the continent's total land area—is forest area. This total includes 1.007 billion hectares of natural forest and 32 million hectares of forest plantation (UN Food and Agriculture Organization, *State of the World's Forests,* 2001).

In terms of total forest area, the holdings of the Russian Federation overshadow those of any other nation on the planet. Indeed, the Russian forest accounts for 22 percent of the world's total forest area (by comparison, Canada and the United States together account for only about 13 percent of the global total). Russian forests cover an estimated 851 million hectares (2.1 billion acres), more than thirty-one times the holdings of Sweden (27.1 million hectares/67 million acres), the European country with the next highest amount of forest area. Other European nations with significant forest area include Finland (21.9 million hectares/54 million acres), France (15.3 million hectares/37.8 million acres), Spain (14.4 million hectares/35.6 million acres), Germany (10.7 million hectares/26.4 million acres), Italy (10 million hectares/24.7 million acres), Ukraine (9.6 million hectares/23.7 million acres), and Belarus (9.4 million hectares/23.2 million acres) (UN Food and Agriculture Organization, *State of the World's Forests,* 2001).

But while these countries contain the largest tracts of remaining forestland in Europe, several of them maintain forests over only a modest percentage of their total land area. Less than 28 percent of the total land area of France, for example, is forested, and only 30 percent of the land within Germany's borders is covered with forest. The remaining land in these countries is either unsuited to support forests or has been sacrificed for farming, transportation, mining, settlement, and other purposes. Moreover, many of the forests that remain in natural and seminatural condition in France, Germany, and other Western European states are small and isolated from one another by cities, villages, farm fields, roads, and rail lines.

Conversely, several Central and Eastern European states, including Austria, Belarus, Estonia, Latvia, Slovenia, and Slovakia, are still graced with forests that blanket more than 40 percent of their land. The highest percentages of forest cover in Europe can be found at the continent's northernmost latitudes, where Sweden (66 percent) and Finland (72 percent) both maintain significant forested areas (UN Food and Agriculture Organization, *State of the World's Forests,* 2001). These percentages are considerably higher than those of Russia, where forests cover half (50.4 percent) the land. Nonetheless, the overall state of Eurasian forest resources remains far more dependent on the extent and health of Russia's forests than that of any other single nation.

The "Endless" Forests of Russia

Armed with the largest land area in the world, Russia has the forest resources to match. Unbroken pavilions of forestland can be found across all ten time zones of Russia's Eurasian landmass, from the vast steppes west of the Ural Mountain Range to the Kamchatka Peninsula in the Russian Far East. But contrary to romantic conceptions, "the Russian forest is no longer a boundless belt of unbroken wilderness. It is better described as a belt of intact fragments that are separated from each other by areas affected either by land use or its side effect" (Dobrynin et al., *Atlas of Russia's Intact Forest Landscapes,* 2002). Large areas of ancient forest untouched by human hand do exist, especially on the Kamchatka Peninsula and among the mountains of southern Siberia. But across much of European Russia, Siberia, and the Russia Far East, industrial logging, agricultural cultivation, mineral and oil exploration and excavation, and road construction—as well as massive human-induced fires that often accompany such activities—have caused significant disturbance and fragmentation of wilderness habitat (ibid.).

Recent analyses indicate that only a little more than one-quarter of Russia's mighty forests remain essentially undisturbed, even though many forests are set in isolated, swampy, and cold regions that make commercial exploitation

Taiga and River near Lake Baikal, Russia WOLFGANG KAEHLER/CORBIS

Table 4.1 Forest Resources in Europe by Subregion

Subregion	*Land area*	*Forest area 2000*					*Area change 1990–2000 (total forest)*	
		Natural forest	*Forest plantation*	*Total forest*				
	000 ha	*000 ha*	*000 ha*	*000 ha*	*%*	*ha/ capita*	*000 ha/ year*	*%*
Northern Europe	129 019	63 332	1 613	64 945	50.3	2.5	70	0.1
Central Europe	196 358	47 766	4 114	51 880	26.4	0.2	152	0.3
Southern Europe	163 750	47 397	4 327	51 723	31.6	0.3	233	0.5
Belarus, Republic of Moldova, Russian Federation, Ukraine	1 770 830	848 742	21 961	870 703	49.2	4.1	423	0.0
Total Europe	2 259 957	1 007 236	32 015	1 039 251	46.0	1.4	881	0.1
Total World:	*13 063 900*	*3 682 722*	*186 733*	*3 869 455*	*29.6*	*0.6*	*–9 391*	*–0.2*

SOURCE: UN FAO *Global Forest Resources Assessment*, 2000.

difficult. Across Russia, a total of 289 million hectares (714 million acres) of forest remain in areas at least 50,000 hectares (123,500 acres) in size that have no signs of infrastructure or modern land use. Eastern Siberia is the most pristine of all regions, with 39 percent of its forest zone intact in large sections. The Russian Far East has 30 percent, while about 25 percent of Western Siberia's forests are intact (ibid.). The forests of European Russia are regarded as the least pristine, with only 9 percent to 14 percent of forests still essentially undisturbed by human activity (ibid.; Yaroshenko, et al., *The Last Intact Forest Landscapes of Northern European Russia*, 2001).

The gradual but steady loss and fragmentation of forestland in Russia has reduced many forests to the point that they can no longer "sustain the full array of components and functions characteristic of a natural forest landscape.

Without decisive action within the next few years, intact forest landscapes may disappear within whole ecological regions and even vegetation zones" (Dobrynin, *Atlas of Russia's Intact Forest Landscapes,* 2002). Indeed, strong concerns have been raised about the long-term viability of some of the region's richest forest ecosystems.

Table 4.2 Total Area within the Forest Zone and within Intact Forest Landscapes in Russian Subregions

Areas of different land categories in Russia, million hectares

Land category	*Russia*	*European Russia*	*Western Siberia*	*Eastern Siberia*	*Russian Far East*
Area of investigation– the forest zone of Russia	1,118.4	345.9	234.1	397.3	141.1
Forest land within the area of investigation	876.9	198.4	160.5	375.5	142.5
Intact forest landscapes	288.5	31.8	58.4	153.9	44.4
Intact forests within intact forest landscapes	216.4	24.0	36.7	125.9	29.8
Intact forest landscapes with special protection within *zapovedniks,* national parks, federal *zakazniks* and nature monuments	14.4				

(*continues*)

Table 4.2 *(continued)*

Portion of the landscape that remains in intact forest landscapes and in intact forest, percent.

Land category	*Russia*	*European Russia*	*Western Siberia*	*Eastern Siberia*	*Far East*
Portion of the entire forest zone (all ecosystems) that remains in intact forest landscapes	26%	9%	25%	39%	31%
Portion of the forest within the forest zone that remains in intact forest landscapes	25%	12%	23%	34%	21%

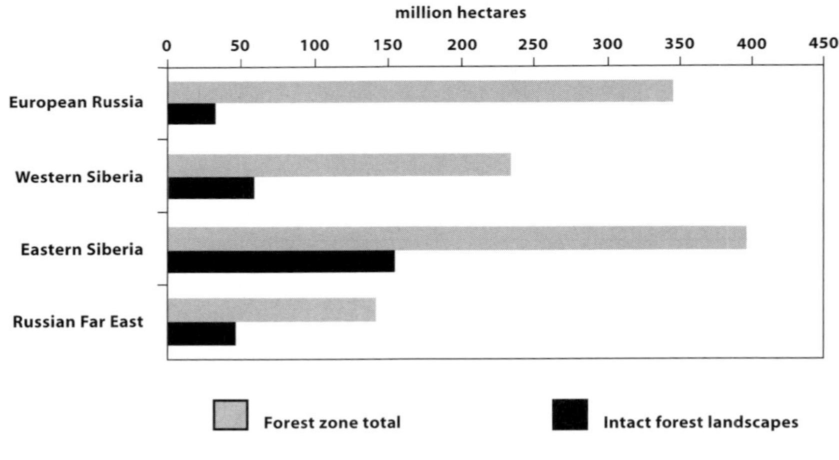

SOURCE: Dmitry Dobrynin et al. 2002. *Atlas of Russia's Intact Forest Landscapes.* Washington, DC: World Resources Institute.

The most biodiversity-rich and productive forest landscapes of southern Siberia, the Russian Far East, and of European Russia are also the most transformed. These areas are steadily diminishing due to continued extensive "development" of natural resources. The situation is most serious concerning temperate broad-leaved and mixed conifer-broad-leafed forests. Such forests are practically extinct in European Russia. The same fate may befall the forests in the area surrounding the mountain range of Sikhote-Alin, which contain the

> richest biodiversity in Russia. Intact landscapes remain, but only in the most inaccessible mountainous locations. Almost all of the unique, far-eastern broad-leaved and mixed conifer-broad-leaved forests have been affected by industrial logging during the last decade. (ibid.)

Conservationists and scientists believe that the leading threats to Russia's remaining forests—and the flora and fauna that make their home within—include industrial logging operations, oil and mineral exploration and extraction, and human-induced fires. Environmental degradation associated with these impacts is already very evident in European Russia and administrative regions in the south, which not coincidentally are among the more highly populated regions of the country. Among the forest conservation options being encouraged by the environmental community is the inclusion of additional forest areas in formal protected area programs. Already, approximately 5 percent of Russia's intact forest landscapes—about 14 million hectares, or 34.6 million acres—enjoy such protection. But in this era of economic growth and international trade, forests that are not chosen for such protection appear increasingly vulnerable to environmentally unsustainable logging practices and other forms of exploitation. These concerns further intensified in 2000 when Russia abolished its forest management authority, which was widely regarded as an effective steward of forest wilderness areas, and transferred its functions to the Ministry of Natural Resources, which has historically exhibited a strong proexploitation orientation.

"Decisions about the conservation and use of the remaining intact forest landscapes [in Russia] must no doubt reflect a complex range of ecological, social, and economic factors," acknowledged one researcher. "At this stage it is reasonable to suggest only that forestry practices observe all possible precautionary measures and make it a concrete goal to preserve sufficiently large and representative reference areas of wild nature. This is especially important and urgent in European Russia and the southern parts of Siberia and the Russian Far East, where intact forest landscapes are particularly rare and threatened" (ibid.).

Major Issues in European Forest Health

As the largest and the most diversified of terrestrial ecosystems, healthy and abundant forestlands constitute a vital part of the global environment. Indeed, the benefits that accrue from healthy forests are both numerous and important. For instance, forested watersheds are less vulnerable to flooding during spring runoff or heavy thunderstorms, and they help to filter out pollutants.

They also minimize erosion and siltation that can damage ecologically vital rivers and streams, and they help regulate climate by acting as sinks for carbon dioxide, a major greenhouse gas that would otherwise enter the atmosphere. Most of all, forests are centers of wildlife habitat, providing shelter, feeding, and breeding areas for a cornucopia of creatures great and small.

But Europe's forests have been buffeted by a host of negative forces over the centuries, rendering them among the continent's most heavily stressed natural resources. More recently, leading obstacles to rejuvenation of Europe's forests have included extensive damage from acid rain and other pollutants (especially in Northern and Central Europe), introduction of plantation sectors that have largely displaced native species, fragmentation of forests into small patches that are unable to sustain wildlife that require large territories, outright destruction of large swaths of forest in the face of ever-growing development pressure, and natural events such as wildfires and severe storms. Following is a brief discussion of some of these forces and their impact on the ecological integrity of Europe's forests.

Acid Rain

Acid rain, which is formed by emissions of nitrous oxides and sulfur dioxide associated with the burning of fossil fuels, has bedeviled European forests, lakes, and streams for more than a century. It has proven particularly menacing in Northern Europe. Forests and waterways in Sweden, Finland, Norway, Austria, and Switzerland have all suffered extensive degradation as a result of acid deposition over the years.

Over the past two decades, however, European nations have made major strides in reducing their emissions of pollutants responsible for acidification. The member states of the European Union, for example, have reduced their emissions of sulfur dioxide—the leading cause of acid rain and a health hazard for children, the elderly, and those with respiratory illnesses—by 70 percent since 1980, with emissions of all acidifying gases falling by 32 percent between 1990 and 1998. These reductions have been realized both through individual initiatives and multilateral agreements such as the 1999 Convention on Long-Range Transboundary Air Pollution (CLRTAP), or Gothenberg Protocol, which established ambitious emission reduction goals for sulfur dioxide, nitrous oxides, and other pollutants. Efforts to reduce nitrous oxide emissions, however, have been less successful, with most of the continent's modest gains in this regard attributed to decreased industrial activity in Eastern Europe in the early 1990s (European Environment Agency, *Environmental Signals 2001*, 2001)

Today, forest loss and other problems associated with acid rain are much less of a problem than they were two or three decades ago. But 10 percent of

Europe's total land area is still suffering excessive levels of acid deposition, and the extent of land subject to acid rain damage has actually increased in France, Greece, and Ireland because of continued high emissions of acidifying substances in those and neighboring nations (ibid.).

Population Density

Europe's forests occupy a landscape characterized by some of the greatest population densities and highest levels of industrial activity in the world. Today, Europe is home to more than 720 million people distributed through forty-seven countries, including the Russian Federation. Not surprisingly, forest cover tends to be lightest in those European countries with the highest population densities. On average, there are about 0.44 hectare of forest for each European (by comparison, per capita forest area in forest-rich, thinly populated Canada is 8.26 hectares per person). Within Europe, the densely populated United Kingdom had only 0.04 hectare of forest per person in 1995. Germany, the country where modern forestry was born, had 0.13 hectare of forest per person, while Russia and Finland, which have relatively sparse populations in a large land-base, had 5.16 and 3.92 hectares per person, respectively (Gardner-Outlaw, *Forest Futures,* 1999).

Ownership and Exploitation

The forests of Europe are primarily controlled and managed by individual governments at the federal level. However, in a number of prominent European countries, including France, Italy, Spain, and Sweden, local public bodies, such as municipalities and communes, account for more than half the publicly owned area. In addition, private landowners (both individual property owners and timber companies) have extensive holdings in some states (UN Economic Commission for Europe, *Forest Resources of Europe,* 2000).

Overall, the proportion of private ownership of forests in Western Europe (excluding countries with economies in transition) is 66 percent. Across Europe, it is estimated that there are about 77,000 forest holdings that are publicly owned and another 10.7 million that are in private ownership. The average size of public holdings is 1,200 hectares and that of private holdings 10.6 hectare. The latter figure reflects the wide divergence that can be found in the size of private forest holdings. Some European timber companies maintain vast forest holdings—both of the natural and plantation varieties—but there are also several million private owners in Europe with holdings of less than 3 hectares (ibid.).

In countries with significant private ownership of forestland, intensive management of the resource is the rule rather than the exception. "Over the last few decades forests have, like farmland, been managed with increasing intensity, and a comparable range of environmental problems has resulted. Plantations and intensively managed forests are changing the nature of forests, narrowing the variety of the tree species mix and genetic variation within species. An expanding area of Europe is covered with conifer monoculture and in many countries, including the UK and Denmark, the majority of these plantation trees are of non-native species" (Institute for European Environmental Policy, *European Environmental Almanac,* 1995). However, increasing areas of forests in some countries, such as Finland and Sweden, are owned by people who maintain the resource primarily for recreational purposes. In these cases, philosophies of stewardship tend to emphasize long-term ecological health over short-term exploitation (ibid.).

In recent years, several Western Europe nations have sought to establish binding regional policies in the realm of forestry management and forest protection, but these have yet to take hold in any meaningful way. For the most part, nations still forge forest management and conservation policies on their own, and regional consensus has been limited to agreements on general principles for sustainable forest management and habitat protections (such as in the First and Second Ministerial Conferences on the Protection of Forests in Europe). In the meantime, ownership of forests in Central and Eastern Europe is rapidly passing from public to private hands as individual countries continue their post-Soviet-era privatization of government assets and their transition to market economies. This trend holds both promise and peril according to those who are urging increased conservation of the region's forest resources. On the one hand, knowledge of environmentally sustainable forestry practices is on the upswing, which may bode well for some forests that enter into private ownership. But it is also feared that some forests will inevitably be exploited for short-term financial gain by logging interests, and they point out that once forestlands pass into private ownership, they are no longer candidates for inclusion in protected area systems.

Natural Events

As they have for countless millennia, Europe's forests continue to be shaped by storms, forest fires, insect infestations, diseases, and other naturally occurring events. In recent years, such events have had a particularly large impact on forest ecosystems. In 2000, for example, prolonged droughts further parched the semiarid Mediterranean region, creating tinderbox conditions in several countries. As a result, Spain, Italy, France, and Greece all endured difficult wildfire years, with Greece alone losing an estimated 150,000 hectares. In

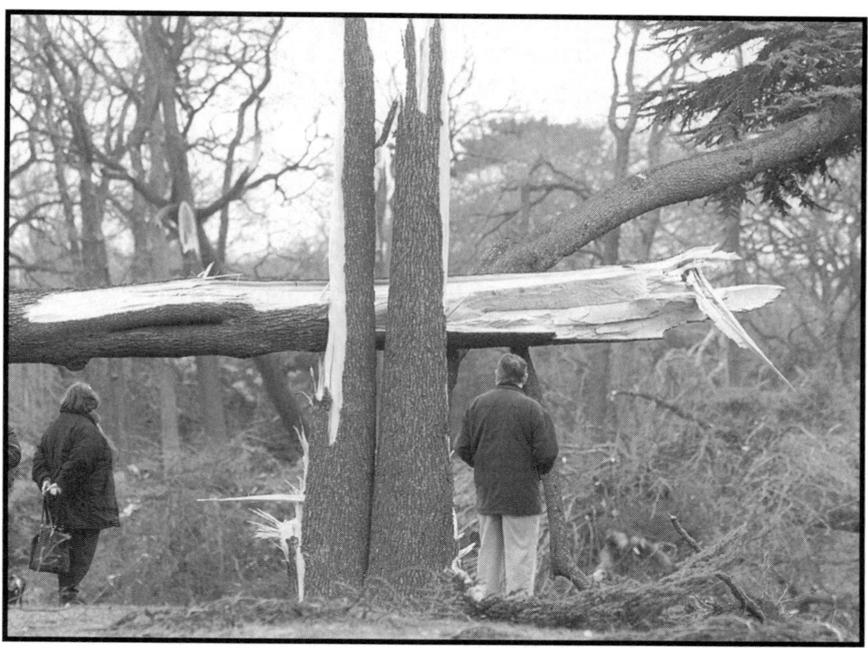

Parisians stand near a large broken tree in Paris's Bois de Boulogne the morning after a freak storm that decimated large swaths of French forestland. REUTERS NEWMEDIA INC./CORBIS

the Balkans, Bulgaria, Romania, and Croatia have also suffered through costly wildfire seasons in recent years, and in Russia, an estimated 4.3 million to 7.1 million hectares of forestland were lost to wildfires in 1998 alone (Mutch and Goldammer, "Special Report on Forest Fires," 2000).

European forests have also suffered extensive damage from windstorms in recent years. In December 1999, for example, severe windstorms wreaked considerable destruction on forest areas in Denmark, Sweden, France, Germany, and Switzerland. These storms left "a changed landscape in their wake," according to the UN Food and Agriculture Organization. "An estimated 193 million meters of material was felled, and windfalls in some countries equaled several years' harvests. In total, the damage represented six months of Europe's normal harvest. The consequences of the storms were far-reaching. They had a substantial impact on many people's livelihoods and severely affected forests, forest-based industries and current and future markets."

France was particularly hard hit by the storms, losing the equivalent of two annual timber harvests in a matter of hours. In the aftermath of the event, France and other countries undertook a somber review of forest management policies in hopes of reducing susceptibility to severe storms in the future.

Potential changes that could take root as a result of these reviews include increased reliance on natural regeneration and the use of a greater variety of species, including hardwoods (UN Food and Agriculture Organization, *State of the World's Forests,* 2001).

Forest Biodiversity and Protected Areas

Not surprisingly, large protected forested areas are currently concentrated in those countries that still have large areas of forest. For example, forty-five of the fifty largest protected areas in Europe are contained in Russia and the Nordic countries. Protected forest areas in much of the rest of Europe, by contrast, tend to be small and isolated from one another. Indeed, 95 percent of Europe's protected forests measure less than 10 square kilometers in size, and all of Europe contains only 329 protected forests that are greater than 100 square kilometers in area (UN Environment Programme et al., *European Forests and Protected Areas,* 2000).

The dearth of large, intact forests outside of Russia has had a major impact on the continent's biodiversity. By the close of the twentieth century, it was believed that Europe was home to more than 230,000 species of birds, mammals, freshwater fish, reptiles, amphibians, invertebrates, and higher plants (Delbaere, *Facts and Figures on Europe's Biodiversity 1998–1999,* 1998). However, large numbers of these species are endangered or in decline (see sidebar, page 87). Europe-wide, half of all mammals and one-third of birds and reptiles are considered to be vulnerable to or threatened with extinction (European Commission, *Natura 2000,* 2000). A great number of these endangered species are forest-dwellers, even in relatively forest-rich Scandinavia. Large mammals—such as the European brown bear, moose, bison, wolf, and beaver—were eliminated from much of their historic ranges over the course of centuries. But as we enter the twenty-first century, even formerly commonplace species are considered endangered. For example, the stag beetle, a formerly widespread insect of deciduous forests, is close to extinction or endangered in a number of European countries.

The protection of endangered species cannot be separated from the protection of their habitats. This relationship has been explicitly and repeatedly recognized by the European Union over the past three decades, a period in which numerous directives promoting stronger habitat protection and greater cooperation among countries have been adopted. Seminal initiatives for the protection of biodiversity and habitats include the International Convention on Biological Diversity (CBD), which grew out of the 1992 UN Conference on Environment and Development (the Rio Summit), and the Habitats Directive of the European Union. The CBD in turn influenced the forest habitat protection objectives laid out in the First and Second Ministerial Conferences on the Protection of Forests in Europe. The CBD also gave rise to the European

A Tale of Two Endangered Species: The European Stag Beetle and the Iberian Lynx

A pair of Iberian lynxes, the world's most endangered feline, huddle together in a special enclosure at Jerez de la Frontera Zoo in southern Spain. REUTERS NEWMEDIA INC./CORBIS

Hundreds of forest-dwelling species, both large and small, are considered to be endangered as a direct result of the decline in the extent and quality of European forests. For example, the European stag beetle (*Lucanus cervus*) is declining because the old oak forests in which it lives are themselves under threat. The stag beetle is close to extinction in the Czech Republic and in several German states. Entomologists report that the species is declining in Hungary, Portugal, the United Kingdom, Switzerland, and Sweden.

The source of the beetle's vulnerability lies in the dependence of its larvae on decaying deciduous trees. The beetles lay their eggs underground next to dead logs or stumps. The larva (or grub) will spend up to seven years inside the logs, slowly growing in size. The larvae use a wide range of woods, especially oak, but also ash, elm, sycamore, lime, hornbeam, apple, cherry, and even some garden tree varieties. However, they usually avoid coniferous species such as fir, pine, and cypress, which are the most common species on tree plantations in Europe (London Wildlife Trust, "Stag Beetle," 2002).

The fortunes of the Iberian lynx (*Lynx pardinus*) are also closely intertwined with those of Europe's forests. This creature has been called the most endangered cat in the world. Through a combination of bad luck, bad planning, and human greed, this nocturnal cat has made the transition from vulnerable (likely to become endangered) to critically endangered

(continues)

Community Biodiversity Strategy. An important objective of this strategy was to encourage sustainable forests management (SFM) with particular regard to maintaining the ecological characteristics of affected areas (European Commission, *Communication to the European Commission and to the Council and Parliament on a European Community Biodiversity Strategy,* 1998).

The most important initiative to come out of the Habitats Directive was Natura 2000, the proposed European ecological network of special conservation areas for the protection of endangered species and habitats. Designated Natura 2000 sites target the protection of 700 species and 168 different habitat types that are deemed at risk throughout the European Union (EU) (European Centre for Nature Conservation, *European Union Nature Conservation Policy and Legislation,* 2002).

The proportion of various EU member countries slated for protection is impressive. For example, Belgium, with a total area just over 30,500 square kilometers, has designated thirty-six sites totaling 4,313 square kilometers, or 14 percent of its national territory. Denmark has nearly completed its Natura 2000 network, which will protect 23.8 percent of its national territory (O'Briain and Papoulios, *Natura Barometer as of 01/03/01,* 2001). However, the designation of Natura 2000 sites in some countries is years behind sched-

(facing an 80 percent chance of extinction in the wild over three generations) over the last forty years. The Iberian lynx is a hunter of rabbits and is at home in the mosaic of open forests and pastures that make up the *dehesa*, a traditional system of mixed farming and goat grazing in Portugal and Spain. The lynxes also use cork oak forests, whose trees yield a sustainable supply of cork bark, to rear their young (Goncalves 2002).

The lynx's bad luck began in the 1950s, when a French doctor imported the rabbit disease myxamatosis to kill off rabbits that were eating his vegetables. Entire rabbit populations were wiped out, which left many lynxes to either starve or fail to reproduce. A few decades later, a fresh virus virtually eradicated rabbits from the Iberian Peninsula, and populations are now only about 5 percent of what they were in 1960 (ibid.).

The advent of the European Union then brought a flood of publicly financed dam-building projects to Spain and Portugal, encouraging the development of industrial agriculture and the deforestation that it often brings in its wake. Today, new dam projects in the Andalusia region of Spain and Portugal's Vale do Guadiana threaten important tracts of the lynx's dwindling habitat. Finally, as part of the expansion of agriculture, lynx were culled by local authorities as "vermin," and poaching continues to this day.

A 1988 survey conducted by the World Wildlife Fund estimated that the region's 1,150 surviving lynx were scattered among forty-eight breeding

(continues)

ule, and member states have failed to meet every deadline for the implementation of the Habitats Directive.

A closer look at challenges facing the successful completion of the Natura 2000 network reveals a number of reasons for the delay. The only lever possessed by the EU to enforce the legally binding Habitats Directive is the withholding of regional aid payments. Another reason for delay has been strong opposition to Natura 2000 from some people living close to designated sites, many of whom may have enjoyed a previous history of unfettered free access to the forest. Local opposition is a potentially serious problem because it is diffuse and difficult to control by law. In fact, the problem was considered so serious that a conference on the subject was organized in 1998 in the United Kingdom. The conference proceedings underlined the complexities of accommodating the traditional claims of diverse user groups, who felt that control of their resource-base was being taken away by EU edict. Addressing these concerns will undoubtedly require "continuing commitment from staff who are locally based, who are known and respected, who understand local needs and aspirations" (Clifford, "Caledonian Partnership LIFE '97 Projects," 1998). Outside of the European Union, meanwhile, forest protection remains predicated on the actions of individual governments.

populations. By 2001 these estimates had been revised downward to 600, or even 200. The WWF has purchased rights to eleven areas of lynx habitat, but many other areas remain in private hands; some are excluded from the Natura 2000 habitat list. Furthermore, there is evidence that habitat protection may not be enough to save the lynx. The WWF reports that the mortality rate of young lynx in Spain's Donaña National Park is between 75 and 80 percent, as lynx are falling victim to automobile traffic in disquieting numbers. Additionally, small, isolated populations are susceptible to inbreeding that increases vulnerability to disease (Anula, "WWF WOrking to Save the Iberian Lynx," 2001).

Sources:

Anula, J. C. 2001. "WWF Working to Save the Iberian Lynx." WWF International Newsroom. http://www.panda.org/news/press/news.cfm?id=2315 (accessed March 28, 2002).

Goncalves, E. 2002. "Lynx on the Brink." *Ecologist* (February 22).

Halkka, A., and I. Lappalainen. 2001. *Insight into Europe's Forest Protection.* Gland, Switzerland: Worldwide Fund for Nature.

London Wildlife Trust. 2002. "Stag Beetle: An Advice Note for Its Conservation in London." London Wildlife Trust, n.d. http://www.wildlondon.org.uk/cons/stagbeet.htm (accessed March 28, 2002).

Sassi, J. F. 2001. "The Cat of La Mancha." *Animals Magazine* (summer).

Criteria for Sustainable Forest Management

If forests are to be managed to sustain multiple biological and economic values, there must be some way to measure the progress of forest management toward sustainability. A number of systems have been developed in Europe to assess the achievements of forest management, including the Pan European Criteria for sustainable forest management and the Forest Stewardship Council's Principles and Criteria. The Pan-European Criteria, originally adopted at the Helsinki Conference in Geneva on June 24, 1994, are as follows:

CRITERION 1: Maintenance and appropriate enhancement of forest resources and their contribution to global carbon cycles.

CRITERION 2: Maintenance of forest ecosystem health and vitality.

CRITERION 3: Maintenance and encouragement of productive functions of forests (wood and nonwood).

CRITERION 4: Maintenance, conservation, and appropriate enhancement of biological diversity in forest ecosystems.

CRITERION 5: Maintenance and appropriate enhancement of protective functions in forest management (notably soil and water).

CRITERION 6: Maintenance of other socio-economic functions and conditions.

(continues)

Forest Conservation Initiatives and Solutions

Over the past three decades, Europe has exhibited an enduring interest in confronting many of its environmental problems. As a body, the EU has responded to environmental challenges with strong directives and legislation. In 1997 alone, the EU passed approximately 170 treaties dealing with environmental issues ranging from emissions of air pollutants to protected areas (Gutkowski and Winnicki, *Restoration of Forests,* 1997). In the realm of forest protection, recent EU measures have included conventions on transboundary air pollution, directives for the conservation and protection of biodiversity (the variety of living things), the development of indicators that assess the quality of forest management, and a Europe-wide initiative to certify sustainable forestry operations. Europe is not a unitary state, however, and individual countries respond to these initiatives with their own national legislation, policies, and guidelines. These initiatives are delivered in different ways and at different rates (ECE Timber Committee, *Forest Policies and Institutions in Europe,* 2001).

Europe has also been an enthusiastic proponent of forest certification schemes, which provide formal recognition to logging operations that manage forests in environmentally sustainable ways. The total area of European forest certified by the international Forest Stewardship Council (FSC) reached 22 million hectares by 2001, more than double the 10.3 million hectares that were accredited three years earlier (see sidebar, page 90). Sweden and Poland alone accounted for more than 60 percent of this growth. National certification schemes that operate outside the FSC process have also expanded rapidly. Fully 95 percent of Finland's 21.9 million hectares of forest have been certified under the Finnish Forest Certification System, and an additional 6.9 million hectares of Norwegian and Swedish forestland have been certified under national certification schemes. In addition, a new European certification process, called the Pan-European Forest Certification Framework (PEFC) has been established to provide a framework for voluntary forest certification and a mechanism for mutual recognition among different European national systems. National PEFC governing bodies have been established in fifteen European countries (UN Food and Agriculture Organization, *State of the World's Forests*, 2001).

This strong support for forest certification programs reflects the fact that restoring the health and vitality of Europe's forests has emerged as a priority across much of Western Europe. Moreover,

A number of indicators have been developed for use in the field to assess whether a particular forest is fulfilling the criteria (Liaison Unit Vienna 2000). These criteria also form the basis of national certification schemes under the Pan-European Certification Initiative.

The nine principles and forty-seven criteria of the FSC's generic Principles and Criteria for managing natural forests cover much of the same territory but are more explicit about the social values to be maintained and the ecological characteristics to be conserved. The term "sustainable forest management" does not appear anywhere in the FSC principles on the grounds that it is difficult, if not impossible, to judge sustainability with current knowledge. Instead, the principles refer to the certification of "well-managed" forests. The principles are as follows (Forest Stewardship Council, 2000):

PRINCIPLE #1: Forest management shall respect all applicable laws of the country in which they occur, and international treaties and agreements to which the country is a signatory, and comply with all FSC Principles and Criteria.

PRINCIPLE #2: Long-term tenure and use rights to the land and forest resources shall be clearly defined, documented, and legally established.

PRINCIPLE #3: The legal and customary rights of indigenous peoples to own, use, and manage their lands, territories, and resources shall be recognized and respected.

(continues)

PRINCIPLE #4: Forest management operations shall maintain or enhance the long-term social and economic well-being of forest workers and local communities.

PRINCIPLE # 5: Forest management operations shall encourage the efficient use of the forest's multiple products and services to ensure economic viability and a wide range of environmental and social benefits.

PRINCIPLE #6: Forest management shall conserve biological diversity and its associated values, water resources, soils, and unique and fragile ecosystems and landscapes, and, by so doing, maintain the ecological functions and the integrity of the forest.

PRINCIPLE #7: A management plan—appropriate to the scale and intensity of the operations—shall be written, implemented, and kept up to date. The long term objectives of management, and the means of achieving them, shall be clearly stated.

PRINCIPLE #8: Monitoring shall be conducted—appropriate to the scale and intensity of forest management—to assess the condition of the forest, yields of forest products, chain of custody, management activities, and their social and environmental impacts.

PRINCIPLE #9: Management activities in high conservation value forests shall maintain or enhance the attributes which define such forests. Decisions regarding high conservation value forests shall always be considered in the context of a precautionary approach.

An additional principle and its associated criteria covers well-managed plantations.

Sources:

Forest Stewardship Council. 2000. *FSC Principles and Criteria.* http://www.fscoax.org/html/noframes/1-2.html (accessed April 4, 2002).

Liaison Unit Vienna. 2000. Second Ministerial Conference on the Protection of Forests in Europe. http://www.mmm.fi/english/forestry/policy/minkonf (accessed March 20, 2002).

forest issues are assuming increasing prominence in areas of Central and Eastern Europe as well. Of course, "whether this good intention is translated into positive management improvements in Europe will depend on how successfully these issues are promoted in international policy forums, how seriously national governments respond to these developments, and the extent to which NGOs and other independent interest groups succeed in shifting opinions," observed one analysis. "More environmentally responsible forestry will only be achieved if forest managers and local people are convinced of the case for change. In the short term, continued threats to Europe's remaining old growth forests, which constitute a vital reservoir of species and natural ecosystems, is probably the most critical issue confronting environmentalists and policy makers in the continent today" (Institute for European Environmental Policy, *European Environmental Almanac,* 1995).

Sources:

Bryant, Dirk, et al. 1997. *The Last Forest Frontiers: Ecosystems and Economies on the Edge.* Washington, DC: World Resources Institute.

Clifford, T. 1998. "Caledonian Partnership LIFE '97 Projects: The Restoration of Atlantic Oak Woods." *Natura 2000: A People, a Partnership.* Bath, UK: United Kingdom Presidency of the European Council and the Unit for Nature Protection, Coastal Zones and Tourism of the European Community.

Council of the European Communities. "Council Directive 92/43/EEC of 21 May 1992 on the Conservation of Natural Habitats and of Wild Fauna and Flora" (last modified January 2001). http://www.ecnc.nl/doc/europe/legislat/habidire.html#ref04 (accessed March 20, 2002).

Delbaere, Ben, ed. 1998. *Facts and Figures on Europe's Biodiversity: State and Trends 1998–1999.* Tilburg, the Netherlands: European Centre for Nature Conservation.

Dobrynin, Dmitry, et al. 2002. *Atlas of Russia's Intact Forest Landscapes.* Washington, DC: World Resources Institute.

ECE Timber Committee. 2001. *Forest Policies and Institutions in Europe, 1998–2000.* Geneva Timber and Forest Study Papers, No. 19 ECE/TIM/SP/19. Geneva: United Nations.

European Centre for Nature Conservation. "European Union Nature Conservation Policy and Legislation." http://www.ecnc.nl/doc/europe/legislat/conveu.html (accessed March 20, 2002).

European Commission. 1998. *Communication to the European Commission and to the Council and Parliament on a European Community Biodiversity Strategy.* Luxembourg: European Commission.

———. 2000. *Natura 2000: Managing Our Heritage.* Luxembourg: European Commission.

European Environment Agency. 1995. *Europe's Environment: The Dobris Assessment.* Copenhagen: EEA.

———. 1998. *Europe's Environment: The Second Assessment.* Copenhagen: EEA.

———. 1999. *Environment in the European Union at the Turn of the Century.* Copenhagen: EEA.

———. 2000. *Are We Moving in the Right Direction? Indicators on Transport and Environment Integration in the EU.* Copenhagen: EEA.

———. 2001. *Environmental Signals 2001.* Oxford: Elsevier Science.

Forest Stewardship Council. "FSC Europe Country Totals." http://www.certified-forests.org/data/eur_table.htm (accessed March 27, 2002).

Gardner-Outlaw, T., and R. Engelmann. 1999. *Forest Futures: Population, Consumption and Wood Resources.* Washington, DC: Population Action International.

Goncalves, E. 2002. "Lynx on the Brink." *Ecologist* (February 22).

Goriup, P., et al. 1999. *The New Forest Woodlands: A Management History.* Oxford: Forestry Commission.

Gutkowski, R. M., and T. Winnicki, eds. 1997. *Restoration of Forests: Environmental Challenges in Central and Eastern Europe.* Dordrecht: Kluwer.

Holley, D. 2001. "Poland: Seeing a Forest for the Trees." *Los Angeles Times,* June 2.

Institute for European Environmental Policy. 1995. *European Environmental Almanac.* Edited by Jonathan Hewett. London: Earthscan.

Kiekens, J. P. 2000. "Certification: International Trends, and Forestry and Trade Implications." European Forest Institute. http://www.efi.fi/cis/english/resources/kiekens.html (accessed March 27, 2002).

Kuusela, Kullervo. 1994. *Forest Resources in Europe, 1950–1990.* Cambridge: Cambridge University Press.

Mutch, R., and J. Goldammer. 2000. "Special Report on Forest Fires." *Global Forest Resources Assessment 2000.* Rome: UN Food and Agriculture Organization.

Natura 2000: A People, A Partnership. Proceedings of Conference held in Bath UK on 28–30 June 1998. 1998. Bath, UK: United Kingdom Presidency of the European Council and the Unit for Nature Protection, Coastal Zones and Tourism of the European Community.

O'Briain, M., and F. Papoulios. 2001. "Natura Barometer as of 01/03/01." *Natura 2000 Newsletter* (April 14).

Pan-European Forest Certification Council. 2001. "Pan-European Forest Certification Framework: Common Elements and Requirements." Luxembourg: Pan-European Forest Certification Council.

Pisarenko, A. I., et al. 2001. *Development of Forest Resources in the European Part of the Russian Federation.* Leiden, the Netherlands: Koninklijke Brill.

Polunin, O., and M. Walters. 1985. *A Guide to the Vegetation of Britain and Europe.* Oxford: Oxford University Press.

Schulz, H. 1993. "The Development of Wood Utilization in the 19th, 20th and 21st centuries." *Forestry Chronicle* 69.

Thirgood, J. V. 1981. *Man and the Mediterranean Forest: A History of Resource Depletion.* New York: Academic.

Tomlinson, G. H. 1990. *Effects of Acid Deposition in Europe and North America.* London: CRC.

UN Economic Commission for Europe and UN Food and Agriculture Organization. 2000. *Forest Resources of Europe, CIS, North America, Australia, Japan, and New Zealand: Main Report.* New York and Geneva: United Nations.

UN Environment Programme, World Conservation Monitoring Centre, and World Wildlife Fund. 2000. *European Forests and Protected Areas Gap Analysis: Technical Report.* Cambridge: UNEP, WCMC, WWF.

UN Food and Agriculture Organization. 2001. *State of the World's Forests 2001.* Rome: United Nations.

Worldwatch Institute. 1998. *State of the World 1998.* Washington, DC: Worldwatch.

Yaroshenko, A. Y., Peter V. Potapov, and S. A. Turubanova. 2001. *The Last Intact Forest Landscapes of Northern European Russia.* Washington, DC: Global Forest Watch and Greenpeace Russia.

Agriculture

—Kathryn Miles

Europe has enjoyed a long and rich tradition of agriculture, and rural farmland has long been a vital and colorful thread in the continent's fabric of landscapes and wildlife habitats. Indeed, many European farming systems have historically worked in harmony with the environment, helping nurture a rich diversity of plants, birds, mammals, and insects. But as European agriculture enters the twenty-first century, it confronts a major challenge to make today's dominant farming practices more environmentally sustainable. Many elements of modern farming, including crop monoculture, irrigation, heavy use of inorganic fertilizers and pesticides, and intensive land conversion, have fundamentally changed the face of Europe's landscape in undesired ways. Negative environmental impacts directly linked to farming practices include habitat loss, aquifer depletion, and land and water degradation. These intensifying problems have made agricultural sustainability an increasingly visible legislative and management priority at the local, national, regional, and continental levels.

Trends in European Agriculture

Approximately 44 percent of Europe's total land area is currently devoted to agriculture, but the amount of land set aside for farming varies dramatically from region to region. In heavily forested Northern Europe, for example, only 10 percent of the land is set aside for livestock or crops. But portions of England, Ireland, and Hungary consist of around 70 percent farmland (European Environment Agency, *Environmental Signals 2002,* 2002). Typical farm size also varies by region. In the European Union, the size and scope of agricultural enterprises range from mammoth corporate-owned operations to small subsistence-style family farms, with some countries housing more of the former and others supporting a greater percentage of the latter. For example, the average farm size in 1989 was only 4 hectares in Greece but 68 hectares in the

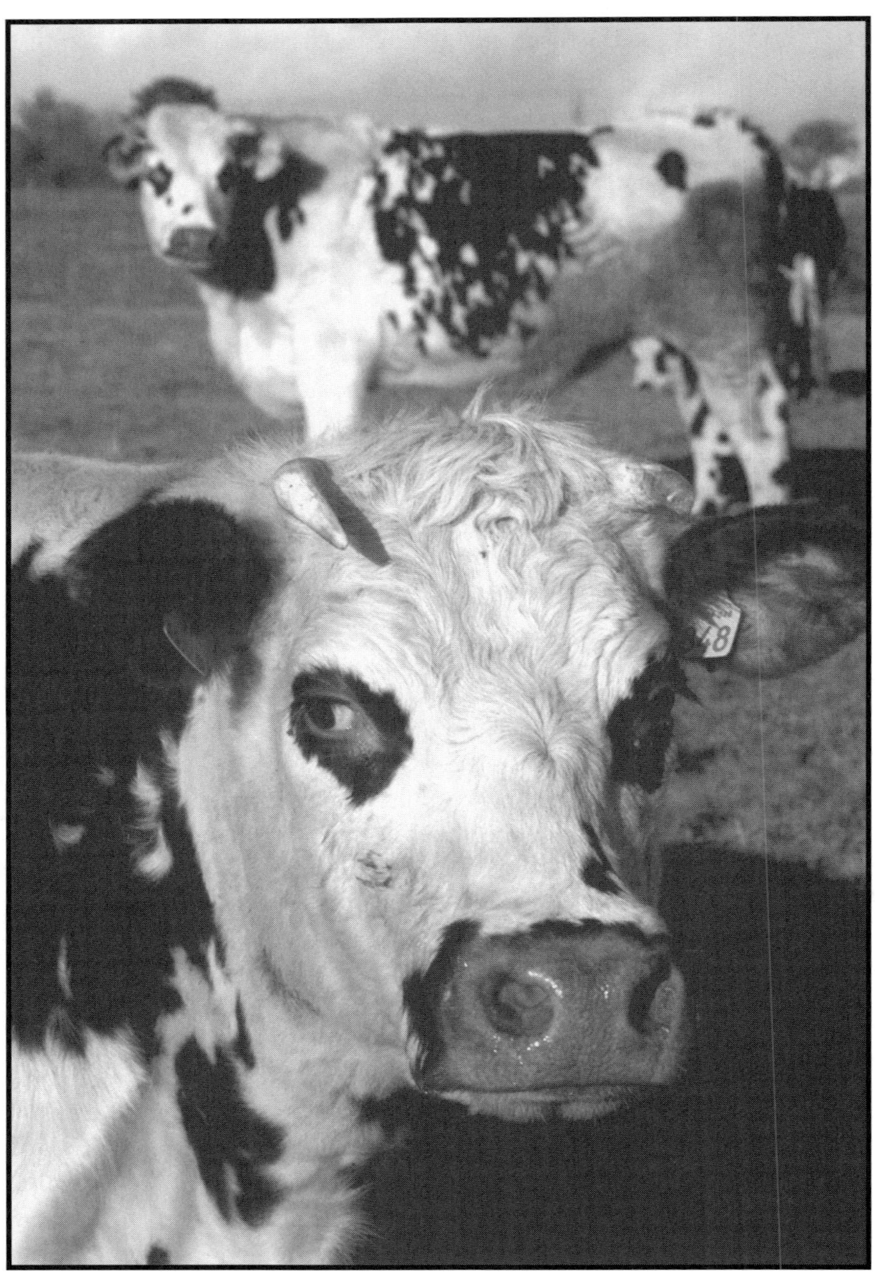

Cows with mad cow disease PREVEL FRANCK/CORBIS SYGMA

United Kingdom (European Environment Agency, *Europe's Environment,* 1995). These variations are due to a host of factors, from land use traditions, population density, and property laws to topography and climate.

Data on farming operations in Eastern and Central Europe have historically been less comprehensive, but it is believed that most farming operations in these regions are fewer than 10 hectares in size (ibid.). The modest size of these plots in comparison to those that are prevalent across much of Western Europe is undoubtedly due to the difference in governmental structures prior to the fall of the Soviet Union and subsequent struggles associated with the transition to market economies. Most Central and Eastern European countries are still oriented toward centralized land management schemes, and subsidies on the scale of those available in Western Europe—which have historically been most beneficial to large farming enterprises—remain largely beyond the financial grasp of this region. Consequently, conditions of economic hardship still prevail in rural communities, and "subsistence farming to meet family needs and bartering or exchange of goods outside formal markets have taken priority in the survival stratagems of many needy farming communities" (Institute for European Environmental Policy, *European Environmental Almanac,* 1995). Even in Eastern and Central Europe, however, the prevailing trend appears to be toward larger monocultural operations, with many new enterprises funded (and sometimes managed) by Western interests.

Mad Cow Disease Rocks Europe

The headlines were at once sobering and shocking: thirty-five people dead, hundreds of thousands of cattle destroyed, proposals to exterminate a million more, all because of a frightening malady that came to be known by the unlikely name of Mad Cow Disease. What had begun as a few cases of an unidentified illness in British cattle had become an epidemic, and it threatened all of European agriculture and the people who rely upon it for sustenance. In the end, the crisis shook European confidence in the safety of its food supplies, devastated farmers who were forced to destroy entire herds of livestock, and prompted a radical reorganization of agricultural procedures and regulations.

"Mad cow disease" is the common name given to bovine spongiform encephalopathy (BSE), a disease that affects the entire neurological system of cattle. The disease, which can lie dormant or manifest no symptoms for several years, is a degenerative

(continues)

neurological condition. Cattle contracting the disease begin to exhibit behavioral changes such as increased aggression or agitation and dementia; they also show a loss of coordination—sometimes being unable to stand or keep balance—and uncontrollable tremors or spasms in individual muscles. These symptoms arise as a result of the disease's effect on the brain: autopsies reveal that the brains of affected animals are rife with holes; the remaining tissue becomes spongy and almost liquid, particularly in the brain stem. There is no definitive explanation for this process, but scientists speculate that the disease creates self-replicating proteins known as prions that burrow into the brain. Another theory is that the disease acts as a virus (World Health Organization, "BSE Factsheet," 2002). There is no known cure for the disease, and affected animals generally die within a year of the onset of symptoms.

The first recorded case of BSE occurred in 1985, when a farmer in Sussex, England, noticed that one of his cows had developed a large tumor in its head. It eventually became unable to right itself, and it died in February of that year. Five other cows owned by the farmer died shortly thereafter. Autopsies revealed a "multifocial spongy transformation of the brain" never before seen in cattle, and the condition was given its current name (BSE Inquiry, "BSE Inquiry Report," 2000).

Scientists eventually deduced that the most common transmission of the disease seemed to be through food containing affected tissue. Indeed, cattle can contract BSE from ingesting as much as a small pebble's worth of contaminated tissue. As a result, the common practice of using slaughterhouse waste as animal feed came under intense scrutiny. This practice is attributed in large part to the intensification of farming, which places a premium on raising larger animals faster and on less land. The easiest way to accomplish those goals is to provide the animals with a high-fat, high-protein feed. In fact, prior to the mad cow outbreak it was common practice throughout Europe to take the rendered remains of animals—lungs, brain, skin, blood, and other parts of the animal not sold for human consumption—and convert it into animal food.

The epicenter of the epidemic was the United Kingdom, where 59 percent of the country's 36,060 dairy herds and nearly 20 percent of its beef herds were stricken by BSE (Kimberlin and Wilesmith, "Bovine Spongiform Encephalopathy," 2000). The World Health Organization estimates that more than 180,000 cattle in the UK contracted BSE between 1986 and 2000. The UK governmental bureau responsible for addressing this rising epidemic was the Ministry of Agriculture, Fisheries, and Food (MAFF), now known as the Department for Environment, Food and Rural Affairs (DEFRA). This agency faced the difficult challenge of simultaneously working to protect the economic interests of farmers while

(continues)

also protecting the public from food-borne hazards.

MAFF initially chose not to institute regulations concerning the spread of BSE. Their response, which may seem careless in hindsight, was based on early scientific assessments of the disease as a relatively innocuous condition similar to scrapie, a transmissible spongiform disease that occurs in sheep. There was no indication that the disease could be transmitted to other species, and thus, initially little was done to keep the affected meat out of the animal and human food chain.

As the disease began to spread, the UK established an advisory committee charged to report to the MAFF. This advisory group subsequently reported that in order to contain the spread of BSE, infected meat must be kept out of animal food chains. The UK responded by introducing a mandatory slaughter and compensation program in 1988. Because there was no indication that BSE could spread from species to species, the EU decided not to ban the use of this meat in feed and, thus, much of it continued to appear in feed destined for animals other than cattle. "One unfortunate consequence of that decision was that for the next six or so years cross-contamination occurred between feed destined for cattle and feed destined for other animals, greatly prolonging the BSE epidemic" (van Zwanenberg and Millstone, "Mad Cow Disease," 2000). It also allowed for transmission of mad cow disease to other regions of the continent, including France, Germany, and Belgium.

Policy on BSE changed dramatically in May 1990, when a domestic cat was diagnosed with a spongiform encephalopathy similar to BSE. This diagnosis raised concerns that BSE might be transmitted to humans. The EU responded by voting to require the compulsory slaughter and destruction of all animals showing signs of BSE. Estimates of the number of animals killed range from 100,000 to over 1 million. Mandatory compensation to farmers cost the EU billions (BSE Inquiry, "BSE Inquiry Report," 2000). In 1994, members of the European Union voted overwhelmingly to adopt bans that prohibit the use of animal products in farm animal feed and to enforce mandatory testing of low-risk cattle at thirty months and high-risk cattle at twenty-four months. Any animal not tested would be removed from the food chain; any animal testing positive would be destroyed.

The real severity of the BSE epidemic was not felt until 1996, when a new variation of a human spongiform encephalopathy known as Creutzfeldt-Jakob (CJ) was identified in the UK. Authorities traced the new strain of the disease to infected meat and BSE. By 1997 there were twenty-three confirmed deaths resulting from BSE-infected meat in the UK, and an estimated five to ten others in the remaining EU countries (Wilesmith, *Manual on Bovine Spongiform Encephalopathy,* 1998). Reported incidents of BSE

(continues)

have dropped dramatically since the late 1990s, and official predictions suggest that the disease will continue to decrease throughout the first decade of the twenty-first century. But while outbreaks of BSE appear to be subsiding, the effects of the epidemic remain pronounced. Intensification of animal husbandry has decreased, and the practice of using rendered slaughterhouse waste as cattle feed no longer provides cattle farmers with an inexpensive protein for their herds. More consumers are turning to organic and free-range beef in order to avoid life-threatening illnesses such as CJ. Finally, European Union agricultural policies now reflect a high level of vigilance and commitment to testing for food-borne hazards to public health.

Sources:

BSE Inquiry. 2002. "The BSE Inquiry Report," *2000*. http://www.bse.org.uk/ (accessed November 15, 2002).

Kimberlin, R. H., and J. W. Wilesmith. 2000. "Bovine Spongiform Encephalopathy." *Veterinary Record* 132.

van Zwanenberg, Patrick, and Erik Millstone. 2002. "Mad Cow Disease 1980s–2000: How Reassurances Undermined Precaution." In *The Precautionary Principle in the 20th Century*. Poul Harremous et al., eds. London: Earthscan.

Wilesmith, John W. 1998. *Manual on Bovine Spongiform Encephalopathy*. Rome: Food and Agriculture Organization of the United Nations.

World Health Organization. "BSE Factsheet." http://www.who.int/inf-fs/en/fact113.html (accessed June 20, 2002).

In Russia, meanwhile, vast farming lands long seen as symbolic of Mother Russia itself are undergoing monumentous change. In 2002 Russian President Vladimir Putin signed legislation permitting the sale and ownership of agricultural land for the first time since the Russian Revolution of 1917. This dramatic embrace of the concept of farmland as private property will almost certainly dismantle the debt-ridden collective farm structure that prevailed across the country for most of the twentieth century. Defenders of the new law contend that the switch to private ownership will facilitate desperately needed new investments in farming, which accounted for only 7.2 percent of gross domestic product in 2001, less than half of what it contributed in 1990. It also hoped that private ownership will enable Russia to reclaim some of the 45 million acres of arable land abandoned during the 1990s (McDonald, "Law Allows for Private Ownership of Agricultural Property in Russia," 2002).

The sheer number of farmers who make their living on European soil is in decline. At the beginning of the twenty-first century, farmers made up only 5 percent of the working population of Europe (European Environment Agency, *Environmental Signals,* 2002). This percentage marks a decline from only thirty years earlier, and it reflects the steep drop in the number of smaller farms in operation across Western Europe. Among the European Union's twelve founding member states, for example, more than 3 million agricultural operations disappeared between 1975 and 1995, a drop of 31 percent (from 10 million to 7 million). This downturn, coupled with an overall 10 percent reduction in agricultural land, reflects the movement toward intensive monocultural crop practices and industrial livestock operations that are most profitable when conducted on a large-scale basis. Other factors in the decreasing number of European farming and ranching establishments include economically devastating outbreaks of livestock disease (mad cow disease and foot-and-mouth disease) and fluctuating commodity prices (see sidebar, page 97). In marginal agricultural areas, rising labor costs and falling crop and livestock prices have been particularly important factors in the rise in afforestation and abandonment of farmland (European Environment Agency, *Environmental Signals,* 2001).

Intensification and Specialization

The face of the modern farm in Europe has changed dramatically over the last fifty years. Although the number of EU farm holdings fell from 10 million in 1975 to 7 million in 1997, agricultural production continued to increase on the strength of steady rises in intensification and specialization. Indeed, by the end of the twentieth century, Europe's farms had increased their production by 18 percent since 1975. These gains are evident in the livestock sector as well. The number of livestock and dairy farms fell by 47 percent and 20 percent, respectively, between 1980 and 1997, but meat and dairy production has remained constant, and in some cases has even risen slightly (European Environment Agency, *Environmental Signals,* 2001).

By the close of the twentieth century, it was estimated that approximately 62 percent of all European farmland was managed through "high-input" or "high-intensity" systems—those in which farmers rely upon frequent soil tillage, fertilizers (mostly inorganic), and chemicals such as pesticides, herbicides, and fungicides to ensure high yields (European Environment Agency, *Environmental Signals,* 2002). Intensification of crop management is most often seen in sections of France, England, Germany, and the Netherlands, while intensification of animal husbandry is most prevalent in Germany, Denmark, and parts of Italy and Spain. The intensification of agriculture

Harvesting wheat in Great Britain in 2000 RICHARD MORRELL/CORBIS

has occurred largely through the mechanization of its practices. Tilling and sowing are now accomplished through automated machinery, which tends to leave a deeper mark on the soil and allows for larger plantings. Armed with improved technologies and fertilizers, farmers have been able to lengthen the growing season and do away with the classic crop rotation system. This has been particularly true in northern countries such as Denmark, Norway, Belgium, the United Kingdom, and even northern parts of France.

In recent years farms have also become larger and highly specialized, and specialized farms now outnumber mixed farms by a ratio of greater than four to one (European Environment Agency, *Environmental Signals,* 2001). On average, existing farms have increased from 15 to 20 hectares in size, and they often produce only one crop or raise a single type of livestock. "Over the last few decades, the range of products generated by European farms has reduced, and become ever more specialised. A loss of genetic potential could result if only a small number of varieties of a crop or livestock covers a large area, or if the number of varieties being used by farmers were to decline" (European Environment Agency, *Europe's Environment,* 1995).

The Common Agricultural Policy and Europe's Environment

The European drift toward larger farming outfits and monoculture-oriented operations has been nurtured by technological changes; cheaper, faster, and more numerous product transport options; and the emergence of a global market for agricultural products. All of these factors have made farming an increasingly capital-intensive business, which further perpetuates the movement toward larger operations. But while all of the above elements have played a part, the European Union's venerable Common Agricultural Policy (CAP) has been cited as perhaps the single greatest factor in the intensification of agricultural production in Europe. Not coincidentally, it also has been criticized as a leading cause of environmental degradation on the continent. In fact, some European environmentalists see CAP reform as essential to the continent's overall efforts to preserve threatened flora and fauna and their habitat. "CAP reform is one of those issues guaranteed to make the eyes glaze over," acknowledged one UK critic. "It seems impossible to discuss the subject without getting bogged down in its complexities, and most people feel that these pan-European taxes—their levying and distribution—affect them in such marginal ways as not to be worth the considerable effort of trying to penetrate their complexities. Yet it is the Common Agricultural Policy—not road-building or urbanisation—which has been the single most destructive force for British environment and wildlife over the last 25 years" (Coward, "The CAP Doesn't Fit," 1999).

Advocates and detractors alike agree that the Common Agricultural Policy has had a profound influence on agriculture and the environment across Western Europe over the past half-century. Established in response to food shortages that followed World War II, the CAP was an early cornerstone of the European Community. The policy regulated markets, food supplies, and pricing, and subsidized a variety of inputs including fertilizers, pesticides, and irrigation schemes, all for the ultimate purpose of improving crop yields and providing European farmers with a stable and financially beneficial environment in which to operate. Working under the philosophy that community cooperation is the cornerstone of success, CAP reduced costs to individual countries by spreading out expenses among all member states. But the expense of maintaining CAP in its present form is considerable, since its rules and regulations govern the management of more than 55 percent of the whole European Union territory (European Commission, Directorate-General for Agriculture, *Common Agricultural Policy: 2000 Review,* 2001). In 2002, for example, the European Union spent half of its budget subsidizing and supporting farmers through the Common Agricultural Policy system (European Environment Agency, *Environmental Signals,* 2002).

During its lifetime, supporters of CAP in the business, agriculture, and political communities have credited its rules and regulations with boosting Europe's self-sufficiency and food security in numerous agricultural sectors. Proponents also believe that it has brought prosperity to numerous farms and their surrounding communities. But the CAP has been condemned for favoring big agribusiness over family farmers, and some members of the scientific and conservation communities contend that the program has had a shattering impact on Europe's ecosystems and the flora and fauna contained therein. Indeed, the Royal Society for the Protection of Birds (RSPB) has characterized CAP as the single biggest threat to wildlife in the United Kingdom, citing "evident links between its application and the loss of birds and other wildlife. The system of incentives to intensive agriculture, in particular, has been recognized by many as the main mechanism responsible for the severe decline

Jadwiga Lopata:
Polish Proponent of Sustainable Agriculture and Ecotourism

Polish environmental activist Jadwiga Lopata was born in the small village of Syryszow, where she learned about the rural values of helping neighbors and enjoying nature. She left the village to attend college and then took a job as a computer programmer. After a few years, however, she was forced to quit her job when it began affecting her eyesight. This experience caused her to reflect upon the state of modern society.

During the late 1980s and early 1990s, Lopata studied the relatively new industry of "nature tourism" or " ecotourism." She gradually became convinced that there was a market for eco tour experiences on Polish family farms, with their healthful, relaxing lifestyle and old-fashioned rural values. Furthermore, she believed that ecotourism could help preserve the Polish countryside and way of life she had enjoyed as a child. Lopata moved to the Netherlands for two years in order to gain work experience in the tourism industry. In 1993 she founded ECEAT (European Center for Ecological Agriculture and Tourism) to promote ecotourism in rural Poland.

Poland is home to 2 million family farms, which account for 60 percent of all farms in the country. The majority of these farms are less than 20 acres (8 hectares) in size. Although family farmers successfully resisted efforts to transform their operations into state-run collective farms under communism, they now face a new threat from the movement toward corporate farming or agribusiness. These large-scale operations generally grow a single crop using highly mechanized and chemical-intensive farming methods. Environmentalists criticize such enterprises for their unsustainable practices, which often cause degradation of land, contamination of water, and decline of rural communities.

Poland's family farmers face significant pressure to consolidate their operations and adopt western agricultural practices as the country prepares to join the European Union (EU). The Polish government has increasingly viewed small-scale farms as inefficient and unsuited to competing in world markets. Yet Lopata and other environmentalists note that family

(continues)

of many farmland bird species over the last three decades" (Royal Society for the Protection of Birds, "The Common Agricultural Policy [CAP]," 2002).

Under the Common Agricultural Policy, farming subsidies are distributed proportionally to levels of production. For example, livestock farmers receive greater levels of economic support with each head of cattle they rear, and arable farmers receive subsidies based on the amount of cropland they maintain and the size of their crop yields. This direct linkage of subsidies to production levels puts enormous pressure on farmers to utilize intensified

farmers have a strong attachment to the land and thus tend to employ sustainable agricultural practices. In addition, they argue that family farms contribute to a diverse landscape that supports a variety of wildlife. Finally, they claim that the modern agribusiness model cannot accommodate the 40 percent of Polish people who work the land. "This is our big treasure, the Polish countryside," Lopata explained. "This is what we can offer to our visitors, this really picturesque landscape still not so destroyed, nature not so poisoned, and good farmers who can in a very short time turn to organic production" (Babb, "Sustainability and Environmental Awareness," 1999).

Lopata developed a plan to help preserve Polish family farms and make them competitive in world markets. The first step in the plan was to begin converting small farms to organic farming methods. These methods were ideally suited to the small size of the farms, and organic produce generally commands premium prices. Poland already had an organic certification process in place through an organization called Ecoland. Once a farm was certified as 50 percent organic, it became eligible for the second part of Lopata's program—ecotourism.

Lopata provides family farmers with orientation and training in small business skills, health, and the philosophy of sustainability. Then these farmers become hosts for tourists who wish to enjoy an immersion experience in rural life. Guests on the farms generally spend their time walking in the countryside, hiking in nearby mountains, riding horses, swimming in lakes and ponds, and participating in farm chores such as harvesting fruit, collecting nuts and berries, milking cows, making cheese, and baking bread. Lopata built a network of eco-farms throughout Poland where tourists could spend a relaxing vacation and learn about the benefits of organic farming. "Tourism is a very good tool to spread the idea of organic agriculture and it's working, really working in practice because people become convinced when they see the production, the atmosphere on the farms," she stated. "They will speak about it to their friends, and so the circle gets bigger and bigger" (ibid.).

The eco-farm movement expanded quickly as Lopata marketed it both nationally and internationally. In 1993

(continues)

she brought 400 tourists from Western Europe to 14 Polish eco-farms. Three years later, her program had expanded to accommodate 1,200 tourists on 60 farms. The network grew to 130 farms by 2002, which played host to 13,000 tourists (70 percent from outside Poland) over a period of three years. The tourists reported high levels of satisfaction with their farm experience, with 95 percent saying that they would repeat the experience or recommend it highly to others. The movement also expanded outside of Poland: ECEAT now includes sixty centers in ten countries.

As the number of eco-farms increased, Lopata began introducing additional benefits of collaboration to the farmers, such as forming cooperatives to handle bulk buying and distribution. She also began expanding upon her idea to create eco-villages based upon sustainable farms. In 2000, Lopata cofounded the International Coalition to Protect the Polish Countryside (ICPPC) to bring public attention to the threat that EU membership poses to Poland's rural countryside. The organization launched a campaign aimed at encouraging the Polish government to make protecting the countryside and its diversity a priority during negotiations over joining the EU. "If financial and promotion aid for bio-farms, ecotourism, and bio-fuel increases, Poland can become Europe's leading organic food and renewable energy producer and ecotourist attraction," Lopata has said. "Poland should only join the EU when a way is found that will clearly support and build on the values of the Polish countryside" ("Goldman Environmental Prize Recipient Profile" 2002). Lobata has received the Ashoka Fellowship and the Goldman Environmental Prize for her work.

Sources:

"Ashoka Fellowship Profile: Jadwiga Lopata." Ashoka website. http://www.ashoka.org/fellows/viewprofile1.cfm?personid=856.

Babb, John. 1999. "Sustainability and Environmental Awareness: Keeping Farmers on Their Farms in Poland." *Changemakers.net Journal.* http://www.changemakers.net/journal/99september/babb.cfm.

"Goldman Environmental Prize Recipient Profile: Jadwiga Lopata." 2002. Goldman Prize website. http://www.goldmanprize.org/recipients/recipients.html.

farming methods that are damaging to land, water, and habitat. Intensified farming practices are heavily dependent on pesticides, fertilizers, and other agrochemicals to boost yields per hectare. Intensification also calls for the conversion of even marginally suitable land to agricultural use, and it encourages farmers to turn to high-yielding monocultural operations that disrupt natural ecosystems. Finally, intensification has created a competitive environment in which farmers can no longer afford to leave fields fallow, as they might have done in an earlier era. This not only puts additional strain on the soil but also harms birds and other creatures. "The biggest blow to bird populations was delivered when farmers abandoned the practice of ploughing back winter stubble into the ground in the spring in favour of burning off the stubble to grow a second crop. This change devastated the populations of ground-feeding birds that previously survived through the winter on the fallen grain. . . . The central principle of the CAP—that farmers should be subsidized to maximize agricultural output, irrespective of market forces—has flogged the countryside to within an inch of its life" (Coward, "The CAP Doesn't Fit," 1999).

Over the years, the CAP's rules and regulations have been repeatedly adjusted to address economic issues, but reforms to address environmental concerns are a relatively recent phenomenon. Even in the late 1990s, habitat protection and other conservation concerns were criticized by environmentalists as an afterthought in CAP implementation. But awareness of environmental problems associated with intensive, monoculture-oriented agriculture has grown, and members of the environmental, organic farming, scientific, and legislative communities are calling for a shift in CAP support away from intensive food production and toward environmental protection and sustainable models of rural development.

Already, some changes to the Common Agricultural Policy have been made to address environmental concerns. One of the first visible manifestations that the European Union was aware of the CAP's environmental shortcomings came in 1987. At that time, the EU formally acknowledged that environmental sustainability should be one of CAP's chief operational priorities. The EU subsequently passed the MacSharry Reform of CAP in 1992 and Agenda 2000, both of which worked to reform the yield-driven support of the original CAP by introducing "accompanying measures"—principally financial initiatives that compensate farmers for environmentally friendly practices. These agri-environment schemes include taking steps to ensure greater biodiversity, implanting drip irrigation, substituting organic fertilizers for inorganic fertilizers, and maintaining or introducing larger riparian buffer zones. By the close of the twentieth century, CAP was supporting agri-environmental measures for 20 percent of Europe's farmland, with some countries, such as Finland, devoting 80 percent of their farmland to agri-environmental schemes (Fay, "Impact of Agri-Environment Measures," 2002). In most countries, administration of these policies is the responsibility of agricultural authorities, and environmental authorities work to develop programs and assess their implementation.

Recent CAP reforms have also belatedly addressed agriculture's role in the diminishment of European wildlife habitat and biodiversity. In 1994 several European countries determined to include "the conservation and sustainable use of agricultural biological diversity" as part of its objectives and provisions (European Commission, *Agriculture, Environment, Rural Development,* 1999). The European Union then followed up by creating the EU-Agricultural Action Plan on Biodiversity. This plan acknowledges both the negative and

Table 5.1 Organic Farming as Percentage of Total Land in European Countries

Country	*1987*	*1991*	*1995*	*1999*
		percent		
Belgium	0.09	0.14	0.26	1.31
Denmark	0.18	0.65	1.50	5.55
Germany	0.18	1.57	2.65	2.67
Greece	0	0.01	0.06	0.41
Spain	0.01	0.02	0.09	1.29
France	0.18	0.27	0.39	1.09
Ireland	0.03	0.09	0.28	0.58
Italy	0.03	0.10	1.22	6.03
Netherlands	0.17	0.46	0.58	1.20
Portugal	0.01	0.05	0.27	1.25
United Kingdom	0.05	0.19	0.28	1.45
Austria	0.24	0.79	9.79	8.44
Finland	0.55	0.52	2.07	6.35
Sweden	0.15	1.21	2.81	9.98
Iceland	0	0	0.03	0.11
Liechtenstein	0	0	0	6.60
Norway	0.03	0.24	0.56	1.79
EEA	*0.10*	*0.37*	*1.03*	*2.47*

SOURCE: European Environment Agency *Environmental Signals 2001* Elsevier Science Ltd. 2000.

positive effects of agriculture on biodiversity. It notes that the presence of farmland can prevent land from becoming developed or urbanized, thereby providing limited habitat for species that might not otherwise be able to exist. But it also acknowledges that high-impact, specialized farming destroys natural habitats and can reduce levels of biodiversity. The European Union's biodiversity strategy seeks to make agriculture more amenable to the preservation of diversity by emphasizing sustainable use of genetic resources (such as crops and domestic animal breeds) and supporting sustainable agro-ecosystems such as "set asides" and organic farming.

With "set-asides," CAP provides financial compensation to farmers that permit arable fields to become fallow. This activity establishes a vegetation canopy that will curb erosion and prevent desertification, encourages biodiversity by preserving wildlife habitat, and regulates runoff and other aspects of regional hydrological regimes (European Environment Agency, *Environment in the European Union,* 1999). In its most extreme manifestation, set-aside can allow for the complete reforestation of agricultural land. Between 1993 and 1997, half a million hectares in the EU were reforested as a result of this initiative (Sondag, "Forestry Measures under the Common Agriculture Policy," 2001).

Organic farming, meanwhile, has enjoyed a renaissance in many regions of Europe. In fact, it now covers 2.5 percent of agricultural land in European Environment Agency nations. This percentage is expected to increase by another 5 to 10 percent by 2005 (European Environment Agency, *Environmental Signals,* 2001). The benefits to the environment from organic farming are myriad. Because organic farmers do not use pesticides or inorganic fertilizers, they cause considerably less ground water contamination. It can also "help to create habitats in which biodiversity is encouraged by management practices" (ibid.). But, because organic farming produces smaller yields and requires considerably more manual treatment (as opposed to machinery)—and because some consumers will pay premium prices for the health benefits of organic foods—prices for organic crops are generally higher.

Environmental groups, members of the scientific community, and some farmers have welcomed these reforms. But they contend that much more drastic reforms to the CAP—and especially its continued practice of rewarding farmers for high-intensity agricultural practices—are still necessary. "The door is now open to more sustainable forms of agriculture and policies that place greater emphasis on good environmental management and less on maximising production," stated the Institute for European Environmental Policy. "Nonetheless, many farmers will react cautiously to this changing climate of opportunity unless it is underpinned by solid economic incentives" (Institute for European Environmental Policy, *European Environmental Almanac,* 1995). This battle to shape the future of CAP will undoubtedly intensify in the coming years, with various constituencies—agribusiness, family farmers, environmentalists, supermarket owners, community leaders—laboring to shape public and legislative opinion and, ultimately, the future landscape of rural Europe.

Environmental Sustainability and the Contemporary European Farm

Europe boasts a tremendous variety of agricultural activities, from fruit production in the Mediterranean basin to sheepherding in the Balkans, and the lives of those who support their families by tending the land vary enormously in large and small ways. But from the United Kingdom to the Ukraine, the challenges of raising crops and livestock in environmentally sustainable ways are largely the same, as are the areas of principal concern.

Habitat Loss and Degradation

Sophisticated drainage, irrigation, and plowing techniques have allowed European farmers to venture ever deeper into the countryside in search of land for crops. The widespread conversion of forest, wetland, and grassland areas to farmland has wiped out entire ecosystems, however, and few countries have been left unscathed. The United Kingdom, for example, has lost an estimated 97 percent of its ancient meadows to farming in the last half-century. Land reclamation also threatens 80 percent of Portugal's coastal meadows, and it is responsible for the drainage of more than 60 percent of Spain's wetlands since the beginning of the 1970s (ibid.). Overall, the development onslaught has produced a 12 percent decrease in permanent grasslands during the last twenty years in member countries of the European Environment Agency (Poiret, "Crop Trends and Environmental Impacts," 2002; Commission of the European Communities, *Agriculture, Environment, Rural Development,* 1999).

The impact of this development of wilderness areas and other natural and seminatural habitat has been further exacerbated by the introduction of pesticides, herbicides, fertilizers, and other tools that have had measurable impacts on freshwater quality and other aspects of the environment. Increased mechanization, overgrazing, and an emphasis on short-term productivity at the expense of long-term sustainability has also contributed to habitat degradation, prompting removal of natural barriers such as hedgerows and trees that nourish an assortment of birds and other wildlife.

Irrigation and Water Use

Traditionally, the relationship between agriculture and water use in Europe has been strictly divided along geographical lines. Many northern countries drained wetlands for agricultural use, while southern countries relied upon irrigation to change their semiarid land into fields more amenable to food production. To some extent, this state of affairs endures. Irrigation continues to be most common in southern countries, with countries such as Greece and Spain earmarking 88 percent and 72 percent, respectively, of their total water consumption for irrigation (Strosser and Vall, "Water and Agriculture," 2001). Moreover, the Mediterranean region's rate of water consumption has steadily increased since 1980, in part because of increases in the amount of land area devoted to farming. Today, more than 8 percent of the total land area in Southern Europe (Albania, Greece, Italy, Malta, Portugal, and Spain) is irrigated, double the percentage of irrigated land area in the rest of Europe. This heavy reliance on irrigation, combined with rampant coastal development, has been cited as a factor in the salinization of nearly 4 million hectares of land across the region (European Environment Agency, *Europe's Environment,* 1998).

Nevertheless, the balance is beginning to shift. In the last twenty years, Northern Europe has increasingly turned to irrigation as a way of meeting high-yield demands. In 1995 approximately 30 percent of all farmland in the Netherlands relied upon irrigation for crop production. Other countries, such as Ireland and France, that have traditionally relied upon rainfall have also become increasingly reliant on irrigation (Strosser and Vall, "Water and Agriculture," 2001). Indeed, by the close of the twentieth century, approximately 31 percent of Europe's total freshwater consumption went to agriculture, mostly for irrigation purposes (Gleick, *The World's Water,* 2000). Experts warn that this rate of consumption is fundamentally unsustainable. They note that many water tables are being drawn down at a pace far exceeding rates of replenishment, and they warn that irrigation is compromising the ecological viability of some rivers and wetlands.

Soil Content and Erosion

Europe ranks the lowest of all continents in terms of erosion rates, but soil erosion is still a serious problem in some regions (Pimentel, *World Soil Erosion and Conservation,* 1993). This is a relatively recent development, however. Early European farmers were limited by rudimentary tools that made clearing rocks and larger indigenous flora difficult. Natural ground cover and wind blocks thus remained in place, helping shield topsoil from the elements. Contemporary farming practices, though, often call for the blanket removal of all native species and the tilling of land previously protected by grasslands and trees. When these features disappear, erosion rates almost inevitably rise, for the practice increases the volume and area of soil that is exposed and thus vulnerable to erosion. It can also remove some of the heavier organic matter that gives lighter soils the weight they need to resist erosion. Vulnerability to erosion is further heightened when farmers engage in continual arable cropping without fallow rotations, or when they plant crops on vulnerable soils and steep slopes (Institute for European Environmental Policy, *European Environmental Almanac,* 1995).

Reliance on mechanization remains more prominent in Western Europe, which has more buying power than countries in the Central and Eastern regions of the continent. In the late 1980s, for instance, it was estimated that Polish farmers still used approximately one million horses for plowing and other farm labor (European Environment Agency, *Europe's Environment,* 1995). But deep plowing techniques and eradication of native fauna are on the increase in those regions as well. This trend has great environmental significance, for once the topsoil is removed an ecological domino effect comes into play. Rocky subsoil tends to have a much lower permeability for water and moisture content; it is, therefore, far more difficult to keep eroded fields irrigated and productive. Erosion also affects fertility, as essential nutrients such as nitrogen, calcium, phosphorous, and potassium that are concentrated in the finer topsoil are lost.

This problem is exacerbated by the modern use of continuous cropping instead of crop rotations, which leave fields periodically fallow. The latter practice, one that allows fields to serve as pasture or hay fields for several years, provides at least a temporary respite from erosion because it allows vegetative cover to take root. The former methodology, on the other hand, encourages runoff and erosion. Other contributors to erosion include heavy use of inorganic fertilizers, which do not feature humus and other weighty materials present in organic fertilizers, and overgrazing and deforestation, both of which can result in the loss of stabilizing root systems (Pimentel, *World Soil Erosion and Conservation,*1993).

Contemporary farmers must also deal with the increased acidification of soil. Although much of the acidification is the result of external forces, such as acid rain generated by industry, farmers are also culpable. "In some countries of Northwestern Europe there is a problem of potential acidification of soils and groundwater as a direct result of ammonia use as fertiliser. . . .Even sufficient liming may not always prevent acidification: if nitrification takes place below the limed depth, then acidification continues, and in sandy areas may lead to groundwater and surface water becoming acidified" (European Environment Agency, *Europe's Environment,* 1995). Finally, application of sewage sludge as a fertilizer, emissions from the transport sector, and air- and waterborne effluent from industrial operations have all increased the levels of heavy metals in Europe's fields. Heavy metals tend to build up in topsoil, and once they reach a critical mass they can reduce yields or render crops unsafe for consumption.

All told, the European Environment Agency estimates that by the mid-1990s, improper soil management had degraded the soil quality of about 3.2 million hectares of farmland across Europe, about 12 percent of the continent's agricultural land. The problem is most pronounced in Southern Europe. Portugal, for instance, is battling serious erosion problems on 20 percent of its land, and Greece and Italy risk losing up to 60 percent of their topsoil through erosion (European Environment Agency, *Europe's Environment,* 1995). These problems, coupled with soil salinization through irrigation, are leading to increased incidence of desertification throughout the region. The European coastal zone of the Mediterranean basin, for instance, includes about 300,000 square kilometers of land that have been classified as undergoing at least moderate desertification (Institute for European Environmental Policy, *European Environmental Almanac,* 1995).

Fertilizers and Pesticides

Perhaps the most environmentally detrimental element of modern agriculture is the heavy application of inorganic fertilizers and pesticides on fields. The application of these chemicals has contributed to the acidification of the soil, a problem exacerbated by industrial pollutants, particularly in the former Eastern Bloc countries. They are also blamed for increased eutrophication of waterways (in this process, excessive nutrient loads deplete affected rivers, streams, lakes, and bays of oxygen, creating an environment in which most marine life cannot survive). Nitrogen overloads of natural ecosystems have been particularly problematic in Western Europe, where economic affluence and high population densities have combined to boost application rates (Harrison, *AAAS Atlas of Population and Environment,* 1999).

Figure 5.1 Fertilizer Use in European Regions, 1961–1995

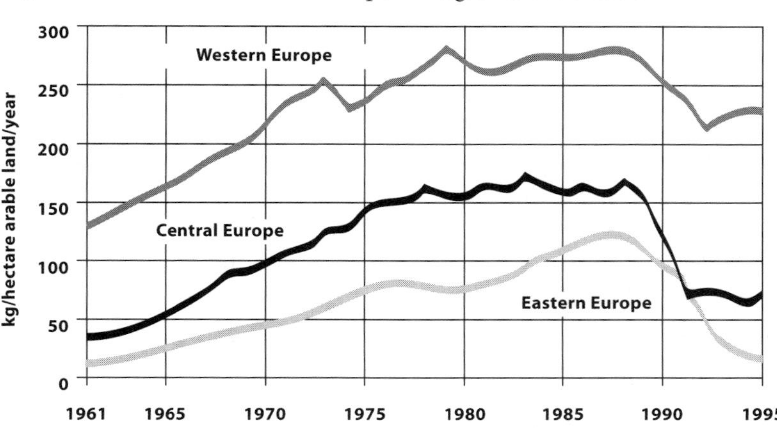

SOURCE: United Nations Environment Programme, *Global Environment Outlook 2000.*

Fortunately, fertilizer use in Europe has actually declined over the past twenty years. Phosphate and potassium fertilizers—two of the most common and potentially noxious fertilizers used in agriculture—now make up less than 45 percent of the mineral consumption in Europe, down from 62 percent in 1970 (Poirett, "Crop Trends and Environmental Impacts," 2002). Moreover, recessionary economic conditions have actually reduced the use of fertilizers and pesticides in many Central and Eastern European countries, which have historically relied on tremendous volumes of agrochemicals in their operations. For example, Poland's fertilizer use dropped by half between 1985 and 1994, while the Czech Republic's use of fertilizers fell from 346 kilograms per hectare in 1985 to 107 in 1994 (European Environment Agency, *Europe's Environment,* 1998).

But whereas European application of some types of fertilizer is in decline, the use of nitrogen-based fertilizers has increased dramatically over the past few decades, from 6.8 to 9.6 million tons annually (Poiret, "Specialized Holdings and More Intensive Practices," 2002). In Denmark alone, more than 800,000 tons of nitrogen fertilizer were being spread on fields on an annual basis. Of that total, less than half (360,000 tons) was actually absorbed by crops; the remainder was released into nearby land and water. Like phosphate and potassium fertilizers, nitrate fertilizers enter major water supplies by way of runoff and irrigation. Levels of contamination depend on a host of factors, including the amount of nitrogen introduced to the soil through fertilizers and livestock waste, and the amount of nitrogen removed by plants or proper manure handling. Levels can increase or decrease depending upon a farmer's ability to protect the soil from leaching by providing adequate ground cover. If fields do not have this cover, nitrates quickly seep into ground water, streams and rivers, which in turn carry the nitrates to coastal regions. "In the EU more than 95 percent of the 7.1 million tonnes of nitrogen surplus is likely to contribute to leakage of nitrogen into waters" (European Environment Agency, *Environmental Signals,* 2002). By the late 1990s, the problem of high nutrient loads in European waters had reached such a level of severity that the European Environment Agency passed a Nitrate Directive requiring member countries to designate Nitrate Vulnerable Zones and install leakproof systems for storing manure—another source of nitrogen pollution in waterways—until soil conditions are ripe for tilling the material into fields.

Pesticides also exact a heavy toll on the European environment. Pesticides—including herbicides, fungicides, and insecticides—continue to enjoy wide use in Europe, although substantial differences in pesticide application rates can be found from region to region, caused by variations in climate and crop choices. Most data on pesticides focuses on the "active ingredient" of the pesticide. Scientists track the active ingredient through its total weight within any given product. This weight, or strength, can reveal what levels of pesticide are being used in agriculture. According to the European Environment Agency, "[A]pparent declining application rates may be misleading because newer generations of pesticide have high potency and require relatively lower application rates" (European Environment Agency, *Europe's Environment,* 1995). Moreover, the most common pesticides—atrazine, simazine, and bentazone—continue to exceed safety standards in most water analyses in Europe (Strosser and Vall, "Water and Agriculture," 2001).

Genetically Modified Organisms

Of the technologies designed to combat worsening field conditions while at the same time meeting the challenge of feeding expanding world populations, none has created quite the stir as the advent of genetically modified crops. In this process, micro-organisms, plants, and animals are modified through the insertion of an altered or borrowed gene, enabling scientists to endow plants with specially chosen characteristics not found in their original genetic structure. Organisms altered through this process are known as GMOs (genetically modified organisms). These organisms are often larger, heartier, and more resistant to insects or disease. Some, such as golden rice, are fortified with vitamins and minerals not commonly associated with the original organism.

Proponents believe that GMOs offer valuable applications in food production, as well as pharmaceuticals and chemical production. They also note that as of the close of the twentieth century, there was no credible evidence of a food safety risk associated with any GMO food on the market in Europe (Nuffield Council on Bioethics, *Genetically Modified Crops,* 1999). However, critics of the push toward GMO food products contend that many uncertainties about their molecular makeup and their long-term effects on the environment remain. In fact, the number of variables and questions regarding GMOs has led the European Union to impose significant restrictions on the production of genetically engineered foods. Beginning in the 1990s, the EU created a series of legislative acts that require a strict approval process before a new GMO can be introduced into the marketplace. This case-by-case assessment requires each GMO proposal to include a report on possible health risks to the proper national authority. That authority must complete a full risk assessment and report to the EU commission, which in turn determines whether the GMO will be approved.

Those GMOs approved by the EU—and those that were on the market prior to the legislation—must be labeled as such so that consumers can make an informed decision about the food products they purchase. The effects of this legislation on European agriculture have been pronounced.

Because most crops pollinate—a process often known as a "gene flow"—across several meters, non-GMO crops must be sequestered, as any cross-pollination between a GMO and non-GMO will effectively create a new GMO. It could also potentially eradicate strains of plants not genetically altered. Cereals and fruits are at a particular risk, as they often pollinate upward of 100 meters.

In any case, the rise of GMO foods has created a resounding stir in the European market, even though genetically modified products still accounted for only a tiny fraction of total food sales at the beginning of the twenty-first century. In Spain, France, and Portugal, where GMOs first came on the market, many consumers have happily embraced them. But other European consumers, concerned over the potential health risks of genetically engineered foods and still reeling from the late–1990s "mad cow disease" crisis, have reacted negatively to the appearance of GMO products on store shelves. Opponents of GMO products have also boycotted products shipped from the United States, which has instituted comparatively liberal rules concerning the use and labeling of GMO products.

Sources:

Barker, Graeme. 1985. *Prehistoric Farming in Europe.* Cambridge: Cambridge University Press.

Brouwer, Floor. 1996. *CAP and Environment in the European Union: Analysis of the Effects of the CAP on the Environment and Assessment of Existing Environmental Conditions in Policy.* Wageningen: Wageningen Academic Publishers.

Clarke, Philip. 2002. "CAP Needs 'Urgent and Radical' Reform." *Farmers Weekly* (June 7).

Commission of the European Communities. 1999. *Agriculture, Environment, Rural Development: Facts and Figures—A Challenge for Agriculture.* Luxembourg: EC.

Coward, Ros. 1999. "The CAP Doesn't Fit." *Ecologist* (August–September).

European Commission. 1998. *The Common Agricultural Policy: Promoting Europe's Agriculture and Rural Areas—Continuity and Change.* Luxembourg: EC.

———. 1998. *Towards a Greening of the Common Agricultural Policy.* Brussels: EC, Directorate-General of Agriculture.

———. 1999. *Agriculture, Environment, Rural Development: Facts and Figures.* Luxembourg: EC.

European Commission, Directorate-General for Agriculture. 2001. *Common Agricultural Policy: 2000 Review.* Luxembourg: EC.

European Environment Agency. 1995. *Europe's Environment: The Dobris Assessment.* Copenhagen: EEA.

———. 1998. *Europe's Environment: The Second Assessment.* Copenhagen: EEA.

———. 1999. *Environment in the European Union at the Turn of the Century.* Copenhagen: EEA.

———. 2001. *Environmental Signals 2001*. Copenhagen: EEA.

———. 2002. *Environmental Signals 2002: Benchmarking the Millennium*. Copenhagen: EEA.

Fay, Frank. "The Impact of Agri-environment Measures." *Europa*. http://www.europa.eu.int/en/comm/agriculture/envir/resport/en (accessed June 10, 2002).

Gleick, Peter H. 2000. *The World's Water 2000–2001*. Washington, DC: Island.

Harris, David R., ed. 1996. *The Origins and Spread of Agriculture and Pastoralism in Eurasia*. Washington, DC: Smithsonian Institution Press.

Harrison, Paul, and Fred Pearce. 1999. *AAAS Atlas of Population and Environment*. Berkeley: University of California Press.

Harvey, Graham. 1997. *The Killing of the Countryside*. London: Jonathan Cape.

Hau, Patrick, and Alain Joaris. "Organic Farming." http://www.europa.eu.int/en/comm/agriculture/envir/resport/en (accessed June 10, 2002).

Institute for European Environmental Policy. 1995. *European Environmental Almanac*. Edited by Jonathan Hewett. London: Earthscan.

Laegreid, M., O. C. Bockman, and O. Kaarstad. 1999. *Agriculture Fertilizers and the Environment*. New York: CABI.

Lucas, Stephanie, and Marie Pau Vall. "Pesticides in the European Union." Europa. http://www.europa.eu.int/en/comm/agriculture/envir/resport/en (accessed June 10, 2002).

McDonald, Mark. 2002. "Law Allows for Private Ownership of Agricultural Property in Russia." *Detroit Free Press* (August 8).

Montanarella, Luca. "Soil at the Interface between Agriculture and Environment." Europa. http://www.europa.eu.int/en/comm/agriculture/envir/resport/en (accessed June 10, 2002).

Nuffield Council on Bioethics. 1999. *Genetically Modified Crops: The Ethical and Social Issues*. London: Nuffield Council on Bioethics.

Paarlberg, Robert. 2000. "Promise or Peril? Genetically Modified Crops in Developing Countries." *Environment* 42 (January–February).

Pimentel, David, ed. 1993. *World Soil Erosion and Conservation*. Cambridge: Cambridge University Press.

Poiret, Michel. "Crop Trends and Environmental Impacts." Europa. http://www.europa.eu.int/en/comm/agriculture/envir/resport/en (accessed June 10, 2002).

———. "Specialized Holdings and More Intensive Practices." Europa. http://www.europa.eu.int/en/comm/agriculture/envir/resport/en (accessed June 10, 2002).

Royal Society for the Protection of Birds. "The Common Agricultural Policy (CAP)." http://www.rspb.org.uk/rspb.asp (accessed June 28, 2002).

Sereni, Emilio. 1997. *History of the Italian Agricultural Landscape*. Translated by R. Burr Litchfield. Princeton: Princeton University Press.

Sondag, Veronique. "Forestry Measures under the Common Agriculture Policy." Europa. http://www.europa.eu.int/en/comm/dg06/com/htmfiles (accessed June 10, 2002).

Strosser, Pierre, and Maria Pau Vall. 2001. "Water and Agriculture: Contribution to an Analysis of a Critical but Difficult Relationship." Agriculture and the Environment (Europa Report), 2001. http://europa/eu.int/comm/agriculture/envir/report/en/eau_en/report.htm (accessed June 10, 2002).

Tangermann, Stefan, ed. 2000. *Agriculture in Germany.* Frankfurt: DLG-Verlag.

Warner, Charles K. 1966. *Agrarian Conditions in Modern European History*. New York: Macmillan.

Freshwater

The environmental condition of European rivers, lakes, and aquifers has improved in some important respects in recent years. Discharges of some pollutants, including ammonium and phosphorus, into waterways have declined markedly because of formal changes in policy, and increased attention has been paid to urban wastewater treatment over the past two decades, further improving aquatic habitat for freshwater fish and amphibians. But nitrate pollution remains very high, particularly in regions where agriculture is dominant, and demands on finite water supplies continue to grow, especially in Southern Europe. In addition, many of the nations of Central and Eastern Europe are still struggling with the legacy of water degradation left by pre-1990s political regimes.

Freshwater Supply and Usage

The countries of Southern Europe depend to a great extent on groundwater aquifers for their water supply, as rivers and lakes are not that abundant in the region. Conversely, Northern and Central European nations generally enjoy sufficient supplies of freshwater from renewable surface sources (in the form of lakes and rivers) for their needs. Indeed, this region features a wealth of freshwater rivers and lakes that are continually replenished by the moderate-to-heavy precipitation levels that characterize much of the continent's length and breadth. Natural lakes of significant size can be found across much of Northern Europe, especially on the northern plains of Sweden and Finland. The continent's many large river systems, meanwhile, originate from deep within its interior, their watersheds draining outward to send freshwater into the region's many seas. For example, the Danube River—Europe's second-longest waterway—empties into the Black Sea, while the Rhone and Po rivers supply the Mediterranean, and the Loire, Seine, and Rhine replenish the Atlantic Ocean and the North Sea.

Figure 6.1 Renewable Freshwater Resources across Europe

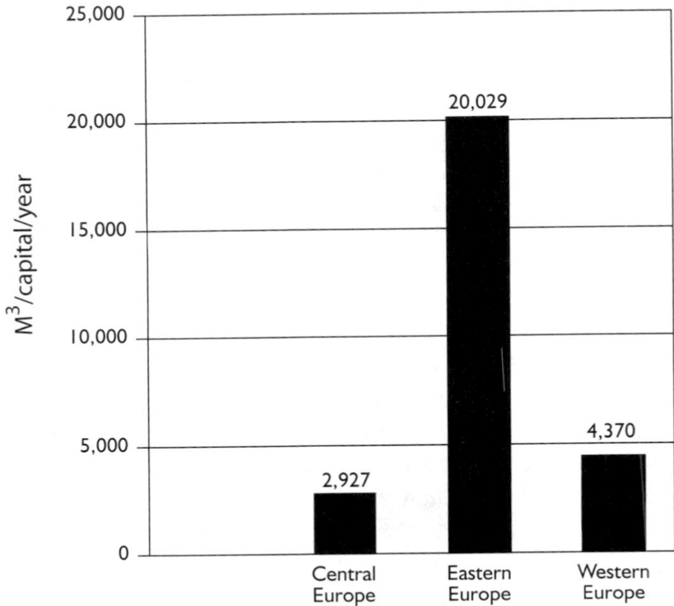

SOURCE: Compiled by UNEP GRID Geneva from WRI, UNEP, UNDP, and WB 1998.

The proximity of many of these rivers' headwaters in the heart of the continent has led to the creation of an extensive canal system that connects them for commercial and recreational purposes. Many of these rivers pass through or by numerous countries as they snake across Europe, enormously complicating the allocation of freshwater resources. Hungary, for instance, obtains about 95 percent of its total freshwater from sources that originate outside its borders, and the Danube River is shared by more than a dozen countries, from Romania (which holds 228,000 square kilometers of the river's length) to Albania (with 140 square kilometers within its borders) (see sidebar, page 125). In recent years, the dissolution of the Soviet Union into fifteen countries, the violent disintegration of Yugoslavia, and the division of Czechoslovakia has further boosted the number of European rivers shared by more than one nation. Given this dynamic of shared ownership, Europe's major rivers are the subject of numerous international agreements meant to preserve the national security and economic welfare of each nation with legitimate water claims. These agreements govern everything from pollution emissions to rates of withdrawal by upstream nations.

Years of Abuse Tarnish the "Blue Danube"

Pollution from a fertilizer plant on the Danube River in Panchevo, Yugoslavia
ED KASHI/CORBIS

The Danube River is one of Europe's most famed—and troubled—waterways. The continent's second longest river, the Danube basin extends into more than a dozen European countries and covers more than 800,000 square kilometers. Utilized for millennia by traders, fishermen, and travelers, the Danube and its many tributaries are deeply interwoven into the history, culture, and self-image of the continent. But while the millions of people who live in this region profess deep affection for the legendary "blue Danube," much of the river's health and vitality have been wrung out of it by centuries of use and abuse.

The modern Danube bears little resemblance to the sparkling waterway conjured up by stories and songs of yesteryear. Dredged, straightened, dammed, and diverted at numerous points for hydroelectric power, transportation, fishing, waste disposal, drinking water, and industrial purposes, the river is now brown in color and sluggish in temperament. It is also terribly polluted in many sections, for it is the primary recipient of waste materials from an estimated 80 million people living in its catchment area. "Dozens of cities and half a dozen countries allow huge amounts of insufficiently purified storm runoff, industrial wastes, and agricultural pesticides to enter the river virtually unmonitored," confirmed journalist Marc de Villiers. "No one has ever added up the total or catalogued the horrors. What is known is that the Danube pours

(continues)

about 80 million tons of contaminated sediments into the Black Sea every average-water-flow year" (de Villiers, *Water*, 2000). In fact, the Danube discharges higher total loads of organic materials, phosphates, heavy metals, and oil than almost any other European river. The pollution problem is particularly egregious on many of the Danube's tributaries, which do not have the necessary stream flows or volumes to mitigate the deadly effects of perennial contamination.

Despite the shoddy treatment it has endured, however, the Danube is not a lost cause. The waterway still nourishes ecologically diverse pockets of forestlands and alluvial plains as it winds its way through the European countryside. In addition, international programs initiated in the public and private sectors have made some progress in establishing protection for ecologically valuable sections of the corridor and reducing pollution. The best known of these international agreements, however—the so-called Danube Action Plan—has been widely criticized for failing to address basic threats facing the river. This initiative called for the adoption of emission limits for fertilizer plants, new industry facilities, and farming operations; establishment of national discharge reduction targets for high-priority tributaries; and the scientific evaluation of discharges of nutrients from the Danube into the Black Sea in order to gauge progress. But the 1997 deadline for these actions came and went with little action taken, giving rise to widespread doubts about Europe's political will to impose actions targeted for implementation by 2005, such as new regulations on agricultural policy, fertilizer and pesticide storage, handling, and use; bans on phosphate detergents; and new investments in wastewater treatment plants.

In the meantime, the Danube's fraying ecosystem received yet another terrible blow in January 2000, when a massive cyanide spill from a gold-mining operation in northern Romania leaked into the waterway. The spill initially entered Hungary's Tisza River, where it reportedly destroyed all aquatic life along a 250-mile stretch. The Tisza then carried the cyanide down to where it joins the Danube. The cyanide spill subsequently poisoned about 450 miles of the Danube, erasing all aquatic life in that stretch of the river and decimating many other river-dependent woodland species.

Sources:

Carter, F. W., and D. Turnock, eds. 1993. *Environmental Problems in Eastern Europe*. London and New York: Routledge.

De Villiers, Marq. 2000. *Water: The Fate of Our Most Precious Resource*. New York: Houghton Mifflin.

Fitzmaurice, J. 1995. *Damming the Danube: Gacikovo/Nagymaros and Post-Communist Politics in Europe*. Boulder, CO: Westview.

Jordan, Michael J. 2000. "Epic Poisoning of Europe's Rivers." *Christian Science Monitor* (February 16).

Land, Thomas. 1992. "The Green Danube." *Contemporary Review* 261 (August).

The European nation with the single greatest amount of freshwater is Russia. The water resources of this country—which extends from Eastern Europe into northern Asia and accounts for about one-ninth of the globe's total land area—include western Russia's Volga River, which is Europe's longest river, and Europe's largest freshwater lakes—Lake Baikal, Lake Ladoga, and Lake Onega (Lake Baikal—the largest freshwater lake in the world by volume—is in southern Siberia, while the latter two bodies of water are located in the country's far northwestern reaches). The sheer scale of Russia's land holdings give it an estimated 4,500 cubic kilometers of renewable freshwater annually. The average annual runoff of freshwater in all of the rest of Europe, meanwhile, is approximately 3,100 cubic kilometers (about 4,500 cubic meters per capita per year for a population of 680 million). Among individual nations, Norway ranks second to Russia in freshwater supply, with an estimated per capita tally of 90,000 cubic meters and 390 cubic kilometers of annually renewable freshwater. Other water-rich European nations include Romania (208 cubic kilometers), Bulgaria (205), France (198), Sweden (180), and Germany (171) (Gleick, *World's Water 2000–2001,* 2000).

On a regional basis, Eastern Europe enjoys the greatest quantity of renewable freshwater, with more than 20,000 cubic meters per capita annually. By comparison, Western Europe has less than 4,400 cubic meters per capita, and Central Europe has approximately 2,900 cubic meters per capita. The area of Europe with the most profound scarcity of freshwater is the Mediterranean territory, a comparatively dry region in south-central Europe that utilizes approximately 60 percent of its freshwater supply for water-intensive agricultural purposes (agriculture accounts for about 80 percent of total demand in Greece, 65 percent in Spain, and 70 percent in Turkey). The rest of Europe, by comparison, uses less than 10 percent of its freshwater resources for irrigation (World Resources Institute et al., *World Resources 2000–2001,* 2000).

The Mediterranean region's rate of water consumption has steadily increased since 1980, in part because of increases in the amount of land area devoted to farming. Today more than 8 percent of the total land area in Southern Europe (Albania, Greece, Italy, Malta, Portugal, and Spain) is irrigated, double the percentage of irrigated land area in the rest of Europe. A few Mediterranean nations have begun augmenting their freshwater supply through desalination of seawater, but that remains a relatively minor factor in most places (Malta is a notable exception, for it obtains about 45 percent of its total freshwater via desalination). In fact, soil salinization is a serious issue in Mediterranean and Eastern European countries, affecting nearly 4 million hectares of land. This trend is primarily attributed to overexploitation of water resources for irrigation, population growth and associated urban and industrial development, and the expansion of tourism in coastal areas. But despite the seriousness of the situation in many regions—manifested by lower crop yields and outright crop failures—coordinated strategies to combat salinization are lacking in most countries (European Environment Agency, *Europe's Environment,* 1998).

Outside of the Mediterranean basin, the majority of the continent's freshwater supply is used by industry. About 55 percent of Europe's freshwater is allocated for industrial use, while the remainder is utilized for agriculture (31 percent) and municipal/public water sectors (14 percent). Leading individual consumers of freshwater by volume are the Russian Federation (77 cubic kilometers annually), Germany (59), Uzbekistan (58), Italy (56), France (35), Kazakhstan (33), and Spain (33). Estimated per capita withdrawal rates in Europe vary wildly, though, ranging from 133 cubic meters per year in Luxembourg to 745 in Portugal and more than 1,550 in Bulgaria. The latter country, hampered by widespread inefficiencies in distribution and usage, pours water into its relatively modest agricultural and industrial enterprises at a phenomenal rate, given its modest size and population (Gleick, *World's Water 2000–2001,* 2000).

Europe's wealth of surface freshwater, though unevenly distributed, has enabled some regions to avoid unsustainable mining of groundwater aquifers. Nonetheless, approximately 60 percent of Europe's large cities are engaged in overextraction of their groundwater resources, and industrial pollution, agriculture, and salt water intrusion have compromised groundwater aquifers in several countries, most notably in Eastern and Southern Europe. Indeed, along much of the heavily developed Mediterranean coastline, overdraws of groundwater have lowered water tables so severely that many city reservoirs have become contaminated by salt water.

In terms of water conservation, the countries of the European Union have assumed a global leadership role. After decades of steadily growing consumption, conservation measures in the industrial arena have produced a small drop in the region's overall rate of water use in recent years. In addition, several countries have enacted national action plans on water resources that cover household water use and water savings. A general European Union policy on water consumption, either in general or for households, remains absent, but analysts believe that implementation of EU-wide regulatory proposals will push member states toward more active management of water use (European Environment Agency, *Environmental Signals 2001,* 2001). Conservation gains have also been made elsewhere in Europe, but these are primarily a side effect of the wrenching struggle to create market economies out of the lumbering, authoritarian economic systems of the communist era. During the 1990s, for instance, water consumption declined in both Central and Eastern Europe because countless manufacturing plants and industrial facilities saddled with notoriously inefficient water use systems shut their doors. Municipal consumption is on the upswing in both of these regions, however, especially as individual countries make halting improvements to their people's standards of living.

Overall, the pressures on Europe's freshwater stocks are significant, and they are expected to grow as Russia and Eastern European nations vie to match the economic success and standard of living enjoyed by countries in the West, although analysts have been heartened by signs of increased water efficiency by Eastern European industries. Expansion of agricultural operations that make extensive use of irrigation will also be a significant draw. And in water-stressed Southern Europe—especially Spain—continued mismanagement of existing freshwater supplies and reliance on environmentally destructive projects such as dams and water diversions still need to be addressed.

The Spanish National Hydrological Plan of 2001, for example, is a controversial "water transfer" law that provides the legal groundwork for the creation of more than 860 dams, reservoirs, and other water infrastructure works. Leading environmental nongovernmental organizations such as the World Wildlife Fund, Birdlife International, and the European Environmental Bureau have warned that the path could lead to the destruction of numerous nature conservation areas and codify unsustainable water use for decades to come. They also contend that the scheme directly contravenes two core European environmental directives—the Habitats Directive and the Birds Directive, both of which are essential components of Europe's Natura 2000 protected area network.

But at the dawn of the twenty-first century, the European Environment Agency provided a relatively reassuring assessment of the continent's overall freshwater supply situation: "Comparisons of total freshwater abstractions [withdrawals] with the total resources available suggest that, potentially, all European countries have sufficient resources to meet national demand, given the rates of replenishment of their resources. More than 60 percent of the countries analysed abstract less than one-tenth of their total resource, with the remainder (apart from Belgium) abstracting less than one-third of the resource. In Belgium, 40 percent of the resource is abstracted" (European Environment Agency, *Europe's Environment*, 1998).

Struggling to Rein in Water Pollution

Europe's inland rivers and lakes have been utilized for centuries as primary sources of drinking water, waste disposal, power generation, transportation, and irrigation. This transformation of most of the continent's waterways into "working rivers" has taken a considerable toll not only on the ecosystems of the rivers themselves but also on the regional seas (Baltic, North, Caspian, Black, Adriatic, and Mediterranean) into which they feed. In addition, most major cities in Spain, Portugal, and other nations of the south have waste treatment facilities, but countless smaller communities dump their municipal waste directly into rivers without any treatment. Not surprisingly, then, many European lakes and rivers are beleaguered by excess amounts of nitrates, heavy metals, pesticides, agrochemicals, and hydrocarbons. These pollutants have contributed to profound eutrophication (a condition in which excess organic nutrients depletes a body of water's supply of oxygen) in many waterways, devastating some regional fisheries. This growing problem has been further aggravated by overfishing. For instance, recent studies indicate that Atlantic salmon are on the verge of vanishing from Northern Ireland's rivers. A 2001 government report warned of the imminent demise of wild salmon stocks from its waterways unless immediate steps are taken to combat pollution and myopic fishing practices. Other regions of Europe are grappling with similar threats to their fisheries and other water-dependent wildlife.

In Northwestern Europe, however, heavy use of waterways has been relieved somewhat by the region's progressive—when compared with other areas of the world—efforts to address environmental issues over the past two decades (see sidebar, page 127). Indeed, many policy initiatives and regulations were developed to protect and heal Europe's rivers and lakes during that time. These measures have produced major improvements in municipal wastewater treatment and significant reductions in discharges from industry. These gains reflect the broad range of environmental concerns that the initiatives address, from continentwide issues to more localized problems. For instance, the European Union (EU)'s Fifth Environmental Action Programme includes quantitative measures to protect ground and surface freshwater and introduce sustainable use practices into other aspects of Europe's culture and economy. Specific programs likely to produce substantial improvements in EU water quality in the coming years include the European Commission's Urban Waste Water Treatment Directive. Meanwhile, the Rhine Action Plan has produced significant improvements in the water quality of one targeted waterway, Northern Europe's Rhine River, which had become so debased that it acquired the nickname "the Sewer of Europe" (European Environment Agency, *Europe's Environment*, 1998).

Environmental degradation manifests itself in numerous ways, however, and many problems created over the past several decades will not subside in a matter of a few years. For instance, acid rain produced in earlier decades by industrial emissions of sulfur dioxide, nitrogen oxides, and ammonia continues to cast its shadow over many Northern European lakes, despite recent reductions in sulfur emissions. Norway has been victimized most significantly by

Great Britain Turns to Water Privatization

In 1989, Great Britain decided to privatize its water and sewage systems after years of mounting frustration with the performance of the country's state-operated water boards. There was universal agreement that under the management of those boards, the United Kingdom's vast and aging waterworks infrastructure had deteriorated significantly. But despite the many horror stories about outdated pipelines and treatment systems that wasted huge volumes of freshwater (about 30 percent of water distribution input, according to the UK's Office of Water Services) or spewed raw sewage into the North Sea, the decision to turn the nation's water supply over to private, for-profit companies stunned and angered many members of the populace. The government responded with assurances that environmental and economic regulations would be imposed that would ensure adequate consumer protection.

Criticism of Great Britain's water privatization scheme intensified in the early 1990s, as the average cost of household water and sewage services nearly doubled. In 1991 water service was shut off to more than 21,000 households for nonpayment of bills. This move was viewed as draconian by many, and the resulting public outrage led to the passage of customer protection legislation and creation of a government agency that monitors the operating needs of the water companies in conjunction with the financial impact of waterworks upgrades and pricing structures on consumers.

Dissatisfaction with the privatization effort crested in the mid-1990s. In 1995, six years after water privatization was launched, the public water supply system in West Yorkshire failed. Over the next few months, the water needs of several million people were met by fleets of water tankers that filled empty reservoirs with water shipments from Northumberland. During the subsequent winter, however, Northumberland's own supply system shut down because of low water levels. "The water companies attributed these failures to an exceptionally hot and dry summer and an exceptionally cold winter, respectively," noted Richard Schofield and Jean Shaoul in *The Ecologist* in 1997.

> The public, however, thought differently. Throughout the country, criticism grew that since the 1989 sell-off of Britain's water and sewerage industry, ordinary customers were being charged higher prices for a deteriorating service, while the profits were going towards high shareholder dividends and vastly-increased directors'

(continues)

salaries. . . . Expenditure on maintenance is now at about the same level it was before privatization when revenues were much lower and when it was widely acknowledged—not least by the water industry's current management—that expenditure on maintaining the infrastructure was inadequate. Indeed, the government justified water privatization on the grounds that large investment was needed in the infrastructure which only the private sector could provide." (Schofield and Shaoul, "Regulating the Water Industry," 1997)

For example, Schofield and Shaoul noted that from 1989 to 1996, less than 1 percent of England's and Wales's "critical sewers"—estimated to comprise 20 percent of the total system—had been renovated or replaced, while only 5 percent of the pipes connecting more than 20 million properties to the infrastructure had been replaced. "If such levels of investment continue, it would take more than one hundred years to reline or replace the water mains and five centuries to renew or replace critical sewers. Victorian civil engineering was good—but not that good" (ibid.).

The water companies have repeatedly defended their record, however, pointing to extensive repair operations in a number of areas of critical importance to the UK water supply and regional ecosystems. They also claim that despite high-profile incidents such as the ones in West Yorkshire and Northumberland, they have made great strides in improving the adequacy of water resources, reducing unplanned interruptions in service, and reducing the risk of sewage flooding.

Today, many of those who initially supported the privatization experiment feel vindicated by the improving state of Great Britain's water supply. After years of replacement and renovation of pipeline networks (private water companies in the United Kingdom invested almost $50 billion in the nation's waterworks system from 1989 to 1999, according to some estimates), Britain's waterworks infrastructure is now more efficient and better able to ensure the long-term viability of the nation's drinking water. Moreover, key environmental benefits have been realized through privatization, most notably in the realm of untreated sewage discharge reductions. After a decade of privatization, for instance, the number of swimmable beaches in England and Wales had risen from 401 to 463. Proponents also point out that in the decade since privatization was instituted, Great Britain's regulatory agencies have been able to transfer money and personnel previously allocated to water and sewage systems to enforcement of pollution laws, producing a surge in pollution-related prosecutions in the late 1990s.

(continues)

Nonetheless, the privatization initiative remains an intensely controversial one in many regions of the United Kingdom. Critics continue to contend that the cost of connection to water and sewage service remains exorbitant, especially given their belief that the water companies have pocketed excessive profits at the expense of a waterworks infrastructure that is still in need of extensive attention. Finally, environmentalists claim that the highly touted pollution reductions registered by the water companies in some sectors, such as sewage discharges, serve to mask unsatisfactory performance in other areas of environmental protection.

Sources:

Department of the Environment. 1986. "Privatisation of the Water Authorities in England and Wales." London: HMSO.

Schofield, Richard, and Jean Shaoul. 1997. "Regulating the Water Industry: Swimming against the Tide or Going through the Motions?" *Ecologist* 27 (January–February).

Swanson, Peter. 2001. *Water: The Drop of Life.* Minnetonka, MN: NorthWord.

this phenomenon, with nearly 30 percent of its freshwater lakes exceeding the "critical load" for sulfur as recently as 1995. But acid rain's deadly effects have been felt throughout the region, contributing to declining fish stocks and disappearing amphibians and migratory waterfowl by means both direct (in which toxins delivered via acid rain poison species) and indirect (in which toxins kill plant food or change water chemistry in ways that make the environment inhospitable to fish and aquatic species). In England, meanwhile, European Environment Agency research suggests that half of all the male fish in low-lying English rivers are changing sex as a result of water pollution. Researchers believe that estrogen-laced urine traced to English women taking contraceptive pills is contaminating the nation's rivers, changing the gender of male fish—and possibly accounting for marked declines in the sperm counts of English men, since these rivers account for one-third of the country's drinking water.

The ongoing challenge to address past and present abuses is being taken up elsewhere as well. For example, the European Environment Agency estimates that total discharge of phosphorus from industrial facilities and urban wastewater sources into rivers and lakes fell by more than 70 percent in several countries from 1980 to 1995 as a result of new regulations and increased public awareness (see sidebar, page 136). But the European Environment Agency (EEA) itself offered a mixed progress report on the effort to combat phosphorus pollution: "The proportion of lakes rich in phosphorus has fallen, while the number of near-natural quality has increased. Although the quality of European lakes appears to be gradually improving, water quality in many lakes in large parts of Europe is still poor and well below that in natural lakes or lakes in a good ecological state. Further action would be needed to improve the overall situation, including action to preserve lakes of high ecological quality from phosphorus inputs from agriculture, forestry, and poor land-management practices" (European Environment Agency, *Europe's Environment,* 1998). Total ammonium concentrations in European rivers also declined during the 1990s, especially in smaller rivers and streams. "The falling concentrations reflect the general improvement in wastewater treatment. In particular, secondary treatment will remove 75 percent of ammonium while primary treatment removes none. Generally the United Kingdom, Denmark, Finland, and France have the lowest concentrations of total ammonium at the monitoring stations; and Austria and Belgium the highest" (European Environment Agency, *Environmental Signals 2001,* 2001). Discharges of organic pollution—linked to agricultural and industrial operations and increased usage of residential sewer lines—have also decreased in many parts of Europe, as new treatment plants came on line.

Efforts to reduce nitrogen pollution, meanwhile, have thus far been disappointing. Implementation of the European Union's Nitrate Directive, for example, has been termed "unsatisfactory" by the European Environment Agency, which noted increases "in nitrate or total oxidised nitrogen concentrations with increasing total agricultural land use in the upstream catchments. In the five European countries with relevant data, the highest concentrations of nitrate or total oxidised nitrogen are found in small- and medium-sized rivers." Indeed, the EEA reports that median concentrations of nitrate in small rivers in those European watersheds with a heavy agricultural focus have often been found to be unsafe to drink (European Environment Agency 2001).

The state of groundwater quality in Europe, meanwhile, is mixed. Groundwater supplies in many regions have been compromised by pollution from nitrates, pesticides, and hydrocarbons. In addition, the EEA reported that groundwater contamination by heavy metals from mining, industrial discharges, and landfills was an issue of concern in ten countries (Bulgaria, Estonia, France, Hungary, Moldova, Romania, Slovak Republic, Slovenia, Spain, and Sweden) out of the twenty-two from which information was obtained (European Environment Agency, *Europe's Environment,* 1998).

Figure 6.2 Nitrogen and Phosphorus Deposition Trends in Large Rivers in the European Union

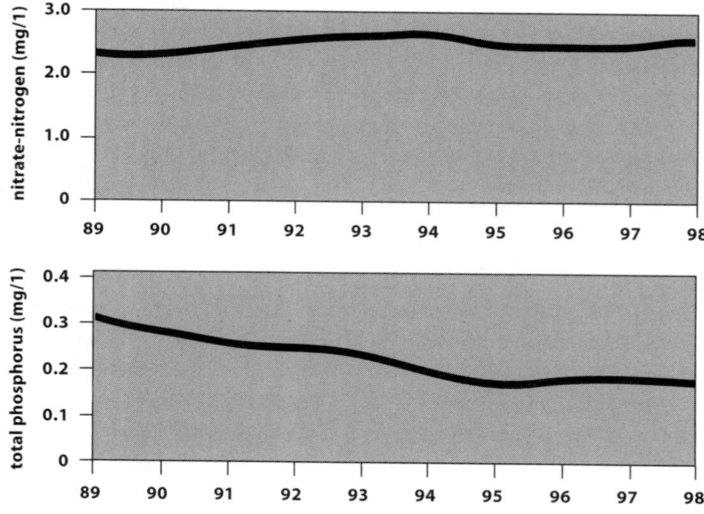

SOURCE: European Environment Agency 2001. *Environmental Signals 2001*. Elsevier Science Ltd.

Most of the nations cited above for excessive groundwater pollution are located in Eastern Europe, indicative of the grim condition of the water supply in much of that region. Most of the countries that were formerly attached to the Soviet empire—either as constituent nations of the USSR or satellite countries under communist rule—now suffer from a legacy of environmental degradation that is stunning in its scope and severity. "Anyone traveling through eastern Europe, the former Soviet Union and its satellites . . . could be forgiven for thinking that the Apocalypse was no longer imminent but in full cry. There's hardly a river, stream, or brook that isn't contaminated with the runoff from human misuse, whether industrial effluents, agricultural pesticides and herbicides or worse [such as] bacterial contamination—the river as disease vector—or the dumping of radioactive wastes" (de Villiers, *Water,* 2000).

Indeed, prior to 1989, when communist governments fell across the region in quick succession, Eastern Europe's rivers and lakes were dumping grounds for a sweeping array of toxic waste materials. Environmental laws designed to block such abuses were generally nonexistent, ignored, or circumvented via bribery. As a result, the aquatic life in countless rivers and streams was decimated by agrochemical, industrial, sewage, and nuclear

The Campaign to Clean Up England's Mersey River

The Mersey River basin covers 4,680 square kilometers in north west England, an area that includes the cities of Manchester and Liverpool. At one time, the river was so dangerously polluted that citizens were warned not to throw lighted cigarettes into its waters for fear of igniting flammable vapors. Very few fish remained in the Mersey basin, and those that survived were subject to public health warnings because of cadmium and mercury contamination.

In 1985 a group of concerned citizens, area farmers and businesses, county authorities, and environmental organizations started the Mersey Basin Campaign. The goal of the campaign was to improve the water quality in the Mersey River and all of its connecting streams and canals so that the whole system could once again support fish by the year 2010. Since its inception, the Mersey Basin Campaign has involved more than 170 cleanup projects, ranging from large-scale efforts to reduce the number of sewer discharge pipes emptying into the Mersey, and improve wastewater treatment, to local projects aimed at picking up litter and planting wildflowers. The campaign has also encompassed educational initiatives to help farmers employ less polluting methods and award programs to encourage companies to implement environmentally friendly work practices.

Since the Mersey Basin Campaign began in 1985, the quality of water in the area has shown steady improvement. The European Environment Agency reported that the percentage of watercourses in the region that were clean enough to support fish improved from 56 percent in 1985 to 80 percent in 2000. The campaign has also paid significant dividends for other species as well. For example, seals and octopuses have been observed in the basin, as well as important indicator species such as otters and kingfishers.

Sources:

European Environment Agency. 2001. *Environmental Signals 2001.* Copenhagen: EEA.

Mersey Basin Campaign. 2000. *A Manifesto for the New Millennium.* Winsford, UK: Mersey Basin Campaign.

Mersey Basin Campaign website. http://www.merseybasin.org.uk

contamination. Human populations suffered as well, as high concentrations of heavy metals and other toxins became part of the drinking water in many major urban centers.

The litany of abuses is too overwhelming to recount in full, but the following glances at individual countries are fairly representative. In central Albania, most of the rivers and streams are organically dead as a result of years of reckless industrial, agricultural, and municipal discharge. In Poland, municipal and industrial sewage treatment was nonexistent across much of the country during the communist era, creating a situation in which the percentage of "rivers with water fit for human consumption declined from nearly a third in the mid-1960s to below 4 percent by the late 1980s; . . .biologically three quarters of Poland's rivers were dead by 1988" (Carter and Turnock, *Environmental Problems in Eastern Europe,* 1993). Romania's waterways are devoid of life for miles at a time, especially in downstream areas that bear the brunt of steadily accumulating pollution, and recent evidence suggests that environmental protection and restoration of these rivers are still not a priority. In January 2000, for instance, a cyanide spill from a gold-mining operation in northern Romania entered the Tisza River. As the spill moved downstream, it ultimately poisoned significant riverine ecosystems in three countries. Since then, critics contend that the Romanian government has done little to prevent similar incidents from taking place. And water supplies in northern Ukraine and southern Belarus continue to be tainted by the deadly reactor explosion at the Chernobyl nuclear power facility in northern Ukraine in 1986. The full scale of this disaster's impact on the regional ecosystem, including its underground aquifers, wetlands, and streams, will not be known for years to come.

The waters of the former Czechoslovakia—sometimes referred to as the "roof of Europe" in recognition of its place as the starting point for several important watersheds—suffered particularly harsh abuse during the Soviet era. By the end of the 1980s, "over two-thirds of Czechoslovakia's rivers and streams were horribly polluted from untreated industrial effluents, raw sewage and run-off from pesticides and fertilizers used on agricultural fields.... The fouling of rivers and streams with untreated sewage from municipalities is a national disgrace. Less than a fifth of the country's sewage is treated properly before being discharged into surface waters.... All of this is made worse by poorly maintained water mains; nearly a third of the total water supply is lost due to defective public drainage systems" (ibid.).

Yet even the ghastly damage visited on the waterways of Slovakia and the Czech Republic pales in comparison to the appalling state of many lakes, rivers, and streams in Russia. Throughout the Cold War era, the factories of the Soviet military-industrial complex polluted lakes, rivers, and seas with impunity. As a result, large swaths of the Russian countryside suffered irreparable damage, and many of its formerly beautiful lakes and rivers were stripped of their natural character and outfitted for industrial use. In the late 1990s, journalist Mark Hertsgaard visited Lake Ledoga and the Neva River, formerly rich aquatic habitats that had been sacrificed to provide water to Leningrad

Rescue workers remove some of the thousands of fish killed by a cyanide spill in Hungary's Tisza River.
REUTERS NEWMEDIA INC./CORBIS

and feed the Soviet military and economy. "In olden days its purity was so renowned that sea captains would insist on stowing Ladoga water aboard before long journeys," wrote Hertsgaard. "Now, however, the lake was ringed with scores of paper mills and other factories that discharged vast amounts of heavy metals, acids, and chlorine. The Neva was further polluted while passing through Leningrad by the city's approximately two thousand factories, only 10 percent of which treated their waste before discharge. Human waste from the hundreds of thousands of households in Leningrad also poured into the Neva, generally without benefit of prior treatment" (Hertsgaard, *Earth Odyssey,* 1998). Yet despite this appalling record, Hertsgaard points out that "Leningrad did not rank among the ten most polluted cities in the Soviet Union. Competition for that honor was stiff in a country where two-thirds of the drinking water did not meet health standards, air pollution in over one hundred cities exceeded legal limits by a factor of ten, a chemically saturated river somewhere in the country burst into flames once a month, and 20 percent of the population (about 40 million people) lived in areas that scientists had labeled zones of ecological 'conflict,' 'crisis,' or 'catastrophe'" (ibid.; Green, *Ecology and Perestroika,* 1991).

Russia's Volga River did not escape the damage visited upon lesser rivers, either, despite its special place in Russian history. "The mighty Volga is no longer a river of plenty," wrote Victoria Pope. "Chroniclers through the centuries remarked on its bounty, especially where the river reached the wide Russian plains called the steppes.... [But] the riverbanks where the famous Volga boatmen once pulled their barges by rope are now crowded with factories, dams, and hydroelectric plants." She goes on to note that much of the Volga's environmental degradation can actually be traced to rampant dam-building along its length in the 1950s and 1960s: "It used to take 50 days for the river water to travel the 2,300 miles from source to estuary. Now it takes a year and a half. The slow pace causes pollutants to accumulate in eight vast man-made reservoirs along the river's course and to settle on the riverbed and its delta. On some stretches of the now sluggish Volga, petroleum byproducts have reached concentrations 100 times the allowable limit or greater. When it reaches the Caspian Sea, the river receives one final insult, from the Kirov district of the city of Volgograd: 40,000 cubic yards of raw sewage every year" (Pope, "Poisoning of Russia's River of Plenty," 1992).

The Caspian Sea is not the only regional sea that is suffering from massive river-borne infusions of pollutants. Indeed, the ecological health of all of Europe's seas, including the North, Baltic, Black, and Mediterranean, have been compromised by feeder rivers carrying toxic cargoes of industrial, domestic, and agricultural waste. In 1990, for example, the Black Sea—which is now biologically dead in many areas—received more than 75,000 tons of heavy metals (including arsenic, mercury, cadmium, zinc, and iron) from the Danube, Dniester, and Dneiper rivers (Hinrichsen, *Coastal Waters of the World*, 1998).

This shocking state of affairs will be immensely difficult to correct. Indeed, the European Environment Programme noted as recently as 1998 that most wastewater generated by cities in Central and Eastern Europe is still discharged into local waterways without any treatment. Cash-strapped governments have little funding to build water treatment facilities or implement other much-needed measures to combat ongoing pollution. Ironically, though, analysts believe that these same recessionary economic conditions have actually relieved the pressure on some of Central and Eastern Europe's

Wastewater Treatment in Europe

As of 1997 about 90 percent of the population had some form of wastewater treatment in Northern Europe (including Norway, Sweden, Finland, and Iceland) and Western Europe (including the United Kingdom, the Netherlands, Germany, Denmark, and Austria). Only about 50 percent of the population was served by wastewater treatment in Southern Europe (including Spain and Greece). These totals include primary treatment, in which solids are removed but not ammonium; secondary treatment, which involves using microorganisms to retain some nutrients and remove about 75 percent of ammonium; and tertiary treatment, in which phosphorus and sometimes nitrogen are also removed.

The percentage of people whose wastewater received tertiary treatment was highest in Northern Europe (about 80 percent), followed by Western Europe (about 50 percent), and Southern Europe (less than 10 percent). The percentage of the population connected to tertiary treatment has increased across all regions of Europe since 1980, as many countries constructed new wastewater treatment plants in the late 1980s and early 1990s. In fact, tertiary treatment more than doubled in Austria and Spain; Greece introduced tertiary treatment for the first time, although only 10 percent of its municipal waste is treated.

In recent years, wastewater treatment in European Union countries has been governed by the Urban Wastewater Treatment Directive of 1991. This directive established three deadlines for member states to implement higher levels of wastewater treatment. By the end of 1993, EU countries were required to identify seriously polluted waterways and environmentally sensitive areas that qualified for strict standards of treatment. The results of that stage affected nearly 3,250 cities, which were required to treat wastewater to the secondary level by the end of 1998. By the end of 2000, all EU cities with

(continues)

pollution-stained waters in recent years. A number of countries have registered considerable reductions in fertilizer and pesticide use as economies have undergone painful transitions away from state-subsidized collective farms, which had historically relied on tremendous volumes of agrochemicals. For example, Poland's fertilizer use dropped by half from 1985 to 1994, while the Czech Republic's use of fertilizers fell from 346 kilograms per hectare in 1985 to 107 in 1994. Another cornerstone of these agricultural systems was massive irrigation projects that damaged freshwater ecosystems by creating areas of profound salination and waterlogged ground. The abandonment of some of these outdated, inefficient irrigation systems has slowed

populations greater than 15,000 were supposed to have secondary treatment of wastewater. This mandate expanded to include all cities with populations greater than 2,000 by the year 2005.

The Urban Wastewater Treatment Directive was expected to precipitate increases in the capacity of treatment plants in all member states except Sweden, Finland, and the Netherlands, which already had high capacity. The greatest increases in capacity were expected to occur in Southern Europe and Ireland. The EEA predicts an overall increase of 22 percent for wastewater collection systems and 69 percent for treatment works by 2005. The total cost of compliance with the directive was estimated at £19 billion.

As of 2002, the EEA reported that the directive had resulted in upgrades to wastewater treatment capacity in many areas, as EU member states built new treatment plants and improved treatment processes. As a result, many European waterways have seen significant reductions in the levels of phosphorus, ammonium, and organic matter in the years since the directive took effect. But some member states have been slow in complying with the directive. For example, the city of Brussels had no wastewater treatment at all by 1998, and only one-third of the city's discharges were treated to the secondary level by 2000. Eleven cities in the United Kingdom had no wastewater treatment by 2001, although work was underway to remedy that situation. The EEA also noted that further action was necessary to control and reduce the impact of runoff from agriculture on Europe's waterways.

Sources:

European Commission. "The Week in Europe, 12 April 2001." European Commission website. http://www.cec.org.uk/press/we/we01/we0114.htm.

European Environment Agency. 2001. *Environment Signals 2001.* Copenhagen: EEA.

———. "Water Indicators." EEA website. http://themes.eea.eu.int/specific_media/water/indicators.

the deterioration of freshwater resources in several regions. In addition, the transition to market economies forced the closure of many state-run industries and factories that dumped large quantities of pollution into local waterways; their demise has undoubtedly helped reduce pollution loads into river and lakes.

Freshwater ecosystems in some other Eastern European countries, meanwhile, have fared comparatively well over the years. In 2001, for example, the World Wildlife Fund (WWF) released a study on water quality in Hungary, Slovakia, Estonia, Bulgaria, and Turkey. According to the WWF, the water resources in some of these nations, while often compromised by years of indifferent stewardship, are actually in better condition than those in some EU member nations. "The belief that these accession countries have overwhelming problems with the state of their rivers and lakes is ill-founded," said a representative of WWF's European Freshwater Programme. "While black spots undoubtedly exist, many rivers and lakes of these countries will offer the EU great natural wealth and contribute strongly to the EU's biodiversity." The study cites the Mesta, Raba, Hornad, Hron, Narva, Kizilirmak, and Goksu rivers; the Rila and Vel'ke Hinbcovo lakes; and the wetland delta of the Gediz as particularly noteworthy freshwater resources in the region (World Wildlife Fund, "Water and Wetland Index," 2001).

The future outlook of Eastern Europe's lakes and rivers is uncertain. Poor economies, outmoded industrial facilities, growing populaces, and ignorance of environmentally sustainable practices all are expected to put additional pressure on regional waterways for the foreseeable future. As the UN Environment Programme stated: "Water pollution problems may persist and worsen as economies recover, with industrial enterprises placing low emphasis on prevention measures and governments taking insufficient measures to enforce pollution reduction strategies" (UN Environment Programme, *Global Environment Outlook 2000,* 1999, p. 110). But some members of Europe's scientific, environmental, and political communities believe that the allure of European Union membership will prove a potent incentive for nations to introduce and enforce environmental regulations that will allow their waterways to begin healing themselves. Meaningful environmental protections for ground and surface water resources are a prerequisite for inclusion in the European Union, as the EU Water Framework Directive requires all member countries to reach quantifiable "good status" for waters.

Europe's Imperiled Wetlands

Europe has taken a number of steps to protect its wetlands, which provide vital habitat for the continent's declining wildlife and are an important facet of its overall freshwater health. As of 2002, approximately 300 wetland areas in Europe and Central Asia have received special protections under the Ramsar Convention on Wetlands (an international environmental convention passed in 1971), and dozens of important wetland areas have been designated as natural biosphere reserves or heritage sites, conveying significant legal protections. All told, approximately 140,000 square kilometers of wetland in Europe were under some safeguards by the late 1990s, according to the European Centre for Nature Conservation. Additional wetlands are also being afforded government protection with each passing year. In early 2001, for example, Albania, Greece, and the former Yugoslav Republic of Macedonia created the first transboundary preserve in the Balkans when they unveiled the 55,830-acre Prespa Park wetland preserve.

Conservationists and scientists are heartened by such set-asides, many of which are of historic importance. But while these and other steps have helped decrease the rate of wetland loss in Europe, many of the Ramsar sites are too small to conserve entire ecosystems, and conversion of wetlands for agricultural purposes or urban development is still occurring at a rate that exceeds replenishment. Continuing development of wetlands is most rampant in Southern Europe, which can least afford to lose them on account of their scarcity relative to the remainder of the continent. The former Soviet republics that line Europe's far eastern ramparts, meanwhile, continue to hold vast wetlands, including the Pripet Marshes of Belarus and Ukraine, the continent's single largest marshland at 270,000 square kilometers (104,000 square miles). Northern Europe also contains large swaths of wetland that remain largely untouched. Indeed, Sweden has the most wetlands of any nation in Western Europe, with an estimated 140,000 square kilometers within its borders. It is followed by neighboring Finland (120,000) and Norway (50,000). But portions of Northwestern and Central Europe are also converting wetlands intensively, despite increasing pressures on habitat. These conversions are most intensive in tourism-reliant coastal areas, where wetlands continue to be drained with little consideration for wildlife habitat, increased vulnerability to flooding, or other factors.

Current initiatives to protect remaining wetlands are strongest in Western Europe, home to long-established canal and reservoir systems that eradicated countless marshes, ponds, and fens over the centuries. But industrial, agricultural, and municipal pollution remain significant threats to many of the region's remaining wetland ecosystems. These pressures continue to push some wetlands to the brink of collapse and change others in fundamental ways. For example, populations of all the United Kingdom's native amphibian species have declined alarmingly in recent years, a development that is most often attributed to the drainage of as much as 80 percent of the breeding marshes, ponds, and other wetlands in the region since the 1950s (Halliday and Heyer, "The Case of the Vanishing Frogs," 1997).

A Landscape Forever Changed by Dams and Canals

Significant stretches of most major European rivers have been dammed, channeled, and otherwise harnessed for human use over the years. These changes range from canal systems used for transportation and large irrigation grids utilized by farming interests to dams that are outfitted to generate tremendous amounts of hydroelectric power. In fact, these rearrangements of river corridors and watersheds by human hand have been so extensive that every significant watershed in Europe has been fundamentally altered.

Dams have been the single greatest factor in this transformation of Europe's landscape. More than 6,000 large dams dot the European landscape. Spain has 1,200 of these dams, fully 20 percent of the continent's total, while Turkey, France, Italy, and the United Kingdom all maintain more than 500 large dams. Most of these dams came on line in the 1950s, 1960s, and 1970s, when dam-building reached its peak worldwide. The rate of dam-building in Europe has declined steadily since that time, although Bosnia, Spain, Turkey, Germany, and Bulgaria, among others, have significant dam projects in the works. Some observers attribute the overall drop in construction to increased awareness of the ecological consequences of such activity in terms of habitat destruction and long-term river health, but others believe that the dropoff can be attributed to the dwindling number of untouched hydroelectric resources left to be exploited and the difficulty of obtaining financing for construction.

Some European countries have signaled a willingness to review the continued viability of some dams, spurred by the growing threat of vanishing fisheries. In France, for example, two high-profile dams were demolished as part of an effort to restore some of the ancient spawning grounds of Atlantic salmon, which have largely disappeared from the major rivers of the European Atlantic coast. In 1998 a small hydroelectric dam on the upper Allier River was removed, making 30 hectares of prime spawning habitat available once again, and in early 1999 a dam that had eliminated a fifth of the entire Loire River basin for migratory fish was removed from the Vienne River, a major tributary of the Loire.

The dams, canals, and concrete embankments that blanket the continent have also been cited as the chief culprits in flooding that has besieged large regions of Europe in recent years. In 1995, for example, rivers in France,

Germany, Belgium, and Holland all overflowed their banks, killing forty people, necessitating mass evacuations, and exacting punishing economic damage throughout the region. The extent of the flooding was widely blamed on the replacement of many of the region's spongelike marshes and floodplains with vast areas of cement, asphalt, and other hallmarks of development.

In many parts of Europe, the river corridors themselves have been altered to benefit regional transportation and business interests. The character of the famous Rhine River, for example, has been intrinsically altered by the machinations of engineers who have changed its course and drained much of the marshland that used to border it. As the *Economist* noted: "The Rhine, over the past few decades, has been put into a kind of corset. . . .Stretches of the Rhine have been straightened and banks heightened, cutting some 50 kilometers off the river's 1,320-kilometer meander to the sea. This has doubled the speed of the water's passage from Basel, at the Swiss border, to Rotterdam. Now, when there is heavy snow or rain upstream, it cascades down to flood at the mouth or half-way along, instead of soaking into marshes nearer its source. These man-created problems have made the river systems less able to accommodate flood waters than they used to be" ("The Drowned Heart of Europe," *Economist,* 1995).

But while criticism of dams—whether for environmental, safety, or economic reasons—has intensified in Europe in recent years, this clean source of energy is an incontrovertibly important element of the established infrastructure of many regions. Approximately 22 percent of total world consumption of hydroelectric power is attributed to Western Europe, and some countries within this region, such as Norway, Iceland, and Albania, rely on hydroelectricity for nearly all their energy needs. France, Norway, and Sweden alone accounted for almost 60 percent of total hydroelectric power consumption in Western Europe in the mid-1990s. Moreover, the economies of many European cities are heavily reliant on the waterways that have been tamed by these towering structures and their ancillary locks and canals. About one-quarter of the continent's large dams serve multiple functions (usually some combination of electrical power, irrigation, water supply, and flood control), making them indispensable to many local and regional economies.

In Eastern Europe and the countries of the former Soviet Union, meanwhile, many existing dams are seen as symbolic of an earlier, authoritarian period in the region's history. During the communist era, all major rivers in the European part of the former Soviet Union were sliced into chains of artificial lakes by massive dam projects. But as with other areas of environmental protection in this region of the world, communist authorities generally did little to address the problems created by the dams, from changing water temperature to high levels of pollution in reservoir waters. Frequently cited examples of the devastation caused by poorly managed dams include the Volga, Kuban, and Don rivers. On each of those waterways, dams were operated with little or no regard for migrating fish or other aquatic life, or for the inhabitants of downstream towns and villages. As a result, most proposed dam projects in this region of the world are now viewed with suspicion and skepticism, even when economic benefits are considerable and planning reflects a recognition of environmental considerations.

Sources:

Abramovitz, Janet N. 1996. *Imperiled Waters, Impoverished Future: The Decline of Freshwater Ecosystems.* Washington, DC: WorldWatch Institute.

Carter, F. W., and D. Turnock, eds. 1993. *Environmental Problems in Eastern Europe.* London and New York: Routledge.

De Bardeleben, J., and J. Hannigan, eds. 1994. *Environmental Security and Quality after Communism: Eastern Europe and the Soviet Successor States.* Boulder, CO: Westview.

Delbaere, B. C. W., ed. 1998. *Facts and Figures on Europe's Biodiversity 1998–1999.* Tilburg, the Netherlands: European Centre for Nature Conservation.

de Villiers, Marq. 2000. *Water: The Fate of Our Most Precious Resource.* Boston: Houghton Mifflin.

"The Drowned Heart of Europe." 1995. *Economist* 334 (February 4).

European Environment Agency. 1998. *Europe's Environment: The Second Assessment.* London: Elsevier Science.

———. 2001. *Environmental Signals 2001: European Environment Agency Regular Indicator Report.* Copenhagen: EEA.

Feshbach, Murray. 1995. *Ecological Disaster: Cleaning up the Hidden Legacy of the Soviet Regime.* New York: Twentieth Century Fund Press.

Gleick, Peter H. 2000. *The World's Water 2000–2001.* Washington, DC: Island.

Green, Eric. 1991. *Ecology and Perestroika: Environmental Protection in the Soviet Union.* New York: American Committee on U.S.-Soviet Relations.

Halliday, Timothy R., and W. Ronald Heyer. 1997. "The Case of the Vanishing Frogs." *Technology Review* (May–June).

Hertsgaard, Mark. 1998. *Earth Odyssey: Around the World in Search of Our Environmental Future.* New York: Broadway.

Hinrichsen, Don. 1998. *Coastal Waters of the World: Trends, Threats, and Strategies.* Washington, DC: Island.

Joyce, Chris B., and P. Max Wade. 1998. *European Wet Grasslands.* New York: John Wiley.

Kirchhofer, A., and D. Hefti, eds. 1996. *Conservation of Endangered Freshwater Fish in Europe.* Basel: Birkhauser Verlag.

Pope, Victoria. 1992. "Poisoning of Russia's River of Plenty." *U.S. News & World Report* 112 (April 13).

Postel, Sandra. 1996. *Dividing the Waters: Food Security, Ecosystem Health, and the New Politics of Scarcity.* Washington, DC: WorldWatch Institute.

Saiko, Tatyana. 2001. *Environmental Crises: Geographical Case Studies in Post-Socialist Eurasia.* Harlow, UK: Pearson Education.

Segerstahl, Boris, Alexander Akleyev, and Vladimir Novikov. 1997. "The Long Shadow of Soviet Plutonium Production." *Environment* 39 (January–February).

UN Environment Programme. 1999. *Global Environment Outlook 2000.* London: Earthscan Publications.

VanDeveer, Stacy D. 2000. *Protecting Regional Seas: Developing Capacity and Fostering Environmental Cooperation in Europe.* Washington, DC: Woodrow Wilson Center.

World Commission on Dams. 2000. *Dams and Development: A New Framework for Decisionmaking.* London: Earthscan Publications.

World Resources Institute, UN Environment Programme, UN Development Programme, and World Bank. 2000. *World Resources 2000–2001: People and Ecosystems, The Fraying Web of Life.* Washington, DC: UN Environment Programme.

World Wildlife Fund. "Water and Wetland Index." European Freshwater Programme. http://www.freshwater.org (accessed March 13, 2001).

7

Oceans and Coastal Areas

Environmental assessments show that the ecological health of Europe's seas has been severely compromised by massive infusions of municipal, industrial, and agricultural wastes during the past half-century. These pollutants—untreated and partially treated human and animal waste, agrochemicals, heavy metals, persistent organic pollutants (POPs) such as PCB and DDT, oil, and radioactive materials—enter the ocean from numerous points along the continent's heavily developed coastline or are deposited into the sea by rivers and streams that carry effluents from polluted areas farther inland. Whatever their origins, this toxic stew has taken a grim toll on many of the continent's ocean resources. In addition, many of Europe's marine ecosystems are reeling from extensive habitat loss and degradation caused by commercial development, decades of overfishing, and the arrival of alien species that have disrupted millennia-old food chains.

The severity of these threats varies somewhat from sea to sea across Europe. After all, each sea's environmental circumstances are predicated on a host of unique factors, including regional climate, seabottom topography and other geographic characteristics affecting water circulation, the nature and extent of human activity within the watershed, the economic might and political philosophy of littoral nations, and regional cooperation (or lack thereof) in addressing environmental issues. Indeed, each European coastal state grapples with environmental issues that are singular to the particular sea on which it sits. But in the final analysis, all of Europe faces the same fundamental challenge: to address trends of usage that threaten to overwhelm the continent's seas and destroy already stressed ecosystems.

An Epidemic of Overfishing in Regional Seas

European Union (EU) member states with access to the sea share a total coastline of 89,000 kilometers (55,200 miles), but the extent of the European coastline expands dramatically when the holdings of non-EU nations in the region—most notably Russia—are considered. When those nations are added to the tally, Europe's coastline is nearly 326,000 kilometers in length, with claimed territorial seas (up to 12 nautical miles from shore) of 2.589 million square kilometers, and a claimed EEZ (Exclusive Economic Zone, which extends 200 miles offshore) of 11.45 million square kilometers.

Much of this shoreline is heavily populated. Of the EU's population of 360 million, some 70 million live on a seacoast, and in several nations the vast majority of the population lives within a few kilometers of the ocean. In Denmark, for instance, about 70 percent of the country's people live along the North Sea or the Kattegat, which connects the North and Baltic seas.

Most of Europe's coastal residents are concentrated in villages, towns, and cities in which fishing has long been closely intertwined with economic vitality and regional identity. Today, centuries after the first nets were cast into the continent's waters, the fishing industry remains integral to hundreds of European communities. In 1998 there were 99,170 registered fishing vessels scattered among the EU member states. Approximately 80 percent of these vessels were under 12 meters in length, indicating a preponderance of small fishing operations. Other characteristics of the European fleet are advanced vessel age (only 16 percent of the total fleet was less than ten years old in 1998) and stagnation in overall fleet size (between 1991 and 1998, the EU saw a nominal reduction in registered fleet capacity of 4.5 percent by tonnage). Both of those trends can be attributed to another, more disquieting trend that has cast a long shadow over Europe's fishing communities: the decline of major fish stocks in European seas over the past two decades.

Ships in the European Union fleet account for only 7.5 percent of global marine capture fisheries by volume, but the total marine fish catch in all of Europe, including EU and non-EU states (such as Russia, Norway, and Iceland), averaged nearly 16 million metric tons from 1995 to 1997, 21 percent of the world total (World Resources Institute, *World Resources 2000–2001*, 2000). Marine scientists and other analysts agree that this current rate of harvest—which is nowhere near historical highs—is unsustainable. But meaningful measures to protect valuable species have only recently been implemented, and some fishermen, environmentalists, and marine scientists openly wonder whether they will be sufficient to counteract years of flawed resource management. In the meantime, more than 100 fish species in Europe and Central Asia

Table 7.1 Coastal Lengths and Economic Zones of European Countries

	Coastal Length (km)	*Territorial Sea (up to 12 nm) (000 km²)*	*Claimed Exclusive Economic Zone (000 km²)*	*Population Within 100 km from the Coast (percent)*
EUROPE	325,892	2,589.4	11,447.1	x
Albania	649	6.2	X	97.1
Austria	0	x	x	2.2
Belarus	0	x	x	0.0
Belgium	76	1.5	x	83.0
Bosnia and Herzegovina	23	x	x	46.6
Bulgaria	457	6.5	25.7	29.2
Croatia	5,663	31.7	x	37.9
Czech Rep.	0	x	x	0.0
Denmark	5,316	24.8	80.4	100.0
Estonia	2,956	24.3	11.6	85.9
Finland	31,119	55.1	x	72.8
France	7,330	73.4	706.4	39.6
Germany	3,624	18.4	37.4	14.6
Greece	15,147	114.9	x	99.2
Hungary	0	x	x	0.0
Iceland	8,506	73.0	678.7	99.9
Ireland	6,437	39.4	x	99.9
Italy	9,226	155.6	x	79.1
Latvia	565	12.6	15.6	75.2
Lithuania	258	2.0	3.6	22.9
Macedonia, FYR	0	x	x	14.3
Moldova, Rep.	0	x	x	9.1
Netherlands	1,914	13.2	x	93.4
Norway	53,199	111.2	1,095.1	95.4
Poland	1,032	10.6	19.4	13.5
Portugal	2,830	64.1	1,656.4	92.7
Romania	696	5.3	18.0	6.3
Russian Federation	110,310	1,318.1	6,255.8	14.9
Slovakia	0	x	x	0.0
Slovenia	41	0.2	x	60.6
Spain	7,268	115.8	683.2	67.9
Sweden	26,384	85.3	73.2	87.7
Switzerland	0	x	x	0.0
Ukraine	4,953	53.9	86.4	20.9
United Kingdom	19,717	168.1	x	98.6
Yugoslavia	x	x	x	8.1

SOURCE: World Resources 2000–2001.

NOTE: Figures should be interpreted as approximations because of the difficulty of measuring coastline length.

were classified as vulnerable, endangered, or critically endangered, according to a 1998 World Conservation Monitoring Centre (WCMC)/World Conservation Union (IUCN) report. Of these species, fully half were judged to be either endangered or critically endangered.

The fisheries of the Northeast Atlantic, which encompasses the open Atlantic and the North Sea as well as semienclosed seas such as the Mediterranean, Black, and Baltic seas, were not always in such terrible shape. Harvests of cod, haddock, and other valuable species were strong throughout the 1950s and 1960s, as expanding regional fleets made effective use of new fishing technologies. In the mid-1970s, the total capture of wild fish by European nations soared to 13 million tons annually. But as with so many other fisheries around the globe, sobering indications of overharvesting became visible during the late 1970s and 1980s. First, catches began to decline in size, despite the steady introduction of new trawlers, equipment, and methodologies. During the 1980s and early 1990s, the annual catch declined to an average of about 10 million tons, 3 million tons less than the peak of only a few years earlier. Even more troubling, analysts noted that the makeup of the catch itself changed significantly during this time. The pattern of total catches in European waters has masked the fact that from 1950 to the mid-1990s the share of the total catch made up by historically valuable or traditional species such as North Atlantic cod, haddock, and herring declined, while harvests of many formerly lower-valued species such as sandeels and blue whiting rose (UN Food and Agriculture Organization, *Review of the State of World Fishery Resources,* 1997).

The FAO and other observers pin much of the blame for the depletion of Northeast Atlantic fishery resources on inadequate resource management. The European Union's fishing industry operates in accordance with the guidelines of the Common Fisheries Policy (CFP), which has the stated goal of protecting commercial fish stocks from overfishing. Toward that end, the CFP includes quotas on the type and amounts of fish that can be harvested (the Total Allowable Catch, or TAC) based on scientific assessments of fish stocks. The CFP also imposes regulations on equipment and restrictions on the number of days that vessels can fish. But in some instances, these regulations have not done enough to maintain fish populations at healthy, sustainable levels. In Atlantic and Mediterranean waters, for instance, the Spanish fleet has become notorious for exceeding permitted tolerance levels for undersized bluefin tuna. In the North Sea, EU nations and Norway—which jointly manage the sea's fisheries—have routinely established TAC levels significantly above advised levels. This problem has been compounded by the stock assessments themselves, which have, at times, wildly overestimated the true size of the fisheries. These inflated numbers have been attributed to several factors. In some

Brent Spar Saga Roils North Sea Waters

Greenpeace occupies the Brent Spar platform in the North Sea before it is dumped at sea in May 1995. GREENPEACE/CORBIS SYGMA

In 1995 a lone oil rig far out in the North Sea became the focal point of one of Europe's most heavily publicized environmental battles in recent memory. This rig, the *Brent Spar*, was a massive oil platform owned by Royal Dutch Shell. The 150-meter-tall facility, which weighed 65,000 tons, had first been installed in 1976. It remained in service until 1991, when Shell closed it down. At that time, Shell carried out extensive decommissioning studies to assess its options. Eventually, however, the company discarded all but two choices: tow the platform to the mainland for dismantling or sink it beneath the waves of the Atlantic. The former option had been used with nine previous decommissioned North Sea oil installations, but all of those rigs had been far smaller than the *Spar*, and industry experts acknowledged that disposing of the *Spar* in the same way would constitute a significant logistical and technical challenge. In 1994 Shell announced that it had decided to dispose of the *Brent Spar* at sea. The company indicated at that time that sinking the installation would be far less expensive than onshore disassembly, and that deep-sea disposal would be safer for workers and have only a minimal, highly localized, environmental impact.

Shell proposed to sink the *Spar* in a deep ocean trench located more than 150 miles northwest of the coast of Scotland. In February 1995, Shell received approval for its abandonment plan from the United Kingdom's

(continues)

instances, political pressures have prompted unduly optimistic assessments. Statistics on fish stocks also have been skewed by illegal overfishing (which is widespread), technological advances that enabled fishing vessels to maintain catch rates despite diminishing stocks, and loss of fish from by-catch (the netting of nontarget species while fishing for target species). "Discarding is a significant factor in the Northeast Atlantic fisheries, and in

Government Department of Trade and Industry. But two months later, members of the Greenpeace environmental organization seized possession of the abandoned platform and occupied it for the next several weeks. These actions triggered extensive media coverage throughout Europe, with Shell and Greenpeace and their respective allies exchanging flurries of angry charges and countercharges.

The crux of Greenpeace's argument against deep sea disposal of the *Brent Spar* was that the rig was a "toxic timebomb" that posed an immediate and significant threat to the regional marine environment. The organization pointed out that according to Shell's own reports, the platform still held 30 tons of low-level radioactive waste and 100 tons of sludge that might contain heavy metals, oil, and PCBs. The group also charged that the *Spar* still held 5,500 tons of oil, a contention that was hotly denied by the oil company. Moreover, Greenpeace observed that Shell's plan violated the 1958 Geneva Convention on the Continental Shelf, of which Britain was a signatory. This law stated that "any installations that are abandoned or disused must be entirely removed." Finally, the environmental group charged that if deep-sea disposal of the *Spar* went forward, it would set an alarming precedent for the disposal of other offshore facilities. As the public relations war intensified, Greenpeace raised the specter of a North Sea in which hundreds of decommissioned oil rigs would be left to rust beneath the waves.

Shell insisted that it had removed most contaminants from the *Spar*—including all oil—in the early 1990s, and Greenpeace eventually retracted its oil claim. But on May 9 the German Ministry of the Environment declared its opposition to the deep-sea disposal plan, and other European countries followed suit over the next several weeks. On May 23 the environmental activists that had occupied the *Brent Spar* were removed, but Greenpeace did not relent. Instead, the group called for a boycott of Shell across continental Europe.

By mid-June, when Shell began towing the *Spar* to its disposal site, the company was under siege. The Greenpeace boycott proved stunningly effective, with business at German Shell stations reportedly down by 30 percent for a three-week

(continues)

part appears to be a consequence of setting quotas on individual species in what are mixed species fisheries," explained the FAO. "Illegal catches are either not reported at all or are reported as different under-quota species, resulting in a deterioration in the quality of fisheries statistics used for stock assessments. This situation is worsening, and is a cause for great concern" (ibid.).

period in June. In addition, dozens of Shell gas stations in Germany were damaged by vandalism. During this same period, European environmental ministers condemned Shell's deep-sea disposal plan at a North Sea conference, and eleven European states called for a moratorium on offshore disposal of decommissioned installations (only Great Britain and Norway, which own the bulk of *Brent Spar*–type facilities in the North Sea, opposed this position).

This sustained firestorm of criticism finally convinced Shell to cancel its deep-sea disposal plan. The environmental community received this news with great happiness, and characterized the entire affair as a prime example of how an empowered and informed citizenry can influence the management of marine and other environmental resources. But the company remained adamant that the only remaining option—to bring the *Spar* to shore for decontamination and dismantlement—would be far more expensive and pose greater environmental risks than deep-sea disposal. A number of observers shared this view. As one marine biologist stated in *New Scientist:* "To float [the *Brent Spar*] to land and dispose of it would be an immense task with many steps and many risks both to workers and to the environment. It would be easier and safer to dump it in the deep ocean" (Pearce, "What to Do with Derricks?" 1995).

The ultimate fate of the *Brent Spar* remained in doubt until January 1998, when Shell announced that the rig's hull would be used as the foundation for a new ferry quay in Norway. The platform was finally dismantled, and in the summer of 1999, the first sections of the *Spar* hull were installed on the North Sea shoreline at Mekjarvik near Stavanger.

Sources:

"The Brent Spar Saga." 1995. *Environmental Health Perspectives* 103 (September).

Jordan, Grant. 2001. *Shell, Greenpeace, and the Brent Spar.* New York: Palgrave.

Knott, David. 1996. "Brent Spar Experience Haunts North Sea Platform Abandonments." *Oil and Gas Journal* 94 (June 3).

Pearce, Fred. 1995. "What to Do with Derricks?" *New Scientist* 42 (June 24).

Rice, Tony, and Paula Owen. 1999. *Decommissioning the Brent Spar.* London: E. and F. N. Spon.

In May 2002 the European Commission proposed drastic cuts to the European Union's fishing fleet in an attempt to save endangered fish stocks. "The alternative is clear," stated EU Fisheries Commissioner Franz Fischler. "Either we take hard but essential reforms now or we hand our industry over to death by a thousand cuts in a few years' time." This plan, which would succeed the CFP upon the latter's expiration at the end of 2002, calls for the institution of multi-year catch quotas, the scrapping of 8,600 vessels—8.5 percent of the EU total—and elimination of subsidies for new vessels. It also calls for a 30 to 60 percent cut in the time trawlers spend at sea, depending on the fish species and region, and funding of programs to encourage fishermen to retire or train for other types of employment. New mandates to protect sea mammals and sea birds are also part of the proposed scheme. But these proposals are bitterly opposed by Spain, Portugal, and other southern European nations with large fleets, and the outlook for the proposed changes is uncertain (Kirby, "EU Proposes Radical Fishing Cuts," 2002).

Years of Overharvesting Haunt Fishermen of Regional Seas

In fact, this dynamic has already wreaked havoc on the North Sea's economically vital cod fishery. "For the past decade the North Sea cod fishery has been shrinking—and everybody knew, or should have known, that a disaster was coming," noted *Newsweek International* in 2001. "Fishermen knew it was getting harder and harder to find cod; most years they haven't even been able to catch their government-set quotas. Scientists warned repeatedly that the cod population was declining steadily, because most cod were being caught and eaten before they could reproduce." But the grim state of the fishery was not fully revealed until the late 1990s, when European fishery scientists adjusted their assessments to better account for misleading catch rates and other flaws in the monitoring data. At that time they discovered that they had been overestimating cod numbers by about 50 percent, and that the stock of spawning-age cod was below 70,000 tons, a quarter of what it had been in the early 1970s (Kunzig et al., "Why the Cod Are Vanishing," 2001).

These findings prompted the European Union and Norway to impose a 40 percent cut in the catch quota for North Sea cod and several other endangered fish species in late 2000 (steep declines in herring, haddock, sole, and other fish stocks have also been blamed on years of catch quotas that exceeded recommended levels). In addition, the survey prompted the EU to increase its efforts to reduce the size of its fleet by buying vessels and taking them out of circulation. Finally, the survey convinced the EU and Norway to close 40,000 square miles of the North Sea to bottom trawling in the spring of 2001 in order to give spawning cod a reprieve. This decision was a tremendous financial blow to Britain's fishing industry, which denounced the cuts. But many scientists believe that even more drastic steps may need to be taken if there is to be any hope of restoring the fishery to a measure of its former glory.

The demise of the cod fishery in the Baltic Sea, meanwhile, has been, if anything, even more precipitous. In the mid-1980s, cod fishermen from Baltic states were hauling in 440,000 tons of cod annually. But ten years later, catches of cod—the most important commercial fishery of the Baltic—had fallen to 66,000 tons (Sheppard, ed., *Seas at the Millennium,* 2000). This rapid decline convulsed countless fishing communities around the Baltic and forced surviving members of the industry to turn their attention to herring and other species.

North Atlantic salmon are another marine species with a hazy future. Over the past three decades they have been buffeted by overfishing, pollution, dams that block ancient spawning grounds, and genetic dilution from breeding with escaped farm-raised salmon. Recently, efforts to introduce fertilized salmon eggs and smolts into rivers draining into European seas have met with some success, but the outlook for wild salmon remains uncertain. In 2001 a comprehensive World Wide Fund for Nature assessment of wild salmon in the North Atlantic found that stocks had fallen by more than 80 percent since 1973, and that wild salmon had been virtually exterminated from the Baltic Sea. The study concluded that in all of Europe, only Norway, Ireland, Scotland, and Iceland still maintained healthy wild salmon populations.

The North Sea and the Baltic Sea are not the only European seas feeling the effects of perennial overharvesting. In the Mediterranean, for example, hake—the seas' most commercially important species—is classified as fully or overexploited in most fishing sectors, and bluefin numbers have plummeted because of extensive purse seine activity. In both cases, catch rates have raised serious concerns about the species' long-term viability.

Of all Europe's seas, however, the Black Sea has suffered the greatest decline in its fish population. For hundreds of years, the Black Sea provided bountiful supplies of fish for the communities scattered along its coastline. But stewardship of this priceless resource was practically nonexistent during the 1950s, 1960s, and 1970s, when littoral states became heavily industrialized and pollution of the sea accelerated. This myopia, coupled with the introduction of exotic species such as the Atlantic comb jellyfish (which is blamed for the collapse of the sea's anchovy fishery), has nearly destroyed the sea's fisheries. In 1986 the Black Sea fishing industry brought in a total catch of 900,000 tons. Within six years, the total catch had fallen to about 100,000 tons, and the fisheries have few signs of recovery since then. Overfishing has also been cited as a factor in the destruction of the Black Sea fisheries. But as others have noted:

"[T]he loss of fisheries resources in the Black Sea is an issue which transcends the usual boundaries of stock management, which is commonly a process of managing the activities of the fishermen themselves. The declining fisheries are a clear consequence of the degradation of the ecosystem itself, which is in turn intimately related to land-based human activities" (ibid.).

Aquaculture Seen as Alternative for Coastal Communities

The declining size of Europe's fisheries has prompted increased investment in aquaculture in many coastal regions. Indeed, aquacultural operations that raise mussels, oysters, trout, carp, salmon, seabass, and other species proliferated during the 1990s, boosting the total output of EU fish farms from 0.94 million tons in 1990 to 1.1 million tons by 1998 (European Commission, "The Future of Aquaculture in Europe," 1999). Buoyed by steadily increasing production, the European Union, led by France, Spain, Italy, and the United Kingdom, now accounts for 3 to 4 percent of world aquaculture by volume, and 8 percent of marine aquaculture production.

Aquaculture has helped cushion the impact of diminished wild fish harvests by generating jobs and economic activity in fishing communities. Nonetheless, the industry's expansion has not been without controversy. Some aquaculture operations have been assailed for compromising the health of wild fish stocks. Critics contend that fish farms dump too much of the waste generated by their product into ecologically fragile bays, and that too many farm fish escape to the open sea, where they compromise the genetic purity of wild species. According to the World Wide Fund for Nature, for example, an estimated 11 million tons of farm salmon escaped from Norwegian aquaculture operations in 1988 alone. Scientists worry that when these escapees reached the open sea, they bred with their wild cousins to create a generation of salmon with diminished spawning instincts. Critics charge that similar dilution of wild fish takes place, albeit on a smaller scale, every time farm-raised species escape their cages and make their way to open water.

Industrialization and Development Take Their Toll on Europe's Seas

During the past half-century, intensive industrialization and coastline development have significantly eroded the ecologic health of Europe's seas. In fact, the European Environment Agency estimates that approximately 85 percent of all European coasts are at high or moderate risk from water pollution, coastal erosion, and overdevelopment. Indeed, while the specifics may vary from region to region, all of the continent's beleaguered seas are grappling with these same basic problems to one extent or another.

For example, eutrophication events are increasingly commonplace in the Gulf of Finland, the Black Sea, the North Sea, the Irish Sea, the Sea of Azov, and other marine areas. This phenomenon develops in bays, estuaries, and other waters where high concentrations of nitrogen-based nutrients generated by sewage and fertilizers accumulate. These pollutants trigger rampant algae growth, which in turn depletes the water of oxygen and makes it impossible for other marine life to survive in the area. Most of these nutrients are deposited in the seas by rivers and streams carrying massive amounts of agricultural, industrial, and municipal effluents from deep within the continent. Indeed, major rivers such as the Danube, Rhine, Vistula, and Volga are the single greatest sources of marine pollution in Europe. In earlier eras, coastal wetlands could have filtered the wastes carried by these and other waterways before they reached open water, thus reducing their impact on marine ecosystems. But most marshlands and other natural defenses once arrayed along Europe's seashores have long since been sacrificed to make way for homes, factories, and harbors. Consequently, even the remote waters of Europe's Arctic seas contain excessive levels of PCB, DDT, heavy metals, and other pollutants. These toxins are generated deep within the European interior but are transported to the Barents and White seas through the atmosphere or via Russian rivers. Remote northern seas have also been degraded by nuclear waste generated by the former Soviet Union (see sidebar, page 58).

Shortcomings in the marine transport of petroleum and other hazardous materials have also bedeviled every European sea. Oil and chemical spills, unlicensed dumping of toxic wastes, discharges of oil-laced ballast water, and other activities have all contributed to the degradation of the marine environment. In fact, the European Commission has bluntly stated that "international marine transport is clearly implicated in the problem of marine and coastal pollution. The huge oil-slicks that have devastated parts of the European coastline over the past 20 years are simply the most spectacular illustration of this phenomenon" (European Commission, *Caring for Our Future,* 1998). But while major oil spills spurred Europe to shore up maritime transport laws and improve spill containment programs during the 1990s, accidents in the transport of oil and hazardous materials continue to occur. At the close of the 1990s, for example, two serious incidents occurred within a few hundred miles of each other off the French coastline. In late 1999 the oil tanker *Erika* sank off the central coast of France, spilling 20,000 tons of crude oil into the sea. One year later, another tanker, the *Ievoli Sun,* sank off the northern coast of France with 4,000 tons of highly toxic styrene in its hold.

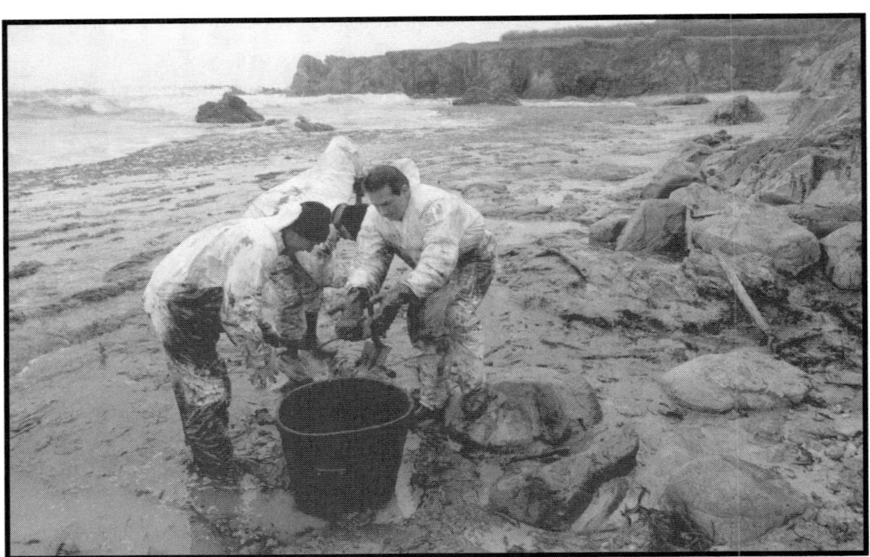

Air force soldiers clean beaches that have been affected by the Erika *oil spill of the coast of France in 1999.*
LE CROISIC, BRITTANY, FRANCE

And in November 2002, a single-hull tanker carrying over 65,000 tons of fuel oil broke in two and sank in the Atlantic Ocean off the northwest coast of Spain. The loss of the *Prestige*—which spewed an estimated 10,000 tons of fuel oil into the sea even before it sank—constitutes a potential environmental catastrophe. The oil spilled in the first days of the crisis blackened beaches and estuaries all along the rugged Spanish coast, and if the remaining fuel cargo housed in the tanker leaks out, the accident could devastate the region's marine ecosystem, and its commercially valuable fisheries, for years to come. Indeed, loss of the cargo currently entombed in the wreckage of the *Prestige* would constitute a spill almost twice the size of the infamous *Exxon Valdez* tanker accident that took place in Alaskan waters in 1989.

Such incidents have convinced Europe to ponder additional safeguards to protect its seas from marine transport calamities. For example, lawmakers, scientists, and environmentalists have all challenged the EU to immediately ban the use of single-hull tankers in European waters (a ban on single-hull tankers like the *Prestige* is currently scheduled to go into effect in 2015).

So the seas of Europe share many of the same pollution problems, from eutrophication to toxic contamination from industrial, agricultural, and municipal sources. But economic, cultural, geographical, and ecological differences exist between these watersheds as well. With that in mind, a summary of the environmental status of each of Europe's regional seas follows:

The North Sea

The North Sea region is a densely populated (more than 85 million people live within 150 kilometers of the coast) and heavily industrialized area that has suffered extensive environmental degradation during the past half-century. Water quality began to decline in the nineteenth century, when mills, tanneries, and other factories began sprouting up along its shoreline. But it was not until the 1960s and 1970s that North Sea water became badly contaminated with pollutants. At that time, industrial, agricultural, and urban expansion ate away at coastal wetlands, river deltas, and other natural areas. In state after state, marshlands, forests, and streams were lost or compromised to accommodate new farms, offices, plants, homes, and roads. These new or expanded enterprises then deposited massive amounts of pollutants into the North Sea and its watershed.

By 1980 studies indicated that the river systems of Western Europe were depositing more than a million metric tons of nutrient pollution (nitrogen and phosphorus) generated by agriculture, industry, and population centers into the North Sea every year. This waste was threaded with an ever-growing assortment of heavy metals; by 1989 an estimated 41,000 metric tons of heavy metals (including zinc, lead, chromium, arsenic, cadmium, and mercury) were being discharged into the North Sea on an annual basis, most of it carried by the region's polluted river systems. This heavy metal contamination thoroughly infiltrated the regional food chain, accumulating in the tissues of harbor and grey seals, dolphins, and seabirds. In addition, every country on the North Sea with the exception of Norway dumped millions of metric tons of sewage sludge and dredge spoils in the North Sea and North Atlantic during the 1970s and 1980s (MacGarvin, *The North Sea,* 1990; North Sea Task Force, *North Sea Quality Status Report,* 1993; European Environment Agency, *Environment in the European Union at the Turn of the Century,* 1998).

The nations of Western Europe belatedly recognized that the North Sea could not withstand such degradation indefinitely. Retarded by a slew of new environmental regulations, the deposition of contaminants into the ocean has leveled off in recent years. Since 1980 nitrate concentrations in major EU rivers draining into the North Sea have remained constant, as increases in industrial and agricultural activity have been offset by reductions in the use of nitrogen-based fertilizers. North Sea states have also curbed their use of the sea as a dumping ground for dredge spoils, imposed new environmental regulations on various industrial operations, improved municipal sewage treatment, and cut their discharges of heavy metals and phosphorus by half since the beginning of the 1990s. In addition, some analysts believe that reforms of the European Union's Common Agricultural Policy (CAP) could eventually reduce the area of arable land under cultivation on the North Sea coast by 10 percent or more, which would further boost efforts to reduce eutrophication in the region.

All of these developments have heartened the scientific and environmental communities, but the discharge of nutrient loads and other pollutants into regional waters still remains far too high in many areas. In the British Isles, for instance, the level of nitrates has roughly doubled within the last 40 years, creating growing eutrophic "dead zones" along the English coastline and in the Irish Sea (Allen et al., "Evidence for Eutrophication of the Irish Sea," 1998). These and other hypoxic zones will continue to expand unless North Sea states dramatically cut the flow of nutrient loads into the sea.

Another environmental issue confronting the North Sea states is oil and gas exploration. At the turn of the century, the surface of the North Sea was pocked with approximately 150 oil and gas production facilities. These extraction platforms and their affiliated pipeline networks supply more than 30 percent of the total energy needs of North Sea states, making them a valuable

Russia's Decaying Nuclear Sub Fleet Threatens Barents Sea

Beginning in the early 1960s, Soviet naval authorities used the Barents Sea and other Arctic waters as a dumping ground for solid and liquid nuclear waste and obsolete reactors from nuclear submarines and icebreakers. In addition, reports indicate that Russia's military leaders have abandoned more than 100 nuclear submarines from its aging fleet in or near Arctic waters without implementing proper environmental or security measures to safeguard the spent nuclear fuel and radioactive reactors still entombed within their hulls. Today these atomic junkyards are seen as a major threat to the ecosystems of Europe's Arctic seas. Indeed, the Norwegian Ministry of the Environment and other parties have cited radioactive pollution as the single greatest threat to the Arctic marine environment.

This growing environmental crisis is due in large part to Russia's poor economic situation. "Obsolete ships withdrawn from service are rusting at sea because there are no means for treating their reactors," reported Thomas Orszag-Land. "And Russia's remaining fleets of nuclear-powered vessels, the largest in the world, continue to produce 20,000 cubic meters of liquid and 6,000 cubic meters of solid nuclear wastes a year without safe storage facilities." Some observers estimate that proper disposal and reprocessing of all abandoned nuclear submarines and radioactive waste in Russia could exceed $100 billion. Russia does not have the financial resources even to begin to address this issue, so analysts say that removing or capping these pockets of nuclear waste will require a concerted, sustained international response. "Without international cooperation and

(continues)

component of the region's economic infrastructure. But the ecological impact of these oil and gas extraction operations is a subject of considerable debate (see sidebar, page 153). Some parties contend that oil spills and seepage from these facilities have caused negligible environmental damage to marine systems; others charge that the platforms are responsible for significant ecological degradation, leaving the surrounding seafloor an oil-contaminated dead zone. Critics also contend that releases of oil and other pollutants from these aging facilities have increased in recent years, further stressing the North Sea ecosystem and its wildlife. "As a result of chronic low-level pollution from ships and discharges from offshore petroleum activity, about 50 percent of seal pups at the largest breeding colony in Norway are polluted each year by oil, though this causes little visible disturbance to the seals' behavior and there has been little mortality," stated one report. "More serious are effects following spills, where animals may be affected by inhalation and suffer physiological damage" (Sheppard, *Seas at the Millennium*, 2000).

financing, a grave situation could arise which can be pictured as Chernobyl in slow motion. If safety measures are not implemented, major accidents and the release of fissile material will be unavoidable," remarked Soviet submarine commander-turned-environmentalist Aleksandr Nikitin and the Bellona Foundation, coauthors of *The Russian Northern Fleet: Sources of Radioactive Contamination.*

The need for prompt international action to address this issue was further underscored on August 12, 2000, when the *Kursk,* a Russian nuclear submarine, sank off the coast of the Kola Peninsula in the Barents Sea after an onboard torpedo explosion. The tragedy killed 118 crew members and heightened international concern about the state of Russia's nuclear fleet and its ability to protect Arctic seas from nuclear contamination. In October 2001, two Dutch salvage firms successfully retrieved the wreck of the *Kursk* without contaminating the Barents Sea with radiation leaks from the sub's reactor. But even though the *Kursk* was brought to dock without incident, the submarine remains a potent symbol of decaying military might and potential ecological catastrophe.

Sources:

Arctic Monitoring and Assessment Programme. 1997. *Arctic Pollution Issues: A State of the Arctic Environment Report.* Oslo, Norway: Arctic Monitoring and Assessment Programme.

Bellona Foundation. 2000. *The Russian Northern Fleet: Sources of Radioactive Contamination.* Oslo, Norway: Bellona Foundation.

Hertsgaard, Mark. "Russia's Environmental Crisis." *Nation* 271 (September 18).

Orszag-Land, Thomas. 1997. "Removing Nuclear Waste from the Arctic." *Contemporary Review* 270 (May).

The Baltic Sea

Environmental restoration of Northern Europe's long-suffering Baltic Sea will be a long and arduous process. Historically, the ecological well-being of the Baltic has been an afterthought throughout its heavily industrialized and densely populated watershed. More than 25 million people from nine littoral states live directly on the coast, while 85 million people live in its drainage basin, including the entire population of Poland (about 38 million people). These households and industries have generated a prodigious amount of household, agricultural, and industrial waste in the past century, an overwhelming percentage of which eventually found its way into the Baltic. This massive deposit of toxic effluents would have taken its toll on any sea eventually, but in the case of the Baltic, the impact of the pollution was heightened by the sea's topography. The Baltic is a shallow and tideless sea that retains its water for an exceptionally long time, since it is connected to the North Sea and the larger Atlantic Ocean only through the narrow Skagerrak Strait. As a result, poisons have accumulated in the Baltic's trapped waters in distressingly high concentrations, permanently transforming the sea's ecosystem.

Today, the decades of abuse are evident throughout the Baltic. Much of the sea bears signs of eutrophication, with 100,000 square kilometers—about one-fourth of its total surface area—significantly impacted. Eutrophication in the Gulf of Gdansk, for instance, is so great that the seabed has been compared to a graveyard. The nutrient pollution that created these oxygen-starved zones has been traced to the usual suspects—untreated and partially treated agricultural runoff (including both fertilizer and animal waste), sewage and other organic matter, and atmospheric deposition from power plant and automobile emissions (Hinrichsen, *Coastal Waters of the World,* 1998).

Blame for the deterioration of the Baltic should be shared by all nations within its catchment area. Even the northern states of Finland and Sweden, which have spearheaded environmental restoration efforts in recent years, bear some responsibility; for many years, their pulp mills were the primary polluters of the Baltic's Bothnian Sea and Bothnian Bay. Still, the mistreatment of the Baltic has been particularly egregious along the eastern shoreline, where the Soviet "Iron Curtain" once fell. Poland's Vistula River, which passes through the industrial and agricultural heart of the former communist state, has been a notorious source of Baltic pollution for decades. Latvia, too, has long used the Baltic as a dumping ground. In 1990 alone, the country released an estimated 250,000 metric tons of hazardous industrial waste and toxic sludge from treatment plants and hospitals into rivers and streams that drain into the Baltic. And Russia's coastal industries have dumped massive quantities of toxic effluents in the Baltic for decades, unchecked by meaningful environmental regulations. "[This] rising tide of toxic pollution, especially elevated levels of mercury, DDT, and PCBs, which bioaccumulate up the food chain, has affected not only fish and shellfish but many marine mammals and seabirds as well," observed one expert. "Populations of grey and ringed seals have plummeted as a result of contamination from PCBs, DDT, and heavy metals. Exposure to these dangerous pollutants causes widespread reproductive disorders in seals, triggering spontaneous abortions and birth defects, among other abnormalities" (ibid.).

The waters of the Baltic, then, are afflicted in numerous ways. But over the past two decades, most of the Baltic states that surround the sea have displayed a genuine commitment to improved stewardship. In 1992 regional governments issued a Baltic Sea Environmental Declaration that called for all littoral nations to "assure the ecological restoration of the Baltic Sea, ensuring the possibility of self-restoration of the marine environment and preservation of its ecological balance." Toward that end, comparatively wealthy countries such as Sweden and Finland have dramatically curbed discharges of pollutants from paper mills and other facilities that once poisoned fragile bays and estuaries. According to the European Environment Agency (EEA), in fact, pollution releases from the region's pulp mill industry have been reduced by nearly 90 percent since 1987 (European Environment Agency, *Environment in the European Union at the Turn of the Century*, 1998). In addition, Lithuania, Estonia, and other nations have invested in new sewage treatment facilities even as they undergo the wrenching transition to free-market economies. As a result of these and other efforts, water quality has improved in some regions, and contamination from heavy metals has dropped significantly in several species, from herring to the rare white-tailed sea eagle.

But while progress has been made in addressing the woeful state of the Baltic, much work still needs to be done. In 1988, for instance, Baltic states agreed to cut pollution from heavy metals, nutrients, and other pollutants in half by 1995, but the nations failed to meet this objective, hamstrung by fertilizer-dependent farming techniques, gaps in sewage treatment, and uneven enforcement of dumping violations.

In addition, experts on the Baltic contend that the pivotal nation in any meaningful effort to cleanse the sea of pollutants is Poland, which contains about 40 percent of the agricultural land in the sea's watershed and almost half of the region's 85 million people. Nitrogen entering the Baltic from Poland's large rivers—the Vistula and Oder—doubled during the 1990s, and most analysts expect Polish fertilizer use to rise, not decline, in the coming years. Yet some government authorities deny that these trends pose a problem.

For example, the Polish government continues to maintain that agricultural fertilizers and chemicals—the single greatest factor in eutrophication—do not constitute a major hazard to the Baltic Sea.

The Black Sea

Much of the Black Sea and the adjacent Sea of Azov has been transformed into a biological wasteland by the nations of Central and Eastern Europe (six nations border the sea, and another dozen lie within its vast drainage basin). "The Black Sea has served mankind well in the past through its provision of food resources, as a natural setting for recreation and transportation and even as a disposal site for waste, including perhaps nuclear wastes. In return, it has been exploited and degraded in many ways" (Sheppard, *Seas at the Millennium,* 2000). This abuse has included unregulated withdrawals from watershed rivers for irrigation purposes, overfishing of commercial species, widespread conversion of coastal areas for business purposes, discharge of untreated industrial, municipal, and agricultural wastes into the Black Sea basin, radioactive fallout from the 1986 Chernobyl disaster, and unregulated (and large-scale) marine transport activity. The combined impact of these forces prompted the coordinator of the Black Sea Environment Programme to state that "the threat to the Black Sea from land-based sources of pollution is potentially greater than in any other marine sea on our planet" (Mee, "The Black Sea in Crisis," 1992). Already, during the past thirty years, much of the sea's natural habitat and marine wildlife has been lost forever. For example, the Sea of Azov—the Black Sea's northernmost section—was once a treasure trove of ecological wealth. But the sea's ecosystem has been annihilated by decades of abuse from Russian and Ukrainian factories and agricultural operations, and by the mid-1990s its waters were almost entirely devoid of fish and other marine life.

The Black Sea's pollution problems are further exacerbated by its geographic character. It is deep and nearly landlocked, so it receives very little replenishment from the Mediterranean, which has its own serious water quality issues, or from regional rivers, most of which continue to empty heavy loads of nitrogen, heavy metals, and man-made chemicals into the sea. Indeed, rivers within the catchment area are the primary source of Black Sea pollution. Many of them pass through heavily populated regions of eastern Europe, where stewardship of natural resources remains spotty. The Danube River alone dumped about 80 million tons of contaminated sediments, 10 million tons of organic waste, and 700,000 metric tons of nitrogen-based pollution into the Black Sea on an annual basis in the early 1990s, making it a major factor in the steadily encroaching eutrophication of the sea (ibid.). In fact, some studies indicate that as much as 90 percent of the sea was suffering from some level of eutrophication by the close of the twentieth century.

Not surprisingly, declining water quality and disappearing coastal habitat have destroyed much of the Black Sea's fish and marine life. In 1950, for example, approximately 1 million common and bottlenosed dolphins surged through Black Sea waters, but by 1995, dolphin numbers had crashed so severely that scientists could not even undertake a proper population survey (Hinrichsen, *Coastal Waters of the World,* 1998). Other Black Sea fish species, including important commercial species, have also declined alarmingly. One of the only marine animals that still thrives in the Black Sea is an alien species of jellyfish. This creature accounts for more than 90 percent of the total biomass of some areas of the sea, and its voracious appetite has been cited as a contributing factor in the decline of numerous fish and crustacean stocks.

The Mediterranean Sea

Perhaps no other ocean on the globe receives as much human pressure as the Mediterranean, Europe's largest sea. Twenty-one nations with a collective population of more than 400 million people surround the sea, including major industrialized nations such as France, Italy, Egypt, and Turkey. In addition, the Mediterranean basin is the world's leading tourist destination. It currently accounts for about 30 percent of international tourist arrivals and one-third of total receipts from international tourism, and some forecasts estimate that the number of tourists that pass through the region could double or triple by 2025.

Not surprisingly, the Mediterranean Sea has suffered enormously from all the demands that have been placed on it by these year-round inhabitants and seasonal visitors. The crowded cities and towns along the Mediterranean coast generate massive volumes of waste, much of which eventually enters the sea in untreated or partially treated form (new wastewater treatment plants have been installed in some littoral states in recent years, but significant amounts of municipal sewage still flow into the Mediterranean untreated). In addition, unrestrained commercial development and robust industrialization were long seen as inevitable by-products of high population density, so few serious efforts were made to incorporate strong environmental safeguards into those activities. As a result, the Mediterranean coastline was utterly transformed over the past half-century, with vast tracts of wetlands and forest sacrificed to development. Water quality also deteriorated swiftly, driven downward by industries that released massive amounts of chemicals into the sea with impunity.

As with other inland seas in Europe, the Mediterranean is particularly vulnerable to pollution because it has only a tenuous connection to the world ocean. The Mediterranean's only connection to the Atlantic Ocean is the narrow and shallow Strait of Gibraltar, so it has a very slow rate of replenishment and lacks tidal currents that might help it flush out pollution. Instead, the waters of the Mediterranean remain trapped for years, absorbing ever greater quantities of pollutants.

Today, eutrophication ranks as one of the chief threats to the Mediterranean. Algal blooms created by high concentrations of nutrients have been detected in numerous sectors, threatening already overfished stocks and bottom-dwelling crustaceans (ironically, increased nutrient loads have boosted capture of pelagic (midwater) fish, enabling the sea's fleet to maintain a fairly constant volume in landings). Alien species are another growing problem. In the Mediterranean's northern reaches, for instance, a giant species of algae (*Caulerpa taxifolia*) has taken over large swaths of the seafloor, smothering sponges, corals, anemones, and other native plants.

Oil pollution has also taken a significant toll on the marine ecosystems of the Mediterranean, a major international shipping route for oil and gas. For much of the past three decades, estimates of the amount of oil discharged into the sea on an annual basis—much of it from routine shipping operations—ranged from 500,000 to more than 700,000 metric tons. These statistics indicate that the Mediterranean, which accounts for only 1 percent of the world's ocean surface, received almost one-fifth of all oil spilled or discharged in the world's oceans. In recent years, littoral states of the Mediterranean have taken strides to monitor environmentally unsound shipping operations and reduce the size and number of spills. Nonetheless, signs of contamination are easy to find. Along the Tyrrhenian Sea, for instance, much of the coastline bears oily blemishes from spills at sea or illegal discharge of petroleum-laced ballast water.

Mediterranean states also succeeded in curbing their release of toxic pollutants into the sea during the late 1980s and 1990s. Nonetheless, heavy metals, dioxin, DDT, and other chemical compounds continue to enter the sea in quantities that degrade sensitive marine ecosystems. In fact, toxic poisoning and vanishing coastal habitat are cited as the two main reasons that sea turtles, dolphins, monk seals, and other marine mammals of the Mediterranean are in danger of being snuffed out entirely.

Preservation and Restoration Depend on Regional Cooperation

All of Europe's seas are held by multiple nations, each one of which possesses the power to profoundly influence the region's marine environment for better or for worse. Given this reality, analysts agree that the future of Europe's seas and coastal areas hinges on effective regional cooperation in addressing overfishing, water pollution, and other sources of marine habitat degradation and loss.

Environmental cooperation on sea and coastal issues is a relatively new phenomenon in much of Europe. In fact, it did not emerge as a major force in Eastern Europe until the post–Cold War era, when one of the most significant barriers to regional environmental cooperation—conflicting political ideologies—was removed. Since that time, however, numerous regional agreements have been struck. Some of these agreements have supplemented or supplanted marine environment treaties that were first forged in the 1970s, when world governments took their first tentative steps to address the declining state of the seas. Others have been shaped to address marine issues—such as overfishing—that have cropped up within the last decade or two by encouraging fleet reduction, fishery certification, and other initiatives.

All together, the nations of Europe have passed approximately thirty major multilateral agreements to halt degradation of coastal and marine environments in the past three decades. Major agreements forged in recent years include the Convention on the Protection of the Marine Environment of the Baltic Sea Area (1992), which includes all ten Baltic littoral states; the Convention on the Protection of the Black Sea against Pollution (1992) and the Black Sea Strategic Action Plan (1996), which has six signatory nations; the Mediterranean Action Program, a twenty-one-party agreement first passed in 1975 and amended repeatedly to address specific issues such as marine preserve creation and transboundary transport of hazardous wastes; and the Convention for the Protection of the Marine Environment of the Northeast Atlantic (1992), a sixteen-state agreement to protect the waters of the North Sea and North Atlantic Ocean. The FAO Code of Conduct for fisheries and the UN Fish Stocks Agreement also include important fishery management and fleet reduction measures. In addition, many major European river basins, which greatly influence the ecological health of the continent's seas and coastal areas, are subject to multistate environmental protection agreements. Together, these agreements have enabled Europe to revitalize some fish stocks and curb exploitation of others.

Europe also has established numerous marine protected areas in recent years. Indeed, protection for ecologically rich but vulnerable marine habitats proliferated in the 1990s. By 1999 the continent had established a total of 246 protected marine areas, according to the World Conservation Monitoring Centre. Conservationists and scientists believe that increased usage of marine protected areas in regions that are under heavy human pressure, such as the Mediterranean Sea region, can be a potent tool in reducing marine pollution and conserving remaining habitat (Goni et al., "The Mediterranean: Marine Protected Areas," 2000).

The nations of Europe deserve praise for these efforts to address the growing threat to their marine resources. "After 25 years, Europe's largest seas . . .

have become subjects of concerted regional scientific assessment and cooperative policymaking," wrote Stacy VanDeveer. "In a continent rife with historical and contemporary conflict, this international environmental cooperation qualifies as an important political achievement." But many observers believe that the multilateral agreements currently in place will not be sufficient to reverse years of environmental abuse if funding to implement and enforce protection measures is not sufficient to meet the size of the task (VanDeveer, "Protecting Europe's Seas," 2000).

Sources:

Allen, J. R., D. J. Slinn, T. M. Shammon, R. G. Hartnoll, and S. J. Hawkins. 1998. "Evidence for Eutrophication of the Irish Sea." *Limnology and Oceanography* 43.

Black Sea Environment Programme. 1994. "Saving the Black Sea." Istanbul, Turkey: BSEP.

Caddy, John. 1993. "Contrast between Recent Fishery Trends and Evidence for Nutrient Enrichment in Two Large Marine Ecosystems: The Mediterranean and the Black Seas." In K. Sherman, L. M. Alexander, and B. D. Gold, eds., *Large Marine Ecosystems: Stress, Mitigation, and Sustainability.* Washington, DC: AAAS.

Carter, F. W., and D. Turnock, eds. 1993. *Environmental Problems in Eastern Europe.* London and New York: Routledge.

De Bardeleben, J., and J. Hannigan, eds. 1994. *Environmental Security and Quality after Communism: Eastern Europe and the Soviet Successor States.* Boulder, CO: Westview, 1994.

De Villiers, Marq. 2000. *Water: The Fate of Our Most Precious Resource.* New York: Houghton Mifflin.

European Commission. 1998. *Caring for Our Future: Action for Europe's Environment.* Luxembourg: EC.

———. 1999. "The Future of Aquaculture in Europe." Luxembourg: PESCA Conference, November.

———. 2001. *Green Paper: The Future of the Common Fisheries Policy.* 2 vols. Luxembourg: EC.

European Environment Agency. 1998. *Environment in the European Union at the Turn of the Century.* London: Elsevier.

———. 1998. *Europe's Environment: The Second Assessment.* London: Elsevier.

Feshbach, Murray. 1995. *Ecological Disaster: Cleaning up the Hidden Legacy of the Soviet Regime.* New York: Twentieth Century Fund Press.

Goni, Raquel, Nicholas V. Polunin, and Serge Planes. 2000. "The Mediterranean: Marine Protected Areas and the Recovery of a Large Marine Ecosystem." *Environmental Conservation* (June).

Hinrichsen, Don. 1998. *Coastal Waters of the World: Trends, Threats and Strategies.* Washington, DC: Island.

Horton, Tom, and Heather Dewar. 2000. "Sea Grasses Vanish, Marine Life in Peril." *Baltimore Sun,* September 26.

Kirby, Alex. 2002. "EU Proposes Radical Fishing Cuts." *BBC News Online*, May 28. http://news.bbc.co.uk/1/hi/world/europe/2012175.stm (accessed May 28, 2002).

Kobori, Iwao, and Michael H. Glantz. 1998. *Central Eurasian Water Crisis: Caspian, Aral, and Dead Seas.* Washington, DC: UN Publications.

Kunzig, Robert, William Underhill, and Michelle Chan. 2001. "Why the Cod Are Vanishing." *Newsweek International* (February 12).

Lamson, Cynthia. 1994. *The Sea Has Many Voices: Oceans Policy for a Complex World.* Montreal: McGill Queens University Press.

MacGarvin, Malcolm. 1990. *The North Sea.* London: Collins and Brown.

McGinn, Anne Platt. 1999. "Atlantic Salmon Face Perilous Waters." *World Watch* 12 (January–February).

———. 1999. *Safeguarding the Health of Oceans: Worldwatch Paper 145.* Washington, DC: Worldwatch Institute.

Mee, Laurence. 1992. "The Black Sea in Crisis: The Need for Concerted International Action." *Ambio* 21 (June).

North Sea Task Force. 1993. *North Sea Quality Status Report, 1993.* London: Oslo and Paris Commissions.

Orszag-Land, Thomas. 1997. "Removing Nuclear Waste from the Arctic." *Contemporary Review* 270 (May).

Saiko, Tatyana. 2001. *Environmental Crises: Geographical Case Studies in Post-Socialist Eurasia.* Harlow, UK: Pearson Education.

Sheppard, Charles, ed. 2000. *Seas at the Millennium: An Environmental Evaluation.* 3 vols. Oxford: Pergamon.

Skjrseth, Jon Birger. 2000. *North Sea Cooperation: Linking International and Domestic Pollution Control.* Manchester, UK: Manchester University Press.

Thorne-Miller, Boyce. 1998. *The Living Ocean: Understanding and Protecting Marine Biodiversity.* Washington, DC: Island.

UN Environment Programme. 1999. *Global Environment Outlook 2000.* London: Earthscan Publications.

UN Food and Agriculture Organization. 1993. "Fisheries and Environment Studies in the Black Sea System." *Studies and Reviews: General Fisheries Council for the Mediterranean.* Rome: FAO.

———. 1997. *Review of the State of World Fishery Resources: Marine Fisheries (Northeast Atlantic).* Rome: FAO.

———. 2000. *The State of World Fisheries and Aquaculture 2000.* Rome: FAO.

VanDeveer, Stacy D. 2000. "Protecting Europe's Seas." *Environment* 42 (July–August).

———. 2000. *Protecting Regional Seas: Developing Capacity and Fostering Environmental Cooperation in Europe.* Washington, DC: Woodrow Wilson Center.

World Resources Institute. 2000. *World Resources 2000–2001, People and Ecosystems: The Fraying Web of Life.* Washington, DC: World Resources Institute.

Energy and Transportation

European society has shown a greater interest in renewable energy technologies than most other industrialized regions in the last thirty years. But despite efforts to increase energy consumption from renewable energy sources and its avowed determination to meet the emissions targets contained in the 1997 Kyoto agreement, Europe's economic prosperity remains closely intertwined with fossil fuels that have been criticized for damaging human health, compromising the ecological integrity of natural habitats, and contributing to global climate change.

Weaning Europe from Fossil Fuel Dependence

The quest for sustainability has dominated national and international energy policy discussions in recent years, especially within the European Union, home to the continent's most prosperous economies. "Coal and oil have fueled the 20th century's economic growth," acknowledged the European Commission. "Yet supplies are limited and some of their side effects are alarming. If we are to avoid a potential environmental catastrophe, we need to change the way in which we use and produce energy. . . .The European Union (EU) is facing the same dilemma as the rest of the world—how to reduce energy use and lessen its impact without jeopardising a way of life to which we have become accustomed or to which we would like to strive" (European Commission, *Energising Europe,* 2000).

Europe's limited reserves of fossil fuels have lent added urgency to this task. Oil and natural gas reserves are relatively small across much of the continent except for Russia and the former Soviet states of the Caspian basin, where extensive new drilling and refining operations are being watched anxiously by international investors and environmentalists alike. Offshore extraction operations, meanwhile, have been complicated by concerns about safeguarding vital fisheries. In 2002, for example, Norway, a major exporter of seafood, called for a moratorium on new oil and gas projects in the Arctic Barents Sea and suggested that it would consider extending its territorial waters toward that end. Coal is much more plentiful than oil and gas in Europe, but many deposits are difficult to extract, and the environmental consequences of coal use—environmental damage to rivers and other habitat at the extraction end, high generation of greenhouse gases and other air pollutants at the consumption end—make dependence on it particularly problematic. Taken together, these domestic production limitations have made Europe a significant net importer of fossil fuels and have cast a large shadow over the continent's economic security, especially during times of political turmoil in the Middle East and other global fossil fuel production centers.

Western European nations have actively moved to address this situation, both individually and collectively within the European Union. "For over a generation, the EU has channeled efforts into finding ways to extend the life of its own limited hydrocarbon reserves and to improve the efficiency of its fossil fuel use. Now, increasing emphasis is also placed on exploiting renewable sources of energy. As a result, [European industries] have won leading positions in a number of key energy markets—notably, in the areas of large wind turbines, advanced coal-fired power generation, and oil and gas exploration and production technologies" (ibid.). European governments also have instituted a variety of measures to curb overall energy consumption, including taxes on fossil fuels, levies on emissions, subsidies for renewable energy industries, and emission reduction agreements—both mandated and voluntary—for various sectors. But efforts to institute a European Union–wide minimum energy tax on coal, natural gas, and electricity use have floundered, thwarted by the resistance of member states who are reluctant to cede power in the realms of taxation or energy. Some Europeans have advocated instituting some exemptions to the proposed tax as a way of increasing support, but critics contend that excessive use of exemptions will undermine the whole purpose of an EU-wide energy tax.

Progress has been made in some important areas, however. One key voluntary emission commitment announced in the late 1990s by the European Automobile Manufacturers Association calls for a 25 percent reduction in emissions of carbon dioxide—a key factor in climate change—from new cars sold in the European Union by 2008. But scientists concede that far greater reductions in consumption will be necessary in the transportation sector, where energy use is climbing more quickly than any other economic sector.

A horse grazes alongside a group of three-bladed wind turbines at a wind farm in Fyn, Denmark. ADAM WOOLFITT/CORBIS

Modern-Day Windmills Light Up Danish Homes

During the 1990s, Denmark emerged as a world leader in renewable energy production by installing extensive wind turbine "farms" that harness the power of wind and convert it to energy that can be used by households and businesses alike. Denmark began experimenting with wind power in the 1980s, but it did not establish itself as a serious player in the renewable energy arena until 1991, when the Danish government introduced a new energy policy that specifically promoted the development and use of renewable energy. Danish policies actively encouraged private investment and ownership of small-scale wind farms by bestowing private owners of wind turbines with a tax refund on the national electricity tax (an estimated 80 percent of Denmark's wind turbines are owned by Danish individuals or cooperatives). In addition, Danish energy regulations guaranteed renewable energy producers that the energy they generated would be purchased at a commercially favorable

(continues)

price. These incentives sparked a rush of wind energy development, and by the late 1990s, Germany was the only European nation with greater installed wind energy capacity than tiny Denmark (Danish Wind Industry Association, http://www.windpower.org).

Boosted by an annual growth rate of 40 percent since 1995, the Danish wind energy industry claimed half of the global wind energy market in 1999. In addition, wind is expected to account for approximately 21 percent of Denmark's total domestic electricity consumption by 2003 (Krohn, "Wind Energy Policy in Denmark," 2002), and in the late 1990s the country's industrial and political leadership expressed confidence that continued growth in wind capacity could enable it to generate 50 percent of its electricity from renewable sources by 2030 (European Environment Agency, *Environmental Signals 2001*, 2001).

Denmark's ability to meet this target is now in doubt, however. Installation of wind turbines in Denmark—as in the rest of the world—has depended to a great extent on government subsidies, and in 2002 Denmark's newly installed center-right government announced that subsidies for the installation of new wind turbines would cease in 2004. Since that time, Denmark has announced its intention to proceed with plans to build two offshore wind farms in 2002 and 2003 with a total capacity of about 300 MW. But four other wind farm projects have been scrapped as a result of the policy change, and environmental groups are concerned that the discontinuation of subsidies will curtail Danish investments in wind energy for the foreseeable future.

Sources:

European Commission. 1997. *Energy for the Future: Renewable Sources of Energy*. White Paper for a Community Strategy and Action Plan. Brussels: EC.

European Environment Agency. 2001. *Environmental Signals 2001*. London: Elsevier Science.

European Wind Energy Association. 1999. *Wind Energy: The Facts*. Luxembourg: EC.

Eurostat. 2000. *Renewable Energy Sources Statistics in the European Union 1989–1997*. Luxembourg: EC.

Krohn, Soren. 2002. "Wind Energy Policy in Denmark Status 2002." Danish Wind Industry Association. http://www. windpower.org (accessed February 22, 2002).

Fossil Fuel Extraction and Delivery Issues

The cumulative environmental impact of locating, extracting, and transporting oil, coal, natural gas, and other energy resources from European soil has attracted considerable attention over the past few decades. Negative impacts associated with coal mining (and associated transport support elements such as roads) include soil degradation and erosion; fragmentation or destruction of species-rich habitats such as forests and meadowlands; and degradation of watersheds from wastewater discharges, toxic tailings, and wholesale landscape alterations (such as during strip mining operations). These harmful side-effects are especially evident in Central Europe, where many nations combine a heavy dependence on coal with a loose regulatory environment that provides inadequate protection for natural resources; and in Eastern Europe, which is saddled with numerous Soviet-era smelting and mining facilities that leak toxins into fragile rivers, streams, and aquifers.

Oil and gas extraction and delivery operations have also come under fire from environmentalists, who claim that they cause significant ecological degradation. Detractors assert that these activities—which require roads and other infrastructure—slice up important breeding and migratory areas, contaminate fragile rivers and aquifers with industrial pollutants, and diminish the wilderness character of undeveloped areas. They charge that these harmful effects are especially acute in Central and Eastern Europe, where limited financial resources intensify historical shortcomings in maintenance and regulatory oversight. Russia's extensive network of oil pipelines, for example, has long been criticized for releasing tons of oil into the country's soil and water on a monthly basis. According to one 1997 study, the Russian Federation experienced more than 100 major pipeline failures between 1991 and 1993 alone (Arctic Monitoring and Assessment Programme, *Arctic Pollution Issues,* 1997). These failures draw the lion's share of attention from authorities and news media, but environmentalists point out that Russia's pipelines are also riddled with leaks that quietly drip oil into woodlands and streams without attracting any notice.

These types of problems are particularly noteworthy because Russia and the former Soviet states surrounding the Caspian Sea basin are expected to take an increasingly prominent role in meeting world energy demand in the coming years. The basin contains significant deposits of untapped oil and natural gas—Russia alone is believed to possess an estimated one-third of the world's total natural gas reserves—and the governments in possession of these reserves are eager to develop them. Indeed, Russia is implementing economic reforms for the express purpose of wringing greater financial benefits from its abundant natural resources (International Energy Agency, *Russia Energy Survey 2002,* 2002). But some of Russia's stated energy development aims are a source of considerable concern to some analysts. For example, Russia has signaled interest in increasing its extraction of coal at a time when many other nations are moving away from the fuel because of associated environmental problems. It also is moving toward greater reliance on nuclear-based electricity generation even though the safety of the country's existing nuclear facilities remains uncertain. "With the current outlook for stronger economic growth [in Russia], more environmental funding will become essential if the country is to limit the environmental damage of heavier resources use" (ibid.).

Marine extraction and transport of petroleum have also proven controversial. Europe's energy industry contends that offshore operations are environmentally safe. Proponents of offshore drilling and transport charge that environmentalists exaggerate the dangers of oil and gas exploration and extraction activities, and they note that Western Europe has implemented major revisions to its maritime transport laws and spill containment programs in order to ward off ecologically devastating spills. They also justify their activities by observing that other energy sectors—such as renewables or nuclear power—do not currently generate enough power to meet Europe's energy needs.

Despite the introduction of new safety technologies and strong environmental regulations, however, significant spills of oil have tainted every European sea. This reality makes every new proposal for offshore oil and gas development a lightning rod for debate. Norway, for example, has plans to formally approve the first petroleum development operation in the Barents Sea, a marine area along the northern coasts of Norway and western Russia that holds major fish stocks, large seabird colonies, and an assortment of marine mammals. The development—dubbed Snowwhite—is seen by environmentalists as the beginning of a massive incursion into the region by oil and gas interests. Conservation groups, joined by the Norwegian Ministry of the Environment, have subsequently appealed for a comprehensive environmental assessment of energy exploration activities in the region prior to launching operations. The Norwegian government has agreed to undertake an assessment of the region's habitat and wildlife, but it refuses to halt the development, saying that the project will provide adequate safeguards for the environment.

Fossil Fuels Remain Cornerstones of European Energy Grid

According to the International Energy Agency (IEA), total European energy production from all sources—including oil, natural gas, coal, hydroelectric dams, and nuclear plants—reached 2.22 billion metric toe (a toe is a unit measurement equivalent to 1,000 metric tons of oil) in 1997. Natural gas accounted for the single greatest share of energy production, with 721 million toe generated in 1997. Other significant energy sources included petroleum and natural gas liquids (649 million toe), hard coal and lignite (416 million toe), nuclear power (300 million toe), and renewable energy sources (139 million toe). The latter sector includes hydropower—the most economically significant of the renewables—wind, solar, wave and tidal, geothermal, and combustible renewables and waste (International Energy Agency, *Energy Balances of Organisation for Economic Cooperation and Development (OECD) Countries,* 1999).

Europe consumed 300 million toe more energy than it produced in 1997, making it a net importer of energy resources. Oil and natural gas liquids met much of Europe's appetite for energy, as the continent consumed 852 million toe of energy in that category. It was followed by natural gas (763 million toe), primary coal, including hard coal and lignite (500 million toe), and nuclear fuels (300 million toe) (ibid.). The single largest consumer of energy in Europe was the industry sector (33 percent), followed by residential (27 percent), transportation (23 percent, with road transportation alone accounting for 17 percent of total European energy consumption), commercial and public services (7 percent), and agriculture (4 percent) (ibid.).

Figure 8.1 Primary Energy Use in the European Union

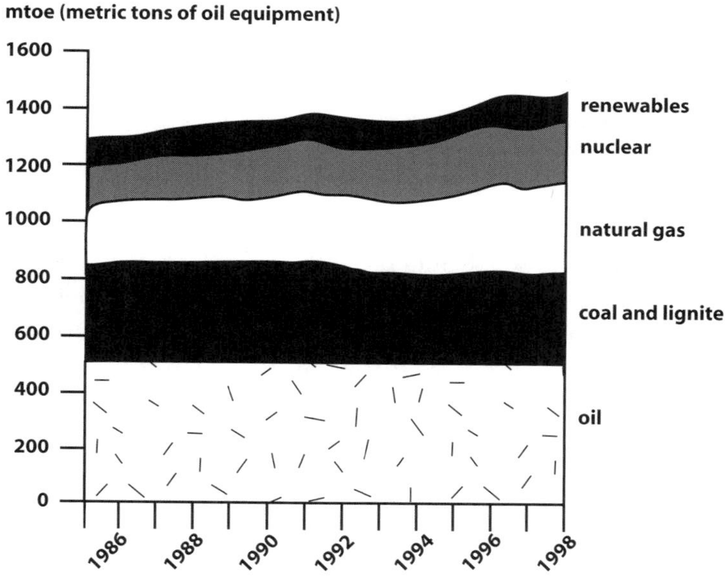

SOURCE: European Environment Agency. 2001. *Environmental Signals 2001.* Elsevier Science Ltd.

Rates of energy consumption differ appreciably as one moves from the EU nations of Western Europe to the countries of Central and Eastern Europe, many of which are just now emerging from years of economic stagnancy and struggle. In the European Union, energy consumption grew in almost all sectors between 1985 and 1998, with the most explosive growth rates registered by the transport sector (one exception was industry, which registered slightly lower consumption levels from 1985 to 1998 because of the implementation of energy efficiency programs and transfers of energy-intensive industries to Central and Eastern Europe). This surge in consumption in the transport sector occurred even though EU member states made improvements in automobile fuel efficiency during the 1990s. Unfortunately, these improvements were not enough to neutralize escalating automobile and truck use.

Despite increased efforts to integrate energy efficiency policies more fully into other policy areas, most analysts believe that EU states will continue to demand greater quantities of energy to run their appliances, operate their cars, and power their businesses. Some observers believe that EU schemes to reorganize its energy markets could spark the creation and implementation of more efficient energy generation technologies, but others believe that reduced energy prices—a likely result of open markets—will diminish the incentive for Europeans to conserve energy (ibid.). In any case, growing numbers of European policy-makers have concluded that further development of renewable energy sources will be essential if the EU hopes to maintain its current level of prosperity in future decades.

In the "Accession" countries of Europe—nations formerly hidden behind the Iron Curtain but now seen as potential candidates for inclusion in the European Union—energy consumption per capita is only two-thirds the average level in the EU. This lower level of consumption is directly attributable to the difficult economic transitions that these countries were forced to make after the collapse of the Soviet empire. Scores of inefficient, heavily polluting factories and plants closed their doors in the early 1990s, which served to reduce levels of environmental degradation but also pushed many communities deeper into economic impoverishment. Today fossil fuels account for most (90 percent) of the energy that is consumed in these countries, with cheap and plentiful—but ecologically dirty—coal a particular staple of the region's energy diet (ibid.; European Commission, *Energy in Europe,* 1996). But many of these countries have initiated programs to squeeze the most out of their energy resources and existing energy infrastructure in an environmentally sensitive manner, often with the active assistance of Western European governmental and academic institutions, industry, and nongovernmental organizations.

Table 8.1 Electricity Consumption per Capita in European Countries

	Electricity consumption per capita 1995	1996	1997	1998
	KWh per capita			
Austria	5.8	6.0	6.0	6.0
Belgium	6.8	6.9	7.1	7.3
Denmark	6.0	6.1	6.0	6.0
Germany	5.5	5.6	5.6	5.7
Finland	12.8	13.0	13.7	14.1
France	5.9	6.1	6.1	6.3
Greece	3.3	3.4	3.5	3.7
Iceland	15.9			
Ireland	4.1	4.4	4.6	4.8
Italy	4.1	4.2	4.3	4.4
Luxembourg	12.3	11.9	12.3	12.5
Netherlands	5.4	5.6	5.7	5.9
Norway	23.9	23.6	23.6	24.6
Portugal	2.9	3.0	3.2	3.4
Spain	3.6	3.7	4.0	4.2
Sweden	14.1	14.3	13.9	14.0
United Kingdom	5.0	5.2	5.2	5.3
EU15	*5.3*	*5.4*	*5.5*	*5.6*
EEA (EU15 + Norway)	*5.5*	*5.6*	*5.7*	*5.9*

SOURCE: Eurostat.

NOTE: Electricity consumption per capita has been calculated by dividing the electricity consumption of the final energy demand sectors (industry, residential, tertiary, transport and agriculture) by the population. It therefore does not include transmission and distribution losses.

Trends in Energy Resource Use

The popularity of various energy sources has ebbed and flowed over the past several decades, affected by a host of economic, political, market, and environmental factors. In the 1970s, for example, nuclear power was hailed worldwide as a relatively abundant, cheap, and clean source of energy at a time when concerns about the availability of other fuel sources was peaking. By the early 1990s, however, the Chernobyl nuclear accident had convinced many European nations to shun nuclear power. "King Coal," on the other hand, relinquished its throne as Western Europe's preeminent source of energy for electricity, industry, and domestic heating in the 1960s, beleaguered by industry restructuring for oil and gas power and mounting evidence that coal consumption was taking a terrible toll on urban air quality. Coal held on for a time in Central Europe, where mines coughed up large quantities of coal that were devoured by government-owned industries and power facilities with little regard for environmental consequences. But here too, coal was eventually eclipsed by natural gas and other energy sources, leading many observers to speculate that "the sun may be setting on the empire of coal" (Dunn, "King Coal's Weakening Grip on Power," 1999). Yet coal refuses to vacate the premises entirely; indeed, power stations in the United Kingdom burned 15 percent more coal in 2000 than in 1999 after soaring wholesale natural gas prices convinced them to look elsewhere for energy.

Road Transport Drives Demand for Oil

Europe relies on oil more than any other energy source, importing massive quantities of petroleum to feed its ever-expanding transportation network and power various industries. In the European Union, energy use for transportation increased by 47 percent and oil consumption increased by 17 percent from 1985 to 1998; by 1997, the average European was burning off 303 liters of motor gasoline annually (International Energy Agency, *Energy Balances of Organisation for Economic Cooperation and Development [OECD] Countries,* 1999; European Environment Agency, *Are We Moving in the Right Direction?,* 2000).

Although European automakers were able to achieve fuel economy gains during the 1990s, demand for oil is expected to increase throughout Europe for the foreseeable future. All the continent's major transportation trends—increased reliance on private automobiles at the expense of public transit, lower vehicle occupancy rates, greater distances between home and principal destinations (work, recreation, shopping), continued new roadway construction, expansion of road-based freight transport—indicate that the continent will demand greater quantities of petroleum in the coming years.

Europe's heightened dependence on automobiles—and thus oil—poses a significant threat to its stated commitment to meet—indeed exceed—the emission standards outlined in the 1997 Kyoto Protocol, a UN-sponsored international agreement on climate change that calls for industrialized nations to reduce their emissions of greenhouse gases to at least 5 percent below 1990 emission levels between 2008 and 2012. The treaty committed the EU to collectively reduce its emissions of greenhouse gases by 8 percent of 1990 levels by 2008–2012, and individual states set even more ambitious emission reduction goals. Germany, for instance, targeted a 21 percent cut in greenhouse gases, primarily carbon dioxide, by 2010 as part of its commitment to the protocol. But since automobile exhaust is a major contributor to greenhouse gases—in 1998 road transport accounted for 20 percent of Europe's total carbon dioxide emissions (European Environment Agency, *Environmental Signals 2001,* 2001)—many European nations, and the EU as a whole, will be hard pressed to meet their stated obligations in this area.

Natural Gas Soars in Popularity

Natural gas now ranks as the single greatest source of energy in Europe, the result of an extended "dash for gas" phenomenon that shook the continent's

Figure 8.2 Surface Transport of Goods

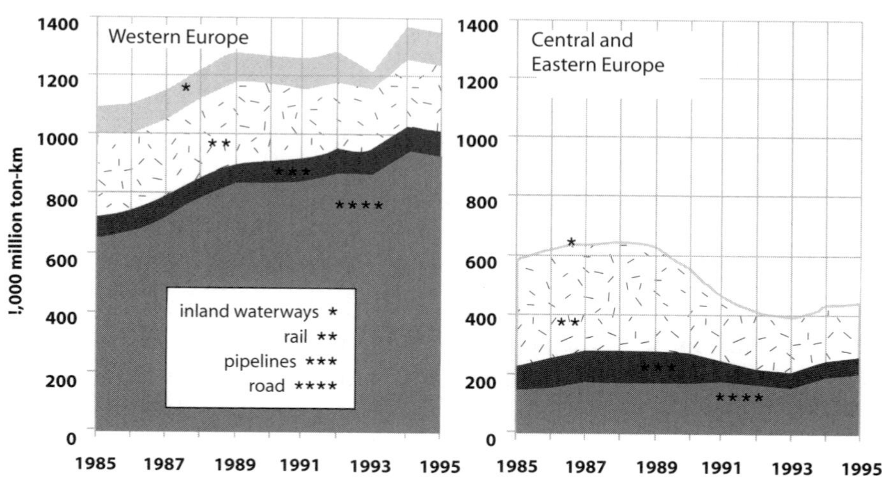

SOURCE: European Environment Agency 1998.

energy industry to its core over the past two decades. Indeed, from 1985 to 1998, consumption of natural gas rose by more than 60 percent (ibid.), spurred by technological efficiencies and increased availability of gas.

This embrace of natural gas has been beneficial for the European environment in several significant respects, especially in the realm of improved air quality. "Emissions of all the major pollutants from the energy supply sector fell between 1990 and 1998 [in the EU] despite increases in total energy output and in gross value added. Much of the overall fall resulted from fuel switching in electricity generation, from oil and coal to natural gas," noted the EEA (ibid.). The environmental community acknowledges that increased reliance on natural gas has helped Europe reduce its emissions of greenhouse gases and other pollutants. But it also points out that dependence on the fuel is not without negative environmental ramifications, since drilling and other extraction activities fragment wildlife habitat and can pollute freshwater sources.

Desire for Cheap Energy Drives Coal Revival

Coal has long been vilified by environmentalists and health professionals for its harm to the environment and human health. It is a major source of atmospheric sulfur, nitrogen oxides, and greenhouse gases when burned, and coal mining has been criticized for polluting rivers, destroying terrestrial habitat, and ruining the scenic quality of natural areas. Nonetheless, it remains an important—though no longer preeminent—source of energy in Europe. In the late 1990s, for example, it accounted for 68 percent of Poland's total energy and 97 percent of its electricity, and Denmark, Germany, and the Czech Republic all relied on the fuel for more than 50 percent of their electricity (Dunn, "King Coal's Weakening Grip," 1999). Fortunately, new technologies have reduced the impact of emissions from coal consumption to some degree. For example, gasifying coal allows some pollutants to be removed prior to combustion. But these advances have yet to be widely implemented because of the heavy capital investments required.

Coal is the primary energy source for 40 percent of Europe's electrical power, but it is utilized more in Central and Eastern Europe than the West. In fact, consumption of coal, lignite, and derivatives fell by almost 30 percent in EU states between 1985 and 1998, during which time electricity generators embraced more efficient fuels with more flexible generating capacity, such as natural gas. Emission-reduction directives and mandates for investing in pollution-abatement technologies provided further impetus for switching to cleaner-burning fuels such as natural gas (European Environment Agency, *Environmental Signals 2001*, 2001).

Coal may be poised for a revival in Europe, however. It remains an essential part of the energy infrastructure in areas of Central and Eastern Europe, and some countries—most notably Russia—see expanded coal mining operations as integral to achieving internal economic and energy security goals. In addition, some analysts anticipate that decommissioning of nuclear power plants in coming years will almost certainly heighten Europe's reliance on coal. Increased coal extraction in Western Europe also appears likely as a result of market forces that have made the fuel more economically attractive than natural gas in recent years. Examples of this renewed interest in coal have proliferated in recent years. In 2000, for example, UK electricity generators resorted to inexpensive coal supplies when confronted with rising natural gas prices. Britain even cranked up coal-fired power stations that had been put in mothballs in the mid-1990s. Norway, meanwhile, announced plans for a major expansion of its coal industry on the Svalbard archipelago in the Arctic, viewed as one of the last intact Arctic wilderness areas in Europe. Opponents of the expansion say that it will compromise unique arctic habitat, endanger fragile species, and jeopardize the EU's ability to meet its Kyoto obligations. But company representatives say that Svalbard coal has high energy content and low sulfur levels, making it preferable to inferior coal currently being consumed in Europe (Kirby, "Norway Defends Arctic Coal Plan," 2001).

Nuclear Industry Faces an Uncertain Future

The outlook for nuclear power in Europe is uncertain. On the one hand, nuclear power remains an important element of the continent's overall energy picture. Eight EU member states possess nuclear power capacity, and approximately 35 percent of electricity generated within the EU originates from the nuclear sector. In addition, nuclear fuel consumption in the EU increased by more than 42 percent from 1985 to 1998, a period during which France greatly expanded its nuclear program in order to compensate for limited supplies of fossil fuels within its borders. This expansion made France the world's top energy exporter and has made the French more dependent on nuclear power than any other European people. In fact, nuclear power currently makes up three-quarters of France's total electricity production (European Environment Agency, *Environmental Signals 2001,* 2001; Johnson, "Nuclear Energy Policy in the European Union," 1999).

But many Western European countries have turned their backs on nuclear power, decommissioning existing nuclear facilities—sometimes years before the end of their economic lives—or declaring moratoria on the construction of new plants. These countries—Belgium, Germany, Sweden, and others—cite concerns about nuclear technology's safety record and the problem of

Graveyard near Chernobyl Power Station, Ukraine, 1991 REUTERS NEWMEDIA INC./CORBIS

disposing of radioactive nuclear waste as decisive factors in their decisions (see sidebar, page 181).

Much of the enduring hostility to nuclear power can be traced back to the April 26, 1986, Chernobyl nuclear accident in the Ukrainian republic of the Soviet Union. That event profoundly altered European—and world—attitudes about nuclear power, and the industry has yet to recover from it. The disaster at Chernobyl produced an immense cloud of radioactive debris that drifted over sections of the western USSR, Eastern Europe, and Scandinavia. It forced the evacuation and resettlement of hundreds of thousands of Soviet citizens and has been blamed for higher cancer rates and other health problems in the region. The accident also was an environmental catastrophe of the first magnitude, contaminating soil, surface water, and groundwater with radioactive fallout over thousands of square miles. "Chernobyl . . . strongly reinforced public fears of nuclear energy," confirmed one analyst:

> These worries were subsequently translated into new policy measures. In 1986 the Danish Parliament decided that no nuclear plants would be built in Denmark. In 1987 in Italy, a referendum blocked the opening of four nuclear reactors, even though the country possessed few indigenous energy resources and was highly dependent on imported energy. In 1989 Belgium imposed a moratorium on the construction of nuclear power stations. Such moratoriums also exist in Spain and the United Kingdom. In 1993 the Finnish government, despite its approval earlier that year to build a nuclear power plant, also voted against further expansion of nuclear power. As a consequence of these decisions, there will be no further expansion of the nuclear industry in Europe for the foreseeable future, with the exception of France, which has not ruled out the possibility of further nuclear construction. (Johnson, "Nuclear Energy Policy in the European Union," 1999)

In Central and Eastern Europe, the future of nuclear power is murky. Nearly 70 reactors were in operation within the territories of the former Soviet Union and its European allies in the late 1990s, with another handful under construction. But while some of these nations would like to expand their nuclear power capabilities, limited financial resources constitute a major hurdle (Land, "Russia: Nuclear Dustbin of the World," 1999).

Eastern European schemes to augment their nuclear industries also must consider the attitudes of the European Union. The nations of Eastern Europe are eager to join the EU, but membership in the organization requires that they handle the nuclear energy issue in a responsible manner. Given the large number of substandard reactors currently generating electricity in Central

The Controversy over Nuclear Waste Shipments in Europe

Although the future of nuclear energy in Europe is uncertain, the continent's past and continued reliance on nuclear power has created problems involving the transport and storage of nuclear waste. As hazardous radioactive materials move between power plants, reprocessing facilities, and storage areas across Europe, citizens of many nations raise concerns about the potential dangers to human health and the environment. Some people fear that the containers holding nuclear waste will accidentally break or spill during transport, while others worry that the shipments are vulnerable to theft, diversion, or terrorist attacks. These factors—combined with growing antinuclear sentiment—have given rise to widespread protests over nuclear waste shipments in Europe and elsewhere. "Nuclear issues have not lost any of their ability to catalyze serious opposition, and transportation has become a lightning rod issue for the antinuclear movement, underscoring serious questions about the safety and viability of the nuclear sector as a whole" (O'Neill, "International Nuclear Waste Transportation," 1999).

Many shipments of nuclear waste within Europe take place between power-generation facilities and the continent's three reprocessing plants for spent nuclear fuel—Cap La Hague in France, Sellafield in Great Britain, and Dounreay in Scotland. Originally, these plants were intended to separate uranium and plutonium from spent fuel rods so that the materials could be reused as fuel. In practice, however, it is more cost effective to use freshly mined uranium in nuclear power generation, so reprocessed materials are seldom used. Critics claim that the main reason that power plants continue to send their spent fuel rods for reprocessing is that they lack adequate storage capacity for their wastes, and reprocessing plants sometimes hold the materials in storage for years. Environmentalists have long favored putting nuclear waste into permanent storage immediately without reprocessing.

All three of Europe's reprocessing plants experienced problems during the 1990s. The French government temporarily halted shipments to Cap La Hague in 1998, when it learned that the company operating the facility had knowingly sent shipments across Europe in containers that were contaminated with surface radioactivity—with some containers registering 3,000 times the legal limit. It turned out that several European utilities were aware of the problem but had failed to alert authorities. This scandal also prompted German, French, and Swiss railways to ban all nuclear shipments pending an investigation of possible harmful effects on workers.

The two reprocessing plants in the United Kingdom experienced problems involving their storage of high-level nuclear waste. Safety issues at the

(continues)

Sellafield complex drew criticism from Ireland, as people worried that an accident in the storage tanks could pollute Dublin. In the meantime, the Dounreay complex struggled to overcome a long history of negative publicity. At one time, workers at Dounreay disposed of nuclear wastes by dumping them into a shaft leading to the sea. The illegal dumping was discovered in 1977, when the wastes caused an explosion that spread contamination over a wide area. In fact, radioactive particles were still found in the area two decades later, and it remains off limits for fishing today.

Germany provides the largest volume of business for Europe's nuclear waste reprocessing plants. The nation lacks adequate storage capacity for its waste, partly because of determined opposition by a strong German antinuclear movement. Germany attempted to develop storage facilities in Gorleben, Lower Saxony, but the first shipment of waste to Gorleben in May 1997 aroused huge protests. In fact, transportation of the waste cost more than $57 million, as 30,000 German police in full riot gear were required to protect the train and prevent sabotage of the railway lines. The following year, Germany shifted its plans for nuclear waste storage to a new site in the northern town of Alhaus. Large-scale demonstrations erupted once again when the first shipment crossed the country by train en route to Alhaus. Thousands of protesters staged sit-ins or chained themselves to the tracks in an effort to stop the train. The German public largely supported the protests, as many people questioned the wisdom of transporting dangerous materials through hundreds of kilometers of densely populated areas.

Partly in response to public pressure, the German government announced plans to shut down the nation's nuclear power plants over a period of ten to twenty years. However, it also stated its intention to honor its reprocessing contracts with Great Britain and France, at least through 2005. For their part, the French and British governments have placed political pressure on Germany to allow shipments of nuclear waste to continue, as those countries stand to lose hundreds of jobs and billions of dollars in revenue if the reprocessing facilities cease to operate. Another factor in Germany's decision to honor its contracts is that the reprocessing plants hold thousands of tons of spent fuel in storage that must eventually return to Germany.

In March 2001 the first shipment of reprocessed nuclear waste since 1997 returned to Germany from France. As the train carrying the materials made its way toward the storage facility at Gorleben, hundreds of protesters blocked the track and 15,000 riot police were called in to forcibly remove them. The following month Germany resumed its shipments of nuclear waste to reprocessing facilities in Great Britain for the first time since 1998. In August 2001, Germany sent twelve containers holding twenty-one spent fuel rods to France—the largest shipment of

(continues)

nuclear waste ever in Europe. As before, large-scale demonstrations took place in an attempt to stop these shipments. Some antinuclear activists view their protests as a way to pressure the German government and Europe as a whole to end its reliance on nuclear energy. "While the government argues that Germany has a moral duty to take back its reprocessed nuclear waste, opponents see disrupting the shipments as the most effective way of forcing an early shutdown of the industry" ("German Nuclear Activists Evicted," *BBC News Online*, March 26, 2001).

Sources:

Broomby, Rob. 2001. "Germany's Nuclear Waste Headache." *BBC News Online*. April 23.

"German Nuclear Activists Evicted." 2001. *BBC News Online*. March 26.

"German Nuclear Waste Crosses France." 2001. *BBC News Online*. August 2.

Kirby, Alex. 2001. "Nuclear Waste: A Long-Lived Legacy." *BBC News Online*. March 28.

O'Neill, Kate. 1999. "International Nuclear Waste Transportation: Flashpoints, Controversies, and Lessons." *Environment* 41 (May).

Rothstein, Linda. 1998. "The Problem Was Not Hidden." *Bulletin of Atomic Scientists* 54 (September–October).

and Eastern Europe, this is a formidable task. Regional governments see many of these facilities as good candidates for retrofitting. But concerns about design flaws, poor maintenance, security problems, and low staff morale at these facilities—as well as perennial worries about safe disposal of nuclear waste—have prompted some Western European nations to call for their outright closure (Wesolowsky, "Sparring over Mochovce," 1998).

Perhaps inevitably, these differing perspectives have created tensions in several regions of Europe. In 1998, for example, Slovakia decided to link a retrofitted nuclear power station built during the Soviet era to its energy grid. This decision was angrily condemned by Austria, which had abandoned nuclear power in the late 1970s. Austrian authorities contend that the facility is unsafe and that it constitutes a threat to the Austrian capital of Vienna, which sits only 90 miles from the power station. In January 2002, meanwhile, two Eastern European nations reneged on deals with the EU in which they were promised financial assistance in return for early reactor closures. Bulgaria decided to delay shutting two old Soviet reactors, and Armenia reconsidered an earlier decision to shut a nuclear plant located in an active earthquake zone. Both countries explained that they were forced to keep the facilities open because the infrastructure for using other sources of energy had not yet been put in place, but their decision was strongly criticized in the EU.

Elsewhere, Lithuania has threatened to keep open a Chernobyl-style nuclear plant in defiance of EU wishes without a guarantee of significant financial assistance, even though the EU has made closure of the facility a stipulation for eventual Lithuanian membership in the Union.

In the meantime, Russia has declared its intention to invest additional money and effort into nuclear power. In 2001, for example, Russia was the only nation in the world to complete a new reactor, and it has publicized plans calling for as many as ten new reactors in the next decade (Worldwatch Institute, *Vital Signs 2002*, 2002). Increased reliance on nuclear energy might help Russia reduce its emissions of greenhouse gases and other pollutants and lessen the need for oil, gas, and coal extraction activities in pristine wilderness areas. But memories of Chernobyl remain fresh in Europe, and Russia's assurances that its nuclear facilities will adhere to high design and safety standards are viewed with some skepticism. Critics also note that Russia has a deplorable history in the area of nuclear waste disposal. "The full extent of nuclear pollution, which was kept under the tightly drawn shroud of state security before perestroika, is still not completely known. What is known, however, is hair-raising. From the beginning of their nuclear program in the 1940s to as late as [October 1993] the Russians have systematically turned much of their own territory and the seas around it into a convenient nuclear cesspool. A report presented to the International Marine Organization by Russian scientists [in the fall of 1993] admitted that 'all dumpings . . . in the northern seas (and most dumpings in the far eastern seas) were performed in gross violation of international standards'" (Burrows, "Nuclear Chaos," 1994). For its part, Russia insists that its days of pitching radioactive waste into the Arctic seas are over, and that it is in the process of building infrastructure that will safely and permanently store large quantities of nuclear waste.

Finally, the future of nuclear power in Europe will undoubtedly depend in large part on the continent's ability to replace its generating capacity with renewable energy sources. Europe's ability to do so is by no means a certainty, and some European industries already claim that phasing out nuclear energy will deprive them of essential electricity supplies that cannot be replaced with increased use of renewables. Germany, for example, has agreed to phase out all nineteen of its nuclear reactors by the mid-2020s. But skeptics contend that in order to do so, it will have to use fossil fuels that generate large volumes of carbon dioxide and other greenhouse gases, making it impossible for the nation to meet its emission reduction goals. Indeed, despite the significant environmental drawbacks associated with nuclear waste and safety, nuclear power's potential as an alternative to fossil fuel combustion in an age of mounting concern about global climate change may ultimately ensure that it occupies a significant place in Europe's energy mix for some time to come (Johnson, "Nuclear Energy Policy in the European Union," 1999).

Investing in Renewables

Europe views renewable energy as a viable means by which it can simultaneously meet its energy needs and reduce its contribution to global warming and its overall impact on the environment. This belief is reflected in the steady rise in consumption of renewable energy on the continent. Between 1985 and 1998, consumption of renewable energy (hydro, wind, solar, wave and tidal, geothermal) rose by approximately 25 percent. By 1998 renewable sources were contributing more than 14 percent of total electricity generation, largely because of energy generated at large hydropower installations.

In addition, European authorities have established specific and ambitious targets for continued growth in renewable energy use. For example, the European Commission's 1997 White Paper on renewable sources of energy laid out a blueprint for boosting renewable energy's share of the EU energy market to 12 percent by 2010. This plan included myriad intermediate goals as well, including installation of 10,000 megawatts (MW) of wind turbine capacity, 1 million installed photovoltaic systems, and 1 million households heated by biomass—which produces clean energy through the consumption of agricultural, forest, and animal waste—all by the year 2003 (European Commission, *Energy for the Future*, 1997). Individual countries have also laid out hard targets for renewables usage. In the United Kingdom, for instance, the government introduced a "renewables obligation" in 2002 that requires electricity suppliers to buy at least 3 percent of their power from "green" (renewable) sources, with the mandate gradually increasing to 10 percent by 2010.

But despite extensive investment in renewables, these resources still account for a relatively modest percentage of Europe's total energy consumption. Renewables' share of total energy consumed rose by only half a percent (from 6.1 percent to 6.6 percent) from 1985 to 1998, and in EU member states the contribution of renewable energy in 1998 was less than 6 percent, well short of the EU's stated goal of garnering 12 percent of its energy from renewables by 2010 (European Environment Agency, *Environmental Signals 2001*, 2000). Accelerated growth in the implementation and use of renewable energy sources will likely hinge on Europe's willingness to set binding targets for use of renewables, eliminate subsidies for fossil fuel industries, institute policies that promote "clean energy" purchases, and further integrate environmental sustainability goals into all major government policy areas.

Some forms of renewable energy have made greater inroads into European society than others. Hydropower, for instance, is a well-entrenched industry that contributes significant amounts of energy in a number of countries without polluting the air with greenhouse gases. But experts believe that hydroelectric power is unlikely to grow appreciably in the coming years. Most sites suitable for large hydroelectric installations have already been developed, and concerns about the destructive impact of dams on fragile freshwater fisheries and other wildlife habitat have sparked considerable debate in recent years.

Sun-based forms of renewable energy have not yet been implemented on a large commercial scale, and solar power is often seen as a supplemental, rather than a primary, energy source. But support for solar cell use continues to grow in Europe and around the world. Biomass is recognized as an important renewable energy source in Western Europe. It accounted for more than 63 percent of total renewable energy production in the EU in 1997, according to Eurostat's *Renewable Energy Sources Statistics in the European Union 1989–1997*, and the cost of electricity produced by this method has already fallen below that from conventional coal-fired power stations. But while use of this technology is expected to grow, high capital investments have limited its utilization. Use of geothermal technology, meanwhile, has grown steadily in the EU, especially in agriculture and residential heating sectors, but it still accounts for only a tiny percentage of the continent's energy production.

Of all Europe's renewable energy options, wind power has enjoyed the greatest growth in recent years (see sidebar, page 171). "These days, wind farms are an increasingly common sight across Europe," confirmed the European Commission. "Countries such as Denmark, Spain, Germany, the Netherlands, Sweden and the UK are all harvesting the wind as a source of energy on a commercial scale. . . .EU energy technology initiatives have already helped to bring turbines to the point at which investors, including large electricity companies, have begun to install them on a fully commercial basis. For machines of up to 1MW, the technological problems are now solved, and their potential is enormous worldwide" (European Commission, *Energising Europe,* 2000).

Certainly, Western Europe has assumed a world leadership position in the research, utilization, and manufacture of wind technology and equipment. Germany alone accounted for more than one-third of the world's total installed capacity of 24,000 MW in 2001, a year in which Europe as a whole increased its wind energy capacity by more than 35 percent. European manufacturers, meanwhile, account for over 75 percent of all the new wind turbines installed worldwide, and the industry is now a significant source of employment in some European nations. In Denmark, for instance, by 1997 some 10,000 new jobs had been created either directly or indirectly as a result of the country's rapidly expanding wind energy industry (ibid.).

Environmentalists have long championed wind power as an environmentally friendly energy alternative. They note that wind energy is an indigenous and freely available resource that does not create any dangerous waste products, and point out that approximately 99 percent of the land area within a typical wind farm site can be utilized for agriculture or other uses. "Wind energy is a clean, renewable and sustainable means of electricity generation," added the European Wind Energy Association. Indeed, wind energy spares the atmosphere from millions of tons of carbon dioxide and other harmful emissions generated by fossil fuel consumption, making it one of the world's most realistic energy options for reducing global climate change (European Wind Energy Association, *Wind Energy,* 1999).

But wind energy is not universally admired. Bird mortality is a problem at many onshore wind farms, and some communities and businesses have registered strong objections to nearby wind turbine operations, citing the loud noise they generate and their impact on the aesthetics of regional landscapes. Critics have also charged that a dearth of suitable sites in densely populated countries and high installation costs could ultimately doom wind energy to a secondary place in Europe's—and the world's—energy infrastructure in the coming decades.

Proponents of wind power, though, argue that many of the criticisms currently being leveled against wind farms can be addressed by moving operations offshore. "Locating wind turbines in shallow coastal waters, rather than on land, solves [the problems of onshore noise and visual impact] while benefiting from higher average wind speeds. In addition, turbulence is less over the smooth surface of the water, producing lower fatigue loads. Further, wind speed is almost independent of height above the surface, allowing engineers to build lower towers" (European Commission, *Energising Europe,* 2000). Indeed, the German Wind Energy Institute (GWEI) calls the notoriously windy North Sea a potential energy "powerhouse" that, if harnessed by wind turbines, has the potential to generate three times the electricity currently consumed by Germany, Netherlands, Belgium, Denmark, and the United Kingdom.

Rising Energy Consumption in Europe's Transportation Sector

Atmospheric degradation problems associated with transportation growth are well-known and have received a great deal of attention from European media and policy-makers. Almost entirely dependent on fossil fuels (they account for 99 percent of transport energy), the transportation sector is a major contributor to emissions of greenhouse gases, acid rain, and other air pollutants that are harmful to city dwellers and woodland creatures alike. But in addition to being a leading culprit in climate change and air pollution, "the transport sector is increasingly contributing to a number of other environmental and human-health problems, such as noise, land take, fragmentation and disturbance of nature conservation areas, as well as an unending toll of accidental deaths (typically 44,000 a year in the EU), injuries and material damage" (European Environment Agency, *Environmental Signals 2001,* 2001).

These problems have been further exacerbated by explosive growth in the transport sector over the past two decades. Between 1985 and 1995, for instance, passenger transport by car increased by 46 percent in the European Union, while air transport of passengers soared by 67 percent (European Environment Agency, *Europe's Environment,* 1995). Freight transport, meanwhile, has become increasingly reliant on trucking, the most environmentally draining of that industry's transport options (air, rail, and short-sea shipping being the other primary means of transport). From 1970 to the late 1990s, trucking's share of total freight transport jumped from 30 percent to 45 percent (European Environment Agency, *Are We Moving in the Right Direction?,* 2000).

This surge in transport activity has fundamentally transformed many landscapes of Europe, as new or expanded roadways, rail lines, airports, and assorted support infrastructure (rest areas, rail yards, parking areas, etc.) are built to accommodate travelers who are negotiating ever greater distances to reach residential areas, shops, schools, and workplaces. This phenomenon, commonly known as "urban sprawl," is in full bloom in most metropolitan areas. From 1990 to 1996, a total of 25,000 hectares—an average of 10 hectares per day—were taken for roadway construction in EU states. This rate of conversion was even higher in heavily industrialized countries such as Germany, which lost an estimated 120 hectares per day to new motorways in 1997. In Central and Eastern Europe, meanwhile, rapid growth in private automobile ownership and progrowth economic policies are creating heightened demand for new highways and airports (ibid.). Increasing rates of tourism are also responsible for much of the pressure on Europe's transportation systems, especially in the sunny Mediterranean and mountainous Alps. In 1998 alone, Europe received 373 million tourists—approximately 60 percent of all international tourist arrivals—and absorbed 3 billion domestic trips taken by Europeans (Ellul, *Tourism and the Environment,* 2000).

Most new transportation development in Europe involves the conversion of farmland, but forests and wetlands are also affected. Not surprisingly, resident flora and fauna often suffer from these changes to their habitat. "Habitats and species are disturbed or damaged by traffic noise and light, vehicle emissions, run-off substances from road surfaces and runways (to which salt and other de-icing chemicals have been applied) and oil discharges, particularly to rivers and seas," reported the EEA. "Some animal species are particularly susceptible to collision with traffic. Proximity to major traffic infrastructure and growth in traffic using such infrastructure can therefore clearly affect habitats and species. Linear infrastructure (roads, railways, canals) may fragment habitats, thereby reducing the living space for endemic species, and can provide new pathways for the influx of other species. They may also act as barriers to movement and genetic interchange between populations, especially for vertebrates" (European Environment Agency, *Are We Moving in the Right Direction?*, 2000).

Increasingly, new roadways are even skirting or passing through formally designated protected areas. By 1997, about 65 percent of the EU's protected bird sanctuaries and Ramsar wetlands were within 5 kilometers of major transport infrastructure. This disturbance to regional ecosystems is regarded as a potentially serious threat to biodiversity and the integrity of designated nature areas (ibid.).

Reducing Transportation's Environmental "Footprint"

European policy-makers are mulling a variety of strategies to reduce the environmental impact of transportation. Increased automobile fuel efficiency is frequently cited as a vital plank in any sustainability platform. Indeed, recent advances in this regard helped Europe's environment weather the continent's 1990s surge in transportation activity, and the European Automobile Manufacturers Association has already pledged to reduce carbon dioxide emissions from new cars sold in the EU by approximately 25 percent by the year 2008. Efforts to increase the percentage of European automobiles outfitted with catalytic converters—which reduce pollutants contained in exhaust gas—have also been cited as essential to reducing air pollution in Europe. As of 1997, less than half of the EU's gasoline-fed automobiles on the road were fitted with catalytic converters, and fewer than three of ten cars in France and Spain (ibid.).

Sales of diesel-engine cars, meanwhile, have increased in recent years. In 1990 they made up 20 percent of sales in Western Europe; by 2000 diesel's share of the new car market had reached 39 percent. Diesel offers superior fuel economy (up to 30 percent improvement in fuel consumption) at slightly higher manufacturing expense, which has the benefit of increasing the region's level of energy security and reducing pressure to engage in oil extraction activities. But diesel engines also produce higher levels of greenhouse gases.

Scientists, environmentalists, city planners, and lawmakers are also looking at ways to halt or even reverse the rapid growth in automobile use. Rejuvenating Europe's declining—but still extensive—public transit systems is central to this goal. Certainly, the European public has indicated strong sup-

Eurostar trains at Waterloo Station in London WILLIAM WHITEHURST/CORBIS

port for increased investment in mass transit. In one survey of 16,000 EU citizens, 70 percent of respondents cited "improving public transport" as the best solution to solving traffic congestion problems in metropolitan areas. Other popular strategies—creating more pedestrian areas (45 percent), reducing automobile traffic (42 percent), creating more bicycle lanes (32 percent)—reflected widespread recognition of Europe's growing problems with addressing transportation needs in environmentally sustainable ways (Commission of the European Communities, *Europeans and the Environment,* 1999).

Maximizing the usefulness of Europe's extensive mass transit system, however, requires confronting several challenges. Fewer numbers of Europeans are utilizing trains, buses, subways, and water ferries—the major transport modes of public transit—than ever before. Instead, they have embraced private transportation by automobile, swayed by its freedom and convenience, the allure of private car ownership, and dissatisfaction with the quality and expense of the mass transit experience. In many urban areas of Western Europe, cars now account for more than 80 percent of mechanized transport, and while rates are lower in Central and Eastern European cities, rising rates of private car ownership will undoubtedly impact transportation choices in those areas as well (European Environment Agency, *Europe's Environment,* 1998).

Proponents of mass transit contend that increasing funding for maintenance, expansion, and other customer service improvements would make it a much more attractive option for commuters, tourists, and shoppers. But that will require a significant reallocation of investment away from motorways, which have received the lion's share of transportation funding from European governments since the early 1990s. Supporters also say that reducing European dependence on the automobile, which will in turn reduce harmful emissions and fossil fuel consumption, will require more projects like the trans-European Transport Network (TEN), a high-speed rail system that will consist of 24,000 kilometers of track by 2010.

Increased use of Strategic Environmental Assessments (SEAs) has also been cited as an important tool in meeting environmental sustainability goals in the transportation sector. Currently, Environmental Impact Assessments (EIAs) are commonly utilized in conjunction with large transportation projects. But critics note that they are not undertaken until the final stages of the development process, when project approval is at stake. At that point, notes the European Environmental Agency, "it is often too late to consider more strategic alternatives such as modal and route choices [in transportation projects]. The effect of EIA is therefore mostly limited to adding certain (technological) mitigation measures to infrastructure design and implementation (e.g., noise screens, tunnels). Furthermore, project EIAs fail to account for cumulative effects (the combined effects of several transport projects)" (European Environment Agency, *Are We Moving in the Right Direction?,* 2000).

By contrast, SEAs—which can be utilized for local as well as national transportation development proposals—are incorporated at all stages and levels of decision-making (European Conference of Ministers of Transport, *Strategic Environmental Assessment in the Transport Sector,* 1998). "SEA helps to ensure that the environmental consequences of policies, plans or programmes are identified before adoption, that feasible alternatives are properly considered and that the public and environmental authorities are fully involved in the decisionmaking process. . . .SEA is particularly useful in assisting decisions on a multi-modal approach. It helps to structure and focus environmental analysis on the key environmental benefits and costs of each transport mode, by comparing alternative planning and management options in an integrated way and providing decision-makers with the relevant information to make the most sustainable decision" (European Environment Agency, *Are We Moving in the Right Direction?,* 2000). By the late 1990s, Denmark, Finland, France, and Sweden had all implemented mandatory SEAs for the transportation sector, and other nations are expected to follow suit.

Finally, individual communities are introducing environmental sustainability models on their own or as part of international sustainability campaigns like Agenda 21 and the Aalborg Charter of European Cities and Towns

Towards Sustainability. In some instances, European communities have made startling reductions in energy consumption and air pollution from the transportation sector. In the early 1990s, for example, the leadership of Strasbourg, France, completely overhauled the city's transportation system. It invested in new bicycle paths and a new light passenger rail system while at the same time imposing restrictions on automobile use within the city. In five years car use fell by 17 percent and use of public transport increased by 30 percent (European Environment Agency, *Environmental Signals 2001,* 2001).

Sources:

Arctic Monitoring and Assessment Programme. 1997. *AMAP Assessment Report: Arctic Pollution Issues.* Oslo: AMAP.

Burrows, William E. 1994. "Nuclear Chaos." *Popular Science* (August).

Carpenter, T. 1994. *The Environmental Impact of Railways.* London: John Wiley.

Centre for Energy Conservation and Environmental Technology. 1997. *Efficiency and Sufficiency: Towards Sustainable Energy and Transport.* Delft, the Netherlands: CEET.

Commission of the European Communities. 1999. *Europeans and the Environment.* Luxembourg: CEC.

Dunn, Seth. 1999. "King Coal's Weakening Grip on Power." *Worldwatch* 12 (September–October).

Ellul, Anthony. 2000. *Tourism and the Environment in European Countries.* Nature and Environment No. 116. Strasbourg, France: Council of Europe.

"Europe on the Rocks: Renewable Energy." 1995. *Nature* 378, no. 6556.

European Commission. 1996. *Energy in Europe: European Energy 2020: A Scenario Approach.* Brussels: EC.

———. 1997. *Energy for the Future: Renewable Sources of Energy.* White Paper for a Community Strategy and Action Plan. Brussels: EC.

———. 2000. *Energising Europe.* Brussels: EC.

European Commission and Eurostat. 2000. *Transport in Figures: Statistical Pocketbook.* Brussels: EC.

European Conference of Ministers of Transport. 1998. *Strategic Environmental Assessment in the Transport Sector.* Paris: ECMT.

European Council. 1999. *Strategy on the Integration of Environment and Sustainable Development into the Transport Policy.* Strasbourg, France: European Council.

European Environment Agency. 1995. *Europe's Environment: The Dobris Assessment.* Copenhagen: EEA.

———. 1998. *Europe's Environment: The Second Assessment.* Copenhagen: EEA.

———. 1999. *Environment in the European Union at the Turn of the Century.* Copenhagen: EEA.

———. 2000. *Are We Moving in the Right Direction? Indicators on Transport and Environment Integration in the EU.* Copenhagen: EEA.

———. 2001. *Environmental Signals 2001.* London: Elsevier Science.

European Wind Energy Association. 1999. *Wind Energy: The Facts.* Luxembourg: EC.

Eurostat. 2000. *Renewable Energy Sources Statistics in the European Union 1989–1997.* Luxembourg: EC.

———. 2001. *Consumers in Europe: Facts and Figures.* Luxembourg: EC.

———. 2001. *Transport and Environment: Statistics for the Transport and Environment Reporting Mechanism (TERM) for the European Union.* Luxembourg: EC.

Flavin, Christopher. 1999. "Bull Market in Wind Energy." *Worldwatch* 12 (March–April).

International Energy Agency. 1999. *Energy Balances of Organisation for Economic Cooperation and Development (OECD) Countries, 1960–1997.* Paris: OECD.

———. 2000. *World Energy Outlook 2000.* Paris: IEA.

———. 2002. *Russia Energy Survey 2002.* Paris: IEA.

Johnson, Debra. 1999. "Nuclear Energy Policy in the European Union: Meltdown or False Alarm?" *Journal of International Affairs* 53 (fall).

Kirby, Alex. 2001. "Norway Defends Arctic Coal Plan." *BBC News Online,* December 12.

Krohn, Soren. "Wind Energy Policy in Denmark Status 2002." Danish Wind Industry Association. http://www.windpower.org (accessed February 22, 2002).

Land, Thomas. 1999. "Russia: Nuclear Dustbin of the World." *Contemporary Review* 275 (October).

Organization for Economic Co-operation and Development. 1987. *Coal: Environmental Policies and Institutions.* Paris: OECD.

———. 2000. *Tourism and Travel Patterns: Tourism and Travel Trends and Environmental Impacts.* Paris: OECD.

Pearce, Fred. "Deals to Prevent Chernobyl-Style Disaster Collapse." *New Scientist Online.* http://www.newscientist.com (accessed January 11, 2002).

Segerstahl, Boris, Alexander Akleyev, and Vladimir Novikov. 1997. "The Long Shadow of Soviet Plutonium Production." *Environment* 39 (January–February).

UN Environment Programme. 1999. *Global Environment Outlook 2000.* London: Earthscan.

Voss, Alfred. 1996. "The Potentials, Prospects and Constraints of Renewable Energy Sources in Europe." *International Journal of Global Energy Issues* 8, no. 103.

Wesolowsky, Tony. 1998. "Sparring over Mochovce." *Bulletin of the Atomic Scientists* 54 (November–December).

Worldwatch Institute. 2002. *Vital Signs 2002: The Trends That Are Shaping Our World.* Washington, DC: Worldwatch.

9

Air Quality and the Atmosphere

Europe has taken a leading role in addressing global air pollution and climate change issues. In many European countries, emissions of sulfur dioxide, nitrous oxide, lead, and various ozone-depleting chemicals that threaten human health or ecosystem integrity have been reduced—substantially in some cases. In Western Europe, these improvements in air quality have been realized through the efforts of individual states as well as policies of cooperation and coordination at the EU and international level.

These endeavors have taken a host of forms, from imposition of emission reduction mandates and energy consumption taxes to shifts toward cleaner burning forms of energy and increased integration of environmental sustainability goals into other policy areas. Pollution abatement measures have made halting advances in Central and Eastern Europe as well, but in those regions, emission reductions in the 1990s were primarily the result of the racking economic changes that accompanied the disintegration of the Iron Curtain. "The changes that have come to [Russia and Eastern Europe] since the end of the cold war have brought stronger controls on air pollution and reductions in industrial emissions, [but] these reductions appear to be largely the result of economic decline and the closing of inefficient, polluting factories. Russia and Eastern Europe now have two possibly conflicting objectives: They must clear the way for accelerated economic growth to improve living conditions for their people, and they must make the investments in pollution control that will allow this to happen without increasing emissions" (McCormick, "Acid Pollution," 1998).

Table 9.1 Emissions of Common Anthropogenic Pollutants in European Countries (1996)

Country	*Sulfur Dioxide (000 metric tons)*	*Nitrogen Oxides (000 metric tons)*	*Carbon Monoxide (000 metric tons)*	*Volatile Organic Compounds (000 metric tons)*
Austria	52	163	1,021	261
Belarus	246	173	1,242	328
Belgium	240	334	1,434	324
Bosnia and Herzegovina	x	x	x	x
Bulgaria	1,420	259	613	147
Croatia	58	67	375	79
Czech Republic	946	432	886	284
Denmark	186	288	597	136
Finland	105	267	430	173
France	1,031	1,641	8,850	2,570
Germany	1,543	1,887	6,717	1,877
Greece	543	374	1,334	409
Hungary	673	196	727	150
Iceland	x	x	x	x
Ireland	147	121	307	103
Italy	x	x	x	x
Latvia	59	35	176	41
Lithuania	93	65	312	87
Macedonia, FYR	x	x	x	x
Moldova, Republic	x	x	x	x
Netherlands	135	501	903	362
Norway	34	223	720	369
Poland	2,368	1,154	4,837	766
Portugal	x	x	x	x
Romania	x	x	x	x
Russian Federation	2,685	2,467	9,312	2,576
Slovakia	227	130	346	105
Slovenia	110	70	95	x
Spain	x	x	x	x
Sweden	83	302	1,082	446
Switzerland	30	130	485	203
Ukraine	1,293	467	2,567	718
United Kingdom	2,017	2,029	5,000	2,046
Yugoslavia	434	57	x	x

SOURCE: World Resources 2000–2001.

Air Pollution by Sector and Region

Europe generates significant quantities of common anthropogenic (man-made) pollutants. In 1996 leading producers of sulfur dioxide, a primary cause of acid rain, included Russia (2.69 million metric tons), Poland (2.37 million metric tons), the United Kingdom (2.02 million metric tons), and Germany (1.54 million metric tons). The biggest producers of nitrous oxides, which contribute to acid rain, global warming, and ozone loss, include Russia (2.47 million metric tons in 1996), the United Kingdom (2.03 million metric tons), Germany (1.89 million metric tons), and France (1.64 million metric tons). Russia is also Europe's leading producer of carbon monoxide, a major pollutant in urban areas; in 1996 the country generated 9.31 million metric tons of the chemical. Other significant producers of carbon monoxide include France (8.86 million metric tons in 1996), Germany (6.72 million metric tons), and the United Kingdom (5 million metric tons). Finally, both France and Russia generated approximately 2.57 million metric tons of volatile organic compounds (VOCs) in 1996; VOCs are partially responsible for smog conditions that can have an adverse effect on the health of human, animal, and plant life (EMEP, *1998 Major Review of Strategies,* 1998).

Western Europe

Within the European Union, states have made significant gains in reducing pollution by the industry sector. Bolstered by the introduction of state-sponsored energy efficiency programs, increased reliance on wind power and other renewable forms of energy, and increased consideration of environmental issues in corporate and governmental decision-making (as well as relocations of energy-intensive industries to development-hungry Central and Eastern Europe), the EU industrial sector actually posted modestly lower energy consumption levels from 1985 to 1998. As a result, emissions from this sector declined as well, and analysts believe that further gains can also be realized, provided that Central and Eastern European states develop environmentally sustainable policies and that lawmakers expand their regulatory net to include smaller companies, which are not yet subject to the same level of environmental regulation as larger firms (European Environment Agency, *Europe's Environment,* 1998).

Western Europe has also made measurable progress in reducing its fossil fuel dependency in industrial and utility sectors. Certainly, oil and coal remain deeply interwoven into the EU's energy grid, and they will undoubtedly remain important elements for some years to come. Nonetheless, other, more environmentally friendly energy sources have made significant inroads over the past two decades. Consumption of energy from renewable sources and natural gas rose by 25 percent and 60 percent, respectively, from 1985 to 1998, enabling some Western European states to dramatically curb their industrial emissions of greenhouse gases and other pollutants. Moreover, emissions of lead and other particulate matter generated by the burning of fossil fuels fell by almost 30 percent between 1990 and 1998 in EU states (European Environment Agency, *Environmental Signals 2001,* 2001).

But air pollution emissions from other sectors—agriculture, municipal, and transport—continue to increase in Western Europe. Of these, transportation has experienced the most troubling rise in emissions. Bloated by an explosion of automobile and truck ownership and use—and a corresponding surge in roadway construction—transportation now ranks as the single largest consumer of energy in the EU and as the leading source of greenhouse gases that contribute to global warming.

According to the European Environment Agency (EEA), energy use for transportation increased by nearly 50 percent from 1985 to 1998, driving a 17 percent increase in oil consumption for the same time period. This growth has occurred even though member states made notable improvements in automobile fuel efficiency during the 1990s. One key to reducing pollutants emitted from Western European automobiles is to expand the use of catalytic converters, but progress in this area has been slow. In the late 1990s, for instance, more than half of the European Union's total automobile fleet was operating without catalytic converters, including more than 70 percent of the cars on the road in heavily populated, tourism-oriented countries such as Spain and France (European Environment Agency, *Are We Moving in the Right Direction?,* 2000).

In addition, Western Europe remains conflicted about the efficacy of diesel-powered engines. Sales of new diesel-engine cars in the West nearly doubled in the 1990s, in part because diesel offers superior fuel economy (up to 30 percent improvement in fuel consumption), which reduces pressure to drill for oil in wilderness areas and decreases reliance on foreign sources of petrol. Increased use of diesel fuel has also been cited as a way to reduce emission of greenhouse gases. But emissions of particulate matter and other pollutants are also higher with diesel engines.

"Most of the emission reductions achieved so far have resulted from economic change and measures directed at large sources in the industry and energy sectors," concluded the European Environment Agency (*Europe's Environment,* 1998). "With the exception of lead from petrol, there has been less success in reducing emissions from diffuse sources such as transport and agriculture; these, by their nature, are more difficult to bring under control, demanding better integration between environmental and other policies."

Industrial power plants such as this one in Czechoslovakia are major sources of air pollution in Europe.
SHEPARD SHERBELL/CORBIS SABA

Central and Eastern Europe

In the states of Central and Eastern Europe, governments are still coming to grips with the dark legacy of environmental degradation left by Cold War–era priorities. Throughout much of this region, "countries . . . obeyed the imperatives to develop heavy industry, factory farming, and militarization, all of which have led to pollution of the region's air, water, and soil by heavy metals, radioactivity, pesticides, and fertilizers" (Brown, "The Worst of Both Worlds," Environmental Health Perspectives, 1999).

The consequences of this skewed set of priorities have manifested themselves in myriad unpleasant ways. More than 400,000 children in Central and Eastern Europe are believed to suffer from lead poisoning, a by-product of the region's poorly regulated zinc, copper, gold, and silver mines and heavy use of leaded gasoline. In addition, the rate of infant respiratory disease in Central and Eastern Europe is nearly 20 times that of North America, in part because of the area's long-time—and continuing—dependence on dirty-burning lignite to keep factories, power plants, and household appliances running. Rampant air pollution has taken its toll on ecosystems as well. For example, annual sulfur deposition in the notoriously polluted "Black Triangle"—an area that includes southwestern Poland and the northern reaches of the Czech Republic—far exceeds safety levels for area forests (National Intelligence Council, *Environmental*

Outlook in Central and Eastern Europe, 1997). Farther west, deep in Russia's interior, nickel and copper smelters in Noril'sk and on the Kola Peninsula continue to emit tremendous volumes of sulfur dioxide that ride air currents to Scandinavia, where they wreak havoc on forest ecosystems.

At the close of the twentieth century, energy consumption per capita in Central and Eastern European states was only two-thirds the average level reported in EU states. This comparatively lower consumption level, mainly attributable to the region's economic problems, resulted in significant downturns in greenhouse gas emissions. In Russia, for instance, the UN Framework Convention on Climate Change reported that emissions fell by more than 35 percent from 1990 to 1998, while emissions in Poland (28 percent decline), Romania (38 percent decline), and Ukraine (50.5 percent decline) also plummeted.

But energy consumption in these and other countries is likely to rise as regional economies grow and diversify. This economically robust vision of the future has both positive and negative environmental implications. On the positive side, populations that attain comfortable standards of living often look favorably on increased environmental protection. In addition, some nations, eager to gain entrance into the European Union, have signaled their willingness to follow environmental protection parameters laid out by that body. Hungary, Poland, Slovakia, Latvia, Estonia, Lithuania, the Czech Republic, Slovenia, Cyprus, Malta, Bulgaria, Romania, and Turkey are all pursuing EU membership, and incorporating significant transboundary polluters such as Poland and Bulgaria into EU environmental programs will be beneficial for Sweden, Norway, and other vulnerable downwind countries (Wettestad, "Clearing the Air," 2002).

But while adoption of new pollution controls will help curb emissions of sulfur dioxide and particulates in these states, which will in turn reduce levels of smog, acid rain, and greenhouse gases, the financial cost of meeting such standards may be prohibitive for some countries. According to one estimate, Poland will have to spend $1.6 billion annually over the next twenty-five years just to meet EU air pollution standards (National Intelligence Council, *Environmental Outlook in Central and Eastern Europe,* 1997).

Finally, resource-rich Russia—which is not lobbying for membership in the EU—exerts considerable influence over the region's air and water quality, and the environmental community is skeptical about its commitment to addressing air pollution and other environmental issues. In 2000, for example, Russia dissolved its State Committee for Environment Protection—Goskomekologii, which was the country's only government agency responsible for environmental protection and regulation—and transferred its responsibilities to the Ministry of Natural Resources, an agency that oversees the exploitation of the state's natural resources (Nierenberg, "Russia Axes Its Environmental Agency,"

2000). In 2002 the Russian Federation announced its intention to ratify the Kyoto Protocol, but it also seemed intent on increasing its use of coal in spite of the fossil fuel's well-documented contributions to climate change (International Energy Agency, *Russia Energy Survey 2002,* 2002).

As in the West, the energy sector in Central and Eastern Europe that concerns analysts the most is transportation. Indeed, there is a danger that surging emission levels from automobiles and trucks could neutralize—and even overwhelm—air quality improvements in other areas. The growth rate for passenger cars in Central and Eastern Europe is three times that of Western Europe, and although highly polluting East European models will be phased out over time, much of the import demand will be met with used cars from Western Europe that are not as environmentally friendly as newer models. Truck transport of goods is also expanding rapidly, even as environmentally sustainable rail and urban mass transit systems decline from disuse and anemic funding. The end result of this expansion of automobile use will be higher emissions of lead, nitrous oxide, and carbon monoxide into the air, at least until catalytic converters and vehicles running on unleaded gasoline become the rule rather than the exception (National Intelligence Council, *Environmental Outlook in Central and Eastern Europe,* 1997).

Addressing the Continuing Threat of Acid Pollution

Acid rain—created by emissions of nitrous oxides and sulfur dioxide associated with the burning of fossil fuels—damages crops and woodlands, corrodes buildings and other architecture, and renders lakes and streams uninhabitable for fish and other creatures. This form of air pollution has been a problem in Europe for more than a century. It was first identified in Great Britain as far back as the 1870s, when the Industrial Revolution transformed the character and landscape of cities around the world. But it was not until the 1950s that Europe passed its first air pollution laws. The impetus for these laws was a 1952 episode in which a blanket of smog settled over London, ultimately contributing to the deaths of an estimated 4,000 citizens.

Most European governments initially chose to address local air pollution problems not by reducing emissions but by building taller smokestacks at power stations and factories. This development merely shifted the problem to neighboring countries. For example, parts of Scandinavia, which lies downwind from the industrial centers of Britain and Germany, experienced a doubling in the acidity of rainfall between 1956 and 1965 (McCormick, "Acid Pollution," 1998). By the mid-1970s, Finland, Norway, Sweden, Austria, and Switzerland all reported that more than half of the acid pollution that was ruining their forests and streams was being generated from foreign sources

(OECD Environmental Directorate, *OECD Programme on Long-Range Transport of Air Pollutants,* 1977).

The chief target of Scandinavia's ire was Britain, which for decades used its windswept location in the North Atlantic to tremendous advantage, counting on wind currents to transport airborne pollutants far beyond its borders. It gained an international reputation as the "Dirty Man of Europe" as a consequence, but the country's leaders shrugged off the criticism until the 1990s, when growing unease with air pollution problems became evident in the UK's own towns and cities. "Many of the local air-quality problems in the southern United Kingdom related to particulate matter and ozone, and in the mid-1990s it was demonstrated that about half of the ozone in the United Kingdom actually originated in other European countries. The fact that much of the United Kingdom's pollution came from outside of its borders made the country more supportive of international regulation [of emissions]" (Wettestad, "Clearing the Air," 2002).

In the meantime, other European nations acted to reduce their own emissions of pollutants responsible for acidification, both individually and in concert with other nations. For example, many Western European nations have participated in a series of international conventions and protocols on reducing transboundary air pollution, the most recent being the 1999 Convention on Long-Range Transboundary Air Pollution (CLRTAP), also known as the Gothenberg Protocol. These conventions have established ambitious emission reduction goals for sulfur dioxide, nitrous oxides, and other pollutants.

These varied efforts have paid measurable dividends. The member states of the European Union have reduced their emissions of sulfur dioxide—the leading cause of acid rain and a health hazard for children, the elderly, and those with respiratory illnesses—by 70 percent since 1980, with emissions of all acidifying gases falling by 32 percent between 1990 and 1998. Thirteen European countries cut their sulfur dioxide emissions by more than 50 percent, and Austria and Sweden both made reductions of more than 80 percent between 1980 and 1993. In 2001 researchers announced that acid rain deposition in the United Kingdom had been cut in half from 1980 to 2000 (National Expert Group on Transboundary Air Pollution, *Transboundary Air Pollution,* 2001). This success—attributed to increased reliance on natural gas and renewables over coal and other fuels with high sulfur content, economic restructuring in Germany, and the introduction of new desulfurization technology in some power plants—has improved environmental conditions across wide swaths of the continent (European Environment Agency, *Environmental Signals 2001,* 2001; UN Environment Programme, *Environmental Data Report 1993–94,* 1993).

However, Europe has enjoyed only limited success in reducing its emissions of nitrous oxides, another major component in the formation of acid rain. According to the European Environment Agency, total nitrous emissions (nitrous oxides plus ammonia) in Europe remained unchanged through the 1980s, and while total emissions declined by about 15 percent between 1990 and 1995, most of the reduction was traced to closures of major polluting factories in Eastern Europe in the aftermath of the Soviet Union's demise. Indeed, a dozen European countries posted increases in nitrous oxide emissions of between 15 and 40 percent from 1980 to 1993 (McCormick, *Acid Earth,* 1997).

Europe's inability to make meaningful reductions in its emissions of nitrous oxide is primarily due to the continent's ever-growing appetite for private car ownership and use. "For nitrogen oxide emissions by transport, environmental policy has not kept up with growth in transport use," admitted the European Environment Agency. "The growth in numbers and use of cars is offsetting the benefits of technical improvements such as the increased use of cleaner engines and exhaust catalysts in passenger cars. This has resulted in the transport sector becoming the dominant contributor to emissions of nitrogen oxides. The large potential for growth in private transport in CEE [Central and Eastern Europe] and in the NIS [Newly Independent States of the former Soviet Union] is likely to exacerbate the problem" (European Environment Agency, *Europe's Environment,* 1998).

Today, about 10 percent of Europe's total land area is still suffering excessive levels of acid deposition. But efforts to further reduce emissions of pollutants responsible for acid rain—and restore acid-damaged lakes and woodlands to their former glory—have been impeded by public perceptions that the issue has been adequately addressed (a perception fed by meager news media coverage in recent years) and by public and industry resistance to paying for new abatement measures. "Unfortunately, while the costs of remedial action [to combat acidification] are relatively easy to estimate, it is difficult to put a precise value on those of acidified forests and lakes, dead animals and plants, corroded buildings, or impaired human health" (McCormick, "Acid Pollution," 1998). However, states in Northern Europe continue to support major acid rain prevention and treatment programs, and proliferating domestic and international initiatives to curb greenhouse gases may have the welcome side-effect of reducing acid deposition as well.

Ozone Concentrations Create Smog Conditions

Whereas Europe has lost ozone density in the stratosphere in recent decades, concentrations of ozone in the troposphere—the layer of the atmosphere from the ground to about 10 miles above the surface—are about three to four times that of preindustrial Europe (UN Environment Programme, *Global Environment Outlook 2000,* 1999). These heightened levels of ozone concentration are decidedly unwelcome, for ozone in the lower atmosphere is a poison that kills trees and other vegetation and damages the respiratory system of humans and other life forms. Moreover, tropospheric ozone is a major greenhouse gas that contributes to global climate change.

Europe has enjoyed some success in reducing its emission of "ozone precursors"—substances that increase the level of ozone in cities, valleys, and other surface zones. Europe as a whole reduced its emissions of ozone precursors by 14 percent between 1990 and 1995. The European Union states, meanwhile, reduced their total emissions by approximately 22 percent between 1990 and 1998, using improvements in transportation technology and new solvent regulations imposed on the industry sector to more than compensate for increased traffic volume (European Environment Agency, *Environmental Signals 2001,* 2001).

But while these reductions have relieved ozone buildup in some areas, authorities note that many Europeans continue to reside in areas that exceed suggested World Health Organization air quality safety levels. High tropospheric ozone concentrations typically manifest themselves in the form of smog, which dogs many European cities. Periodic winter smog incidents impact an estimated 25 million people annually, and smog is a grim reality all summer long in many European metropolitan areas. Indeed, in 1999 an estimated 42 percent of the continent's population was exposed to concentrations above the limit level on between one and twenty-five days, and 12 percent on more than fifty days. Only Portugal and the nations of Northern Europe managed to limit their annual number of such days to less than ten (ibid.).

Clearly, further reductions of tropospheric ozone-generating substances will be necessary for Europe to get its smog problem under control. Measures such as the Gothenburg Protocol—which among other things calls for the EU to halve its emissions of nitrous oxides from 1990 levels by 2010—and the National Emission Ceilings Directive (NECD) will be vital to those efforts.

LRTP Pollutants

Reducing transboundary air pollution is another important element of Europe's overall efforts to improve air quality. This focus reflects a recognition that even the continent's remote Arctic regions have become scarred by pollutants generated hundreds or even thousands of miles away. "Airborne pollutants have turned the Arctic into a 'sink' for contaminants from all over the world," confirmed the World Resources Institute (WRI). "Persistent organic pollutants

Indoor Air Quality

When most people think about air pollution, they tend to picture factory smokestacks, automobile tailpipes, and vistas clouded by smog. But air pollution is also a serious problem indoors—within the homes, office buildings, and shopping malls where people spend up to 90 percent of their time. In fact, the concentration of pollutants can reach much higher levels indoors than outdoors because there are no natural air currents to disperse them. The problem has been compounded in recent years by the airtight construction of newer homes and office buildings, as well as the increased use of materials like particle board and synthetic carpeting, which contain high levels of chemicals that continue to be released for years after installation.

Some of the most common indoor air pollutants include tobacco smoke; volatile organic compounds such as formaldehyde, which are released from carpets, furniture, and building materials or contained in pesticides and household cleaners; radon, a naturally occurring gas that seeps upward from the soil in some areas and can enter the foundations of buildings; asbestos, a fibrous material once commonly used in insulation; emissions from combustion appliances, such as gas stoves, wood stoves, fireplaces, and even candles; biologic contaminants such as mold, mildew, bacteria, and viruses; and outdoor air pollutants that enter dwellings from windows or ventilation systems and become trapped. As people inhale these substances, it triggers defense mechanisms such as coughing and sneezing. Eventually, as the defense mechanisms become overwhelmed through chronic exposure, the pollutants can destroy tissue and cause disease or even death.

Although national governments around the world have spent decades monitoring outdoor air quality and developing pollution standards, indoor air quality is a relatively new issue that is only beginning to be recognized and addressed. In the United States, the Environmental Protection Agency ranked indoor air pollution among the top five environmental risks to public health in recent years (Meyer, "Every Breath We Take," 1999). At the same time, however, the government has made little progress in addressing the problem because several different agencies share statutory jurisdiction over it. Some measures that have been put in place in an attempt to improve indoor air quality in the United States include voluntary industry codes, product safety standards, and guidelines for dealing with radon and handling asbestos.

Experts recommend a number of steps that individuals and businesses can take to help improve the indoor air quality in their homes and offices. For example, they should restrict smoking to outdoors; encapsulate or remove asbestos; test for radon and take

(continues)

remediation steps if necessary; reduce humidity and prevent leaks to make the indoor climate inhospitable for biologic contaminants; properly maintain cooking and heating equipment to eliminate the buildup of fumes; avoid the use of toxic cleaners; and open windows whenever possible or improve ventilation by installing an air filter or cleaning device.

Another option to address indoor air quality is to incorporate natural ventilation into new commercial and residential structures. Natural ventilation—which involves systems of windows, vents, wind scoops, wind towers, and fans designed to bring outside air into structures—has become fairly common in Europe and is gaining popularity in the United States and other regions. Natural ventilation offers several benefits, including improved indoor air quality, a 25 to 40 percent reduction in energy costs, and greater occupant satisfaction because of increased daylight and control of temperature (Jones and West, "Natural Ventilation and Collaborative Design," 2001).

There are a number of notable examples of European buildings that have incorporated natural ventilation into their design. For example, the RWE AG building in Essen, Germany, is a multistory office building with a cylindrical shape that allows natural air currents to enter. The Bluewater Shopping Center in Dartford, England, is a mall that was designed with large wind scoops that provide a fresh natural breeze along the concourse. The Queens Building at De Montfort University in Leicester, England, uses cross ventilation and wind towers and has become known as one of the coolest buildings on campus in hot weather. Finally, the World Trade Center in Amsterdam, Netherlands, is a convention center with a waveform roof that permits natural ventilation.

Although natural ventilation is well suited to a wide variety of structures, experts suggest that it works best when the building site is open or when nearby buildings or land forms funnel breezes toward it. It is also limited to regions of the world where average outdoor conditions fall in the thermal comfort range during the cooling season. In order to be used successfully, natural ventilation should be incorporated into new buildings during the design phase (ibid.).

Sources:

Hansen, David. 1999. *Indoor Air Quality Issues.* New York: Taylor and Francis.

Jones, Jim, and Aaron W. West. 2001. "Natural Ventilation and Collaborative Design." *ASHRAE Journal* 43 (November).

Maroni, Marco, Thomas Lindvall, and Bernd Seifert, eds. 1995. *Indoor Air Quality: A Comprehensive Reference Book.* Amsterdam: Elsevier.

Meyer, Pamela, David Mannino, and David Homa." 1999. "Every Breath We Take." *Forum for Applied Research and Public Policy* 14 (winter).

O'Neil, Kathleen. 2000. "The Inside Scoop." *E: The Environmental Magazine* 11 (November–December).

(POPs) and other toxic chemicals travel on air, water, and wind currents until they settle in the Arctic, where they bioaccumulate in the food chain. Radioactive materials have also accumulated in the Arctic; sources are fall-out from nuclear bomb tests, the accident at Chernoybl, and releases from European nuclear fuel reprocessing plants. . . . The effects of POPs on wildlife are not fully understood, but it is clear that the biomagnification effects on certain species—birds, seals, polar bears, and others at the top of the food chain—are grave and will continue to worsen" (World Resources Institute, *World Resources 2000–2001*, 2000).

Efforts to reduce the impact of Long-Range Transmission of Air Pollutants (LRTPs) on Arctic ecosystems and other regions range from domestic programs undertaken by single states to EU-wide and international agreements. The first major multilateral agreement in this arena was the 1979 Convention on Long-Range Transboundary Air Pollution (CLRTAP), which was passed by the UN Economic Commission for Europe (UNECE). The UNECE—composed primarily of European countries but also of the United States, Canada, and other industrialized nations—has since passed eight additional protocols to the 1979 convention. Together, these protocols represent the world's largest international set of agreements on transported air pollution to date. UNECE nations have agreed to limits on emissions of sulfur dioxide (1987, 1994, 1999), nitrous oxides (1991, 1999), volatile organic compounds—VOCs (1997, 1999), heavy metals (1998), POPs (1998), and ammonia (1999).

The most recent protocol in this area was the December 1999 Gothenburg Protocol, a comprehensive agreement to limit the export of pollutants that cause acid rain, tropospheric ozone, and other environmental problems. Indeed, this convention calls for Europe to pare back its emissions of sulfur dioxide, nitrous oxides, VOCs, and ammonia to 1990 levels by 2010.

The Gothenburg Protocol has not been signed by Russia, Ukraine, and a number of other significant polluters (although Poland signed in May 2000), but it still constitutes a potent symbol of Europe's commitment to reining in environmentally destructive emissions. "The European parties to this accord [agreed] that new emissions reductions should be mandated in the agreement based on the levels necessary to protect human health and ecosystems in specific downwind areas. That presents a departure from other international agreements, which have been based on countries' reducing emissions by a percentage that they deem economically or technically feasible" (Reuther, "Winds of Change," 2000).

Several other programs designed to address air pollution problems have also been unveiled by the European Union in recent years. In 1998, for instance, the EU launched a Clean Air for Europe (CAFE) Programme meant to encourage greater integration of emission concerns into other policy areas and among all states. Under the CAFE timetable, a comprehensive blueprint for realizing significant reductions in air pollution will be in place by 2004. In September 2001, meanwhile, the EU adopted a National Emission Ceilings Directive (NECD) that complements the Gothenburg Protocol. The NECD aims for an overall 63 percent cut of sulfur dioxide emissions and 40 percent cuts in nitrous oxide, VOC, and ammonia emissions by 2010.

In 2001, meanwhile, delegates from 122 countries reached agreement on a pact calling for a worldwide phaseout of the twelve worst persistent organic pollutants. The treaty covers dioxin, PCBs, DDT, aldrin, chlordane, dieldrin, endrin, heptachlor, mirex, toxaphene, hexachlorobenzene, and furans, and it will go into effect after fifty nations ratify it.

Environmentalists, scientists, and policy-makers all acknowledge that even if these gains are realized, acid deposition and ground-level ozone will continue to bedevil some European communities and ecosystems. But these policies—if fully implemented—will nonetheless substantially reduce the gap between present levels of acid deposition and critical loads by 2010, and since several of the air pollutants targeted in the Gothenburg Protocol and the NECD are also greenhouse gases, these instruments will also help Europe in its grim struggle to meet the threat of accelerating global climate change (Wettestad, "Clearing the Air," 2002).

Atmospheric Issues

Europe and the Ozone Layer

Protection of the stratospheric ozone layer from ozone-depleting chemicals is another environmental priority in Europe. Efforts to preserve the ozone layer from thinning and loss are critically important for several reasons. First, ozone in the stratosphere (between 6 and 30 miles above the surface) protects earth's life from the full force of the sun's ultraviolet radiation, which is a cancer-causing agent. But other negative impacts associated with increased exposure to ultraviolet radiation include damage to valuable food crops and other vegetation and declines in plankton, a vital link in the world's marine food chain. These losses can in turn lead to escalating levels of carbon dioxide, the primary cause of global warming, and prompt dramatic changes in the character of regional ecosystems.

Europe—which lost an estimated 5 percent of its ozone layer between 1975 and 1995—and other industrialized nations have already taken significant steps to protect the ozone layer from ozone-depleting chemicals. Chlorofluorocarbons (CFCs)—chiefly chlorine-laced chemicals used in refrigerants and aerosol sprays—were banned across much of the world with the passage of the 1987 Montreal Protocol on Substances that Deplete the Ozone Layer and its subsequent extensions. In 1995 more than 100 countries agreed to end their use of the pesticide methyl bromide, another major cause of ozone depletion. And in 2002 the European Union formally adopted a law that requires member countries to ensure that ozone levels do not exceed World Health Organization standards more than twenty-five times annually. But while implementation of various multilateral environmental agreements over the past two decades has reduced Europe's—and the world's—total production and emission of ozone-depleting substances by an estimated 80–90 percent, experts caution that full recovery of the stratospheric ozone layer will be slowed by the lingering presence of CFCs, methyl bromide, and other contaminants in the upper atmosphere (European Environment Agency, *Europe's Environment,* 1998).

Researchers also point out that use of hydrochlorofluorocarbons (HCFCs)—a substitute for CFCs—is increasing in Europe and other areas of the world. These substances are not as damaging to the ozone layer as CFCs, but they are still greenhouse gases that constitute a threat to the long-term integrity of the earth's atmosphere. Any effective ozone protection program will require curbs on usage of HCFCs in Europe and elsewhere. Current multilateral environmental agreements call for a global phaseout of HCFCs over the next two decades.

Efforts to reduce global dependence on HCFCs and other ozone-depleting substances (such as nitrous oxides and CFCs, which are still produced in some developing nations) are particularly important to Antarctica and the northern Arctic, since ozone loss has been most severe at the world's poles. Both of these polar regions have seen massive "holes" develop in their ozone layers in the past two decades. In September 2001, the size of the Antarctic hole was estimated at 9.8 million square miles (25.4 million square kilometers). European nations with significant holdings above the Arctic Circle, including the Russian Federation, Greenland (a protectorate of Denmark), Norway, Sweden, and Finland, fear that increased exposure to ultraviolet radiation could do extensive and permanent damage to marine and terrestrial ecosystems and spark epidemics of skin cancer and cataracts in northern communities (UN Environment Programme, *Scientific Assessment of Ozone Depletion,* 1998). Fortunately, scientific evidence suggests that the global response to ozone depletion may be stabilizing ozone levels in the upper atmosphere, including areas above the Antarctic and Arctic regions.

Grappling with Climate Change

At the same time that airborne pollution degrades the air upon which the earth's people, plants, and animals depend, it also is transforming the planet's atmosphere so that it takes on greater insulating properties. Under this "greenhouse effect," the sun's heat is trapped in the atmosphere under an ever-growing blanket of "greenhouse gases." The main source of these gases—which include carbon dioxide, nitrous oxide, methane, CFCs, and HCFCs—is human activity, specifically the burning of oil, gas, and coal to operate cars, trucks, airplanes, and power plants. This burning of fossil fuel generates huge quantities of carbon dioxide, the main greenhouse gas. Lesser sources of greenhouse gases include methane emissions from cattle and landfills, nitrous oxides from agricultural fields, emissions of fluorinated gases from industry, emissions of carbon dioxide from volcanic activity, and releases of carbon dioxide from "slash-and-burn" deforestation (forests are significant repositories of carbon dioxide) (European Commission, *Environment 2010,* 2001).

If left unchecked, the earth's accelerating retention of greenhouse gases in the atmosphere will fundamentally transform the planet. Probable elements of this transformation include rising temperatures, increasingly severe and numerous storm events, altered rain and snowfall patterns that will bring greater incidence of flooding and drought, inundation of islands and coastal areas by rising sea levels (precipitated by melting glaciers and polar ice caps), expansion of malaria and other tropical diseases into previously temperate zones, and possible mass extinctions of species of flora and fauna.

Several of these manifestations of global warming are already apparent, such as polar melting and rising temperatures (according to the UN's Intergovernmental Panel on Climate Change, nine of the world's ten hottest years in recorded history occurred between 1990 and 2000). Other consequences are expected to become more evident in the next half-century. And while some of these sweeping changes may prove beneficial in certain respects to some regions (by transforming arid and semiarid areas into productive farmland, for example), many of the consequences are expected to be devastating for people and ecosystems around the world. With this in mind, a host of international and state-sponsored programs and initiatives were launched during the 1990s to reduce greenhouse gas emissions, the root cause of climate change. "We do not have the usual option of seeking definitive empirical evidence before acting [against global warming]," concluded one joint panel of the WHO, World Meteorological Organization, and the UN Environment Programme. "A wait-and-see approach would be imprudent at best and nonsensical at worst" (McMichael et al., *Climate Change and Health,* 1996).

According to the Intergovernmental Panel on Climate Change (IPCC), the world's most authoritative scientific voice on climate change, the planet will warm by an unprecedented 2.5 to 10 degrees Fahrenheit during the twenty-first century without major reductions in greenhouse gas emissions. The IPCC already estimates that the average temperature in Europe increased by as much as 0.8 degree Celsius in the twentieth century, with the continent's northern reaches becoming wetter and its southern states becoming even more arid (Intergovernmental Panel on Climate Change, *Climate Change 2001: Summaries,* 2001).

Both of these trends, if left unchecked, would have tremendous consequences for major economic sectors such as tourism, agriculture, and forestry. It would also alter the character of Europe's rivers, lakes, woodlands, marshes, and other natural areas, triggering dramatic change in the fortunes of countless species of flora and fauna. For example, climate change may come so quickly that plant and animal species in different climatic zones will be unable to survive in their old habitats or migrate to areas that can meet their nutritional and breeding requirements. These extinctions will not only reduce European biodiversity—which is already under enormous pressure on other fronts—but also disrupt delicately balanced ecosystems, which will in turn trigger surges and crashes in the populations of other species (European Commission, *Environment 2010,* 2001).

Among developed nations, though, the states of Western Europe have shown the greatest willingness to address the issue of climate change. The European Union, for example, has been one of the most visible proponents of the 1997 Kyoto Protocol. This UN-sponsored international agreement seeks to address the threat of global warming by calling on developed nations to reduce their emissions of greenhouse gases to at least 5 percent below 1990 emission levels between 2008 and 2012 (the treaty calls for EU states to make even greater reductions). Western Europe's strong pro-Kyoto stance reflects the EU's belief that climate change is fast-emerging as "the dominant environmental issue of the 21st century" (European Environment Agency, *Environmental Signals 2001,* 2000). But analysts concede that Kyoto constitutes only a first step in combating global warming. Moreover, prevailing trends of energy consumption and emissions in Europe suggest that meeting its Kyoto obligations will be no easy task. "Overall, achieving sustainable levels of environmental pressure and use of resources is likely to require major technological advances and major shifts to less resource-intensive and environmentally harmful activities," acknowledges the European Environment Agency (*Europe's Environment,* 1998).

Declining Emissions in Europe

Historically, Europe has been one of the world's leading generators of carbon dioxide, the single most important greenhouse gas. Over the course of the twentieth century, it is estimated that the continent accounted for 21 percent of cumulative global carbon emissions from industrial sources and land-use changes (Carbon Dioxide Information Analysis Center, *Trends,* 2000), and in 1996 Europe accounted for 6.124 billion metric tons of the world's total output

Automobiles are a major source of greenhouse gases in Europe. BOSSU REGIS/CORBIS SYGMA

of 23.88 billion metric tons of carbon dioxide. Leading producers of carbon dioxide in Europe included Russia (1.58 billion metric tons), Germany (861 million metric tons), the United Kingdom (557 million metric tons), Italy (403 million metric tons), and Ukraine (397 million metric tons) (Carbon Dioxide Information Analysis Center, *Global ... Fossil Fuel Burning,* 1999).

But Europe is the only continent on the planet in which per capita emissions of carbon dioxide have actually declined over the past twenty years. Moreover, numerous countries, including Denmark, France, Germany, the Netherlands, and the United Kingdom, adopted comprehensive national programs in 1999 or 2000 to further reduce greenhouse gas emissions, and several member states have instituted energy taxes to encourage greater use of "green" power sources.

In addition, the European Union has produced an array of global warming policies and measures that are binding on its member states. These include minimum energy efficiency standards for manufacturers and importers of appliances; a negotiated agreement between the European Commission and the European automobile industry to reduce carbon dioxide emissions from new passenger cars by 25 percent between 1995 and 2008; implementation of the Integrated Pollution Prevention and Control (IPPC) Directive, which mandates use of best available technology in energy efficiency and other areas;

Figure 9.1 Total CO_2 Contribution, 1950–1996 (as a Percent of Global CO_2 Emissions)

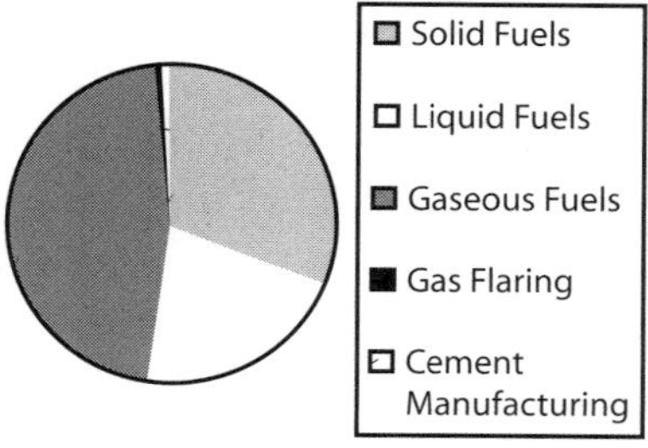

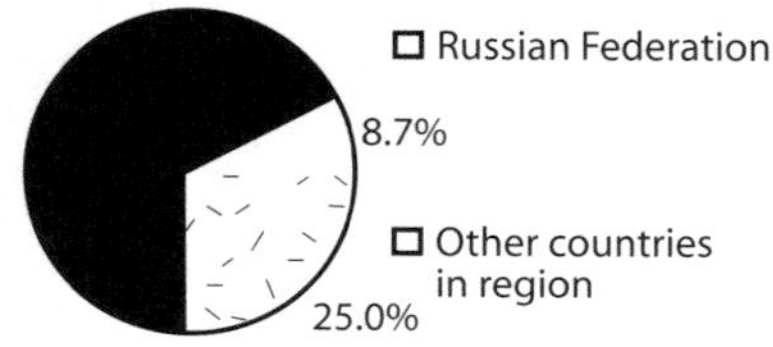

SOURCE: EarthTrends 2001. World Resources Institute.

and passage of the Landfill Directive, which provides for greater collection of landfill gas for energy use while simultaneously reducing methane emissions by cutting the amount of organic waste deposited in landfills (European Environment Agency, *Environmental Signals 2001*, 2001).

All of these measures are expected to help Europe reduce its volume of greenhouse gas emissions in those areas that have thus far been targeted. But they may go for naught if the continent fails to significantly reduce its releases of carbon dioxide in the transportation and utility sectors. Carbon dioxide, generated by fossil fuel combustion, currently accounts for 81 percent of Europe's total greenhouse gas emissions. Other greenhouse gases generated in Europe include methane (9 percent), nitrous oxide (9 percent), and fluorinated gases (1 percent) (ibid.).

Thus far, Europe has had only limited success in reducing its emissions of carbon dioxide, although some individual states have made impressive strides. In 2001, for instance, the United Kingdom reduced its output of greenhouse gases to a ten-year low as a new generation of clean-burning gas power stations came on line, replacing older plants fueled by coal and oil, both of which produce large amounts of carbon dioxide. At the continental level, emissions of carbon dioxide fell by 12 percent between 1990 and 1995 as Western European countries shifted from coal to natural gas for electricity generation and notoriously dirty Eastern European factories shut their doors (European Environment Agency, *Europe's Environment,* 1998). But increased economic activity in Central and Eastern Europe, where environmentally sustainable business and policy practices are being introduced fitfully, may negate some or all of these gains. Moreover, increased traffic volumes, coupled with minimal improvements in fuel efficiency, pushed total EU carbon dioxide emissions up by 3 percent between 1994 and 1998 (European Environment Agency, *Environmental Signals 2001,* 2001).

European nations have had far greater success in reducing methane emissions. Output of this greenhouse gas fell by a total of 40 percent between 1980 and 1995 among the nations of Central and Eastern Europe, including former satellites of the Soviet Union (European Environment Agency, *Europe's Environment,* 1998). Meanwhile, the EU reduced its emissions of methane by 17 percent between 1990 and 1998, primarily because of reductions in livestock and improved landfill emission controls (European Environment Agency, *Environmental Signals 2001,* 2000). Emissions of CFCs have also declined dramatically throughout Europe, and by 1998, EU states had reduced their emissions of nitrous oxide 10 percent from 1990 levels. But reliance on HCFCs, the class of chemicals that replaced CFCs in industrial processes, remains strong.

Europe and the Kyoto Protocol

The Kyoto Protocol is a 1997 UN-brokered agreement that calls on developed nations to reduce their emissions of greenhouse gases to at least 5 percent below 1990 emission levels between 2008 and 2012. The protocol enters into force when it has been ratified by at least fifty-five parties to the convention, including developed countries accounting for at least 55 percent of carbon dioxide emissions from this group in 1990.

Among developed nations, the states of the European Union have emerged as the protocol's most vocal champions. Ultimately, the region's leadership has determined that climate change constitutes a threat of such severity that it trumps all other considerations, including potential negative impact of abatement measures on economic growth and energy security. In fact, during the Kyoto negotiations, most of Western Europe agreed to seek an 8 percent reduction in greenhouse gas emissions below 1990 levels by 2010 (Kyoto requires only a 5 percent reduction). Other countries in Central and Eastern Europe, meanwhile, committed themselves to reductions of between 5 and 8 percent, while the Russian Federation and the Ukraine agreed to stabilize their emissions at 1990 levels.

In May 2002 all fifteen European Union nations ratified the Kyoto Protocol as a single voting bloc. As a vocal advocate of the Kyoto Protocol, the EU has been sharply critical of the U.S. decision to opt out of the agreement. Indeed, much of Europe sees the U.S. decision as an abdication of responsibility for its role in global warming (the United States accounts for one-quarter of all greenhouse gases generated on the planet) and a serious impediment to reining in worldwide emissions. But despite its disappointment with the U.S. stance, Europe is forging ahead to meet its Kyoto obligations.

Reaching its stated emission reduction goals, however, has proven difficult. Many Kyoto targets for Europe's "accession" countries—those seeking membership in the EU—were met by the late 1990s, but those emission reductions stemmed primarily from economic recession rather than new abatement measures, and analysts fear that soaring rates of private ownership of cars in Central and Eastern Europe, combined with new investment in the industrial sector, will produce a resurgence of greenhouse gas emissions. In the EU, meanwhile, some studies carried out at the close of the twentieth century indicated that EU abatement policies and measures would produce only a 1 percent drop in total greenhouse gas emissions by 2010 from 1990 levels, and that EU emissions of carbon dioxide—the most prevalent greenhouse gas—might increase by 3 to 8 percent during that time period (European Commission, *Report … for a Monitoring Mechanism of Community Greenhouse Gas Emissions,* 2000; Commission of the European Communities, *Council Conclusions on Climate Change,* 1998). The forecasted increase in carbon dioxide emissions is directly related to the rapid expansion of automobile use in Western Europe, where rates of private auto ownership are rising and new roadways are proliferating.

As a result, Europe is continuing to explore various means by which it can further reduce emissions. Options currently being investigated—and implemented in some states—include new energy consumption taxes, which would provide households, businesses, and governments with incentives to embrace energy conservation. Another proposal would eliminate subsidies for fossil fuels such as coal and diesel, which are major sources of greenhouse gases. In fact, a coalition of environmental campaign groups operating under the banner of the European Environmental Bureau (EEB) has repeatedly urged EU states to phase out all environmentally harmful subsidies to industry, transport, and agriculture and shift the savings to renewable energy development. "If you focused on one single issue that would be important for the future [of Europe], it would, of course, be to get away from the environmentally unsound subsidies and to replace them with environmentally sound incentives," stated Kjell Larsson, Sweden's environment minister. "As long as we subsidize, for example, the mining of coal, it will be extremely difficult for green energy to break through in the marketplace" (Peltola, "Sweden Says Subsidies Endangering Environment," 2002).

Table 9.2 Change in Greenhouse Gas Emissions since 1990 and the Kyoto Protocol Target or the EU Burden Sharing Agreement (Excluding Land-Use Change and Forestry)

Country	*Actual emission trend (% change 1990–1998)*	*Kyoto Protocol target/EU burden sharing 2008–2012 (% from 1990)*	*1998 total greenhouse gas emissions (tonnes per capita)*	*1998 carbon dioxide emissions (tonnes per capita)*
Austria	6	−13.0	10	8
Belgium	7	−7.5	14	12
Denmark	9	−21.0	14	11
Finland	6	0.0	15	12
France	1	0.0	9	7
Germany	−16	−21.0	12	11
Greece	15	25	11	10
Ireland	20	13	17	11
Italy	5	−6.5	9	8
Luxembourg	−58	−28	14	12
Netherlands	8	−6.0	15	12
Portugal	18	27	7	5
Spain	21	15	9	7
Sweden	1	4.0	8	6
United Kingdom	−9	−12.5	11	9
EU Total	*−2*	*−8.0*	*11*	*9*

SOURCE: UNFCCC, EEA.

NOTES: All six Kyoto Protocol gases are included, but fluorinated gas emissions are indicative. Base year is assumed to be 1990 for all gases (except for fluorinated gases, where it is 1995). Emissions from Denmark are not adjusted for electricity trade. Emissions and removals ("sinks") due to land-use change and forestry (LUCF) are excluded because of major uncertainty in their estimates and because no decisions have yet been taken which LUCF activities can be included to meet the Kyoto Protocol targets.

But mustering the political will to erase these subsidies is a challenge. In 2002, for example, EU member states cobbled together an energy agreement that enabled Germany to continue handing out subsidies to coal miners in exchange for allowing other nations to subsidize truck fuel. This trade-off satisfied various national interests but did nothing to further the cause of greenhouse gas reduction. Indeed, Europe's environmental community charged that the agreement exposed a chasm between EU rhetoric and actions in addressing the threat of climate change.

For their part, European environmental ministers and agencies acknowledge that additional steps need to be taken. "Achieving the Kyoto Protocol target for greenhouse gas emissions for the EU and the Member States will require substantial further reductions, particularly in carbon dioxide emissions," stated the European Environment Agency. "However, energy and transport demands, and the associated carbon dioxide emissions, are likely to continue to increase. It is unlikely that current measures, including improvements of energy efficiency and increasing the share of renewable sources of energy, will achieve enough to offset these increases. Major policy changes will be needed beyond the Kyoto target dates (2008–2012) if sustainable development is not to be seriously jeopardised by climate change" (European Environment Agency, *Environmental Signals 2001,* 2001).

Indeed, even Europe's most committed Kyoto advocates acknowledge that halting global warming trends will ultimately require far greater emission reductions than those set in the 1997 protocol. Climate change experts contend that the world will ultimately have to reduce its emissions of greenhouse gases by as much as 70 percent from 1990 levels if it hopes to meet "provisional limits for sustainability" of a 0.1 degree Celsius temperature increase per decade and 2-cm sea level rise per decade (European Environment Agency, *Europe's Environment: The Second Assessment,* 1998; European Environment Agency, *Environmental Signals 2001,* 2001).

Sources:

Austin, D., and R. Repetto. 1997. *The Costs of Climate Protection: A Guide for the Perplexed.* Washington, DC: World Resources Institute.

Baumert, Kevin A., and Nancy Kete. 2001. *The United States, Developing Countries, and Climate Protection: Leadership or Stalemate.* Edited by Christian Layke and Wendy Vanasselt. Washington, DC: World Resources Institute.

Brown, Valerie J. 1999. "The Worst of Both Worlds: Poverty and Politics in the Balkans." *Environmental Health Perspectives* 107 (December).

Bunyard, Peter. 1999. "How Global Warming Could Cause Northern Europe to Freeze." *Ecologist* 29 (March–April).

Carbon Dioxide Information Analysis Center. 1999. *Global, Regional, and National Annual CO2 Emissions from Fossil-Fuel Burning, Hydraulic Cement Production, and Gas Flaring: 1951–1996.* Oak Ridge, TN: Oak Ridge National Laboratory.

———. 2000. *Trends: A Compendium of Data on Global Change.* Oak Ridge, TN: Oak Ridge National Library, DOE.

Commission of the European Communities. 1998. *Council Conclusions on Climate Change.* Brussels: Commission of the European Communities.

Downie, David. 1993. "Comparative Public Policy of Ozone Layer Protection." *Political Science* 45 (December).

———. 2002. "Global POPs Policy: The 2001 Stockholm Convention on Persistent Organic Pollutants." In David L. Downie and Terry Fenge, eds., *Northern Lights against POPs: Combating Global Toxic Threats at the Top of the World.* Montreal: McGill-Queens.

EMEP—Co-Operative Programme for Monitoring and Evaluation of the Long-Range Transmission of Air Pollutants in Europe. 1998. *1998 Major Review of Strategies and Policies for Air Pollution Abatement.* Report No. ECE/EB.AIR/65. http://www.emep.int/emis_tables/tab1.html.

Energy Information Administration. 1999. *International Energy Annual 1999.* Washington, DC: EIA.

———. 2001. *International Energy Outlook 2001.* Washington, DC: EIA.

European Commission. 1996. *Energy in Europe: European Energy 2020: A Scenario Approach.* Brussels: EC.

———. 1997. *Towards Sustainability.* Brussels: EC.

———. 2000. *Energising Europe.* Brussels: EC.

———. 2000. *Report under Council Decision 1999/296/EC for a Monitoring Mechanism of Community Greenhouse Gas Emissions.* Brussels: EC.

———. 2001. *Environment 2010: Our Future, Our Choice.* Brussels: EC.

European Council. 1999. *Strategy on the Integration of Environment and Sustainable Development into the Transport Policy.* Strasbourg, France: European Council.

European Environment Agency. 1995. *Europe's Environment: The Dobris Assessment.* Copenhagen: EEA.

———. 1998. *Europe's Environment: The Second Assessment.* Copenhagen: EEA.

———. 1999. *Environment in the European Union at the Turn of the Century.* Copenhagen: EEA.

———. 2000. *Are We Moving in the Right Direction? Indicators on Transport and Environment Integration in the EU.* Copenhagen: EEA.

———. 2001. *Environmental Signals 2001.* Copenhagen: EEA.

Gelbspan, Ross. 1997. *The Heat is On: The High Stakes Battle over Earth's Threatened Climate.* Reading, MA: Addison-Wesley.

Intergovernmental Panel on Climate Change. 2000. *The Regional Impacts of Climate Change: An Assessment of Vulnerability.* Geneva: IPCC.

———. 2001. *Climate Change 2001: Mitigation, Impacts, Adaptation, and Vulnerability: Summaries for Policymakers.* Geneva: IPCC.

———. 2001. *Climate Change 2001: The Scientific Basis.* Geneva: IPCC.

International Energy Agency. 2000. *Energy Policies of IEA Countries: 2000 Review.* Paris: OECD/IEA.

———. 2002. *Russia Energy Survey 2002.* Paris: IEA.

Martens, Willem J. M., et al. 1995. "Potential Impact of Global Climate Change on Malaria Risk." *Environmental Health Perspectives* 103 (May).

McCormick, John. 1997. *Acid Earth: The Politics of Acid Pollution.* 3d ed. London: Earthscan.

———. 1998. "Acid Pollution: The International Community's Continuing Struggle." *Environment* 40 (April).

McMichael, A. J., A. Haines, R. Slooff, and S. Kovats, eds. 1996. *Climate Change and Health: An Assessment Prepared by a Task Group on Behalf of the World Health Organization, the World Meteorological Organization and the United Nations Environment Programme.* Geneva: World Health Organization.

Moe, Arilde. 2000. *The Kyoto Mechanisms and Russian Climate Politics.* London: Royal Institute of International Affairs, Energy and Environment Programme.

National Expert Group on Transboundary Air Pollution. 2001. *Transboundary Air Pollution: Acidification, Eutrophication, and Ground-Level Ozone in the UK.* National Expert Group on Transboundary Air Pollution.

National Intelligence Council. 1997. *The Environmental Outlook in Central and Eastern Europe.* Washington, DC: NIC, December.

Nierenberg, Danielle. 2000. "Russia Axes Its Environmental Agency." *WorldWatch* 13 (September/October).

Nilsson, Annika. 1996. *Ultraviolet Reflections: Life under a Thinning Ozone Layer.* New York: Wiley.

Nilsson, Sten, and David Pitt. 1992. *Mountain World in Danger: Climate Change in the Mountains and Forests of Europe.* London: Earthscan.

Organization for Economic Cooperation and Development Environmental Directorate. 1977. *OECD Programme on Long-Range Transport of Air Pollutants: Summary Report.* Paris: OECD.

Peltola, Anna. 2002. "Sweden Says Subsidies Endangering Environment." Reuters News Agency, May 24.

Reuther, Christopher G. 2000. "Winds of Change: Reducing Transboundary Air Pollutants." *Environmental Health Perspectives* 108 (April).

UN Economic Commission for Europe. 1995. *Strategies and Policies for Air Pollution Abatement.* New York and Geneva: UN.

UN Environment Programme. 1993. *Environmental Data Report 1993–94.* Oxford: Blackwell.

———. 1999. *Global Environment Outlook 2000.* London: Earthscan.

———. 1999. *Synthesis of the Reports of the Scientific, Environmental Effects and Technology and Economic Assessment Panels of the Montreal Protocol.* Geneva: UNEP.

Wettestad, Jorgen. 2002. "Clearing the Air: Europe Tackles Transboundary Pollution." *Environment* 44 (March).

World Meteorological Organization, National Oceanic and Atmospheric Administration, National Aeronautics and Space Administration, and European Commission. 1998. *Scientific Assessment of Ozone Depletion: 1998.* Geneva: UNEP.

World Resources Institute. 2000. *World Resources 2000–2001, People and Ecosystems: The Fraying Web of Life.* Washington, DC: World Resources Institute.

Environmental Activism

The history and character of environmental activism in Europe vary by region as well as by country. In Western Europe, for example, some nations can trace environmental activism all the way back to late nineteenth-century conservation and naturalist movements. In Eastern Europe, on the other hand, such activism arose a century later, when citizens used widespread degradation of the environment as a rallying cry in their efforts to topple communist governments during the late 1980s. Awareness of global environmental issues is generally thought to be highest in Northern Europe, where industrialization has long been coupled with a sense of responsibility toward the natural environment. In Southern Europe, however, global environmental consciousness is limited and public concern instead centers around local issues and campaigns.

A few similarities can also be found in examining environmental activism across various European regions and nations. For example, the main players in the environmental debate include local groups concerned about issues in their communities, environmental nongovernmental organizations (NGOs) operating at the national level, and international environmental organizations working on issues of regional or global concern. In addition, Europe is notable for its concentration of green political parties, which are active in many national governments as well as at the European Union (EU) level. In recent years, the EU has expanded its role in setting environmental policy for much of Europe—including not only EU member states but also Eastern and Southern European nations that aspire to join the EU. The influence of the EU has helped to homogenize environmental regulations across Europe, although the level of enforcement varies from country to country.

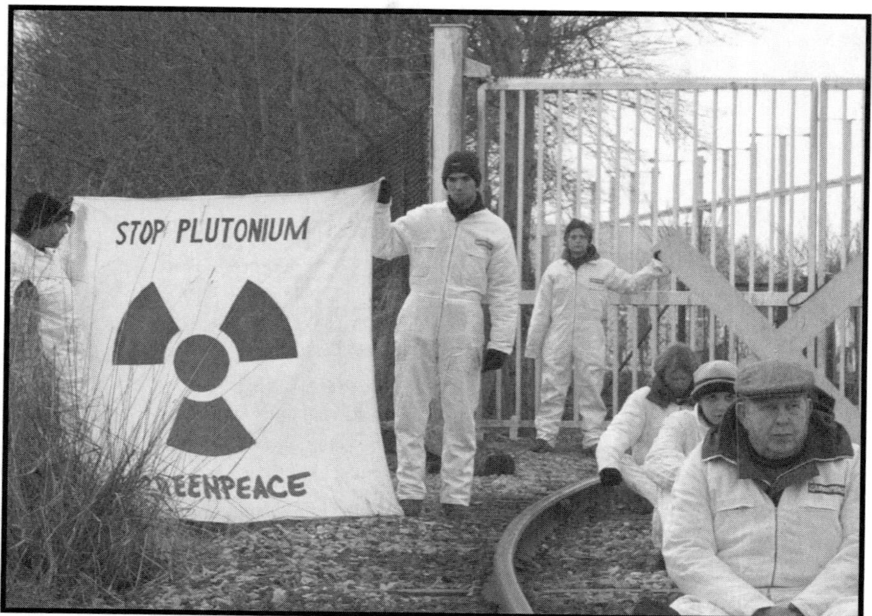

Greenpeace militants protest on the railway of the French nuclear industry giant COGEMA in Valognes, 18 January 2001, against the arrival of a shipment of nuclear waste from Borselle, the Netherlands.
AFP/CORBIS

Environmental NGOs and Green Political Parties

In many European nations, environmental NGOs play an active role in raising public awareness of environmental issues and influencing government policy. The nation with the highest proportion of its population involved in environmental groups is the Netherlands, at 17 percent, followed by Denmark at 10.9 percent, West Germany at 7.5 percent, Great Britain at 4.7 percent, and Belgium at 3.4 percent (Rootes, "Environmental Movements and Green Parties in Western and Eastern Europe," 1997). European NGOs have been credited with helping to secure international regulation of hazardous waste management, bans on whaling and trade in endangered species, and reduction of the use of chlorofluorocarbons (CFCs) that damage the ozone layer.

International environmental organizations have also established a strong presence in Europe. The World Wide Fund for Nature (WWF) was one of the first environmental groups to stake a position in Europe, forming a national organization in the United Kingdom in 1961. By the mid-1990s, WWF had grown to include nearly 5 million members in twenty-eight organizations around the world, with half centered in Europe (Bomberg, *Green Parties and*

Politics in the European Union, 1998). Initially concerned with the protection of habitats and species, WWF later added goals of promoting sustainable use of resources and reduction of pollution.

Friends of the Earth (FoE) is another international group with a strong European base. Created in 1969 by U.S. activist David Brower, FoE formed French, British, and Swedish offices the following year and eventually grew to include fifty national affiliates. The group tackles issues such as nuclear power and industrial pollution, and focuses on active campaigns such as street protests and boycotts.

Greenpeace is probably the best known environmental pressure group in Europe. It began as an antinuclear protest movement in North America in 1969, then expanded into protests against whaling and sealing during the 1970s. Greenpeace formed organizations in several European countries in the late 1970s, then set up Greenpeace International in the Netherlands in 1985 to act as a governing body. Always known for its direct action campaigns, the group's profile was raised in Europe that year when the French intelligence service blew up a Greenpeace ship—killing one activist in the process—that was taking part in protests against French nuclear tests in the Pacific.

Europe is also notable for the participation of green political parties in the governance of many countries. Green parties are generally concerned about protecting the environment, as well as such related issues as human rights, exploitation of the Third World, nuclear power, and peace and disarmament. "Greens want basic changes in the ways humans protect the natural environment, produce and consume goods, discard their waste, use and promote science and technology, and defend themselves against aggressors," one expert explained. "The kind of society that would incorporate these ideological changes is often referred to as the 'sustainable society' or 'conserver society.' Its key components are decentralization and reduced consumption of resources and material goods, or what Greens call the 'economics of enough.' Greens see 'profligate' consumption and the materialist values underlying it as the main cause of resource depletion and pollution. They argue that the finite productive limits of the globe make continued consumption at increasing levels impossible, and thus human aspirations to consume must be curtailed" (ibid.).

In Western Europe, the rise of green political parties was tied to the emergence of new social and political movements during the 1960s and 1970s. In Eastern Europe, green parties emerged as opposition forces in former communist countries as they began to make the transition to democracy in the late 1980s. Supporters of green parties tended to be young, educated urban-dwellers who were active in politics and critical of the government (Frankland, "Green Revolutions? The Role of Green Parties in Eastern Europe's Transition,"

1995). As of the late 1990s, green party members held office in the national governments of three of the four largest Western European states (Wall, *Environmental Movements: Local, National, and Global,* 1999). The most powerful green political party in Europe is the German Greens (die Grunen), which has held seats in both the German Bundestag and the European Parliament during the 1990s.

In general, green parties have enjoyed the most success in smaller countries with volatile party structures and proportional electoral systems (Frankland, "Green Revolutions? The Role of Green Parties in Eastern Europe's Transition," 1995). Yet neither environmental awareness nor the presence of a strong environmental movement seems to have a strong correlation with the success of green political parties. In the Netherlands and Denmark, for example, awareness of environmental issues is high, but the number of environmental activists is low; green parties tend to be small and poorly supported. Sweden has a modestly successful green party and high levels of environmental awareness, but almost no independent environmental movement despite high levels of awareness. Belgium and France have lower levels of environmental awareness than the Nordic countries, but they still have relatively successful green parties (Rootes, "Environmental Movements and Green Parties in Western and Eastern Europe," 1997). Regardless of the differences between countries, there have been several examples of international cooperation between green parties, such as the Green-Alternative European Link (GRAEL), the Green Group in the European Parliament (GGEP), and the European Greens Coordination.

Eastern Europe

Environmental activism arose in Eastern Europe in the late 1980s, when citizens rallied around the issue of environmental degradation during the popular uprisings against communist governments. "Environmental problems and Green parties and movements were key factors in the collapse of the old regimes," wrote one expert. "For example, they paved the way for broader political demands and served as 'breeding grounds' for democratic attitudes and practices" (Frankland, "Green Revolutions? The Role of Green Parties in Eastern Europe's Transition," 1995).

The main reason that environmental activists played a leading role in the revolutions that swept through the Eastern Bloc in the late 1980s was the extreme environmental damage that had occurred under communism. The communist governments had focused their economic expansion goals on extractive and heavy industries, and those industries had utilized older technologies and instituted few environmental safeguards. As a result, Eastern Europe gradually became the most severely polluted region of the industrialized world, with high levels of air pollution, water pollution, and deforestation (ibid.).

These factors took a significant toll on human health as well as natural resources throughout Eastern Europe. For example, a 1989 United Nations report found that pollution had damaged 82 percent of forests in Poland, 78 percent in Bulgaria, and 73 percent in Czechoslovakia. Another study found that nearly all river water in Poland was unfit for municipal use, and that one-fourth of all cities and towns in Hungary were forced to use bottled water because of contamination of their water supplies with heavy metals and hazardous wastes (French, "Green Revolutions: Environmental Reconstruction in Eastern Europe and the Soviet Union," 1991). Furthermore, environmental problems in one country tended to spread throughout the region via air currents or the Danube River.

For the people of Eastern Europe, concern over the state of the environment came to be regarded as a matter of survival. Environmental movements formed throughout the region during the 1980s. Although some groups faced government harassment, many communist regimes allowed ecological groups to exist, viewing them as relatively harmless outlets for the people's political frustration. Environmental groups employed such means as nonviolent protests and grassroots networking to draw attention to pollution and other problems resulting from government policies. Before long, people moved from questioning policies to questioning the government, and the environmental movement became linked with other grassroots movements aimed at securing peace and human rights.

These popular uprisings were successful in bringing about the fall of communism in several Eastern European nations in 1989. Since then, however, green groups have largely failed to translate their success into the political arena under the new governments. Experts offer a number of explanations for that situation. For example, some environmental groups suffered from internal strife during the transition period, as they struggled to decide whether to participate in the new governments or retain their grassroots status. In many cases, the green message of cleaning up pollution and protecting the environment was appropriated by other political parties. In addition, the environment lost some of its saliency with voters as they grew increasingly concerned about political and economic issues during the transition to democratic governments. Finally, all forms of social activism tended to decrease as the authoritarian regimes became more democratic and activists were drawn into institutionalized political activity (Rootes, "Environmental Movements and Green Parties in Western and Eastern Europe," 1997). "Their very grassroots, fluid nature seems to doom them to minority status," one expert wrote of Eastern European green groups, "but they still influence politics by exposing issues, mobilizing the people, and acting as the creative conscience for the government" (Frankland, "Green Revolutions? The Role of Green Parties in Eastern Europe's Transition," 1995).

Political reform in Eastern Europe has allowed for more formal management of the environment. Many of the newly democratic governments have formed environmental ministries, agencies, and monitoring bodies and have strengthened environmental legislation. In addition, environmentalists have enjoyed greater opportunities and influence in the political arena. But real changes in the state of the environment remain slow in many countries.

Poland

The first green political party to emerge in Eastern Europe was the Polish Party of Greens. Founded in 1988 by Polish activist Zygmunt Fura, the group traced its origins to the Polish Ecology Club, which had been founded eight years earlier. In June 1989, the Polish Party of Greens held a convention that seemingly unified hundreds of small environmental groups. This apparent unity disappeared when the greens made a poor showing in the 1989 elections, however, and the following year Poland's three major green parties fragmented into 140 local organizations and movements (Jordan, "Greenway 1989–90: The Foundation of the East European Green Parties," 1991). Although the groups reunified as the Polish Greens later in 1990 and managed to elect 120 local officials, they still received no seats in the national parliament.

Despite their failure to elect candidates to national office, the Polish Greens still raised public awareness of environmental problems and influenced government policy. Through such means as protests over construction of a nuclear power station and dam, they encouraged the government to implement progressive environmental policies. One initiative that resulted from the influence of green parties was the Green Lungs of Poland program, which was intended to protect the relatively pristine northeastern section of the country from pollution. The government also established industrial pollution standards, compiled a "hit list" of the nation's eighty worst polluters, and committed to cleaning up its portion of the notorious Black Triangle region. "The environmental movement in Poland has, as an increasingly mature interest group, contributed to the development of civil society by introducing substance to the formal shell of democratic politics," wrote one expert. "In its practice, the movement has increasingly demonstrated the civic virtues of tolerance, cooperation, and responsibility as well as helping to fill the void of middle-level social organization between state and individual left by decades of state socialist domination" (Rootes, "Environmental Movements and Green Parties in Western and Eastern Europe," 1997).

Hungary

Environmental activism in Hungary arose in response to a joint Hungarian-Czech proposal to build the Gabcikovo-Nagymaros dam on the Danube River.

The dam grew out of a 1977 treaty between the two countries and was intended to address a joint energy shortage. A group of young scientists and professionals formed the Blue Danube Circle in the early 1980s in order to oppose the dam project. This group raised public awareness of the environmental problems associated with the dam through public gatherings and articles in the news media. In 1988–1989, the Blue Danube Circle collected 200,000 signatures on a petition opposing the dam. The public pressure led the Hungarian government to create the first Environment Ministry in Eastern Europe and, in October 1989, to withdraw from the dam project. This marked the first major victory for an independent environmental movement in Eastern Europe.

The Hungarian Party of Greens (HGP), founded in 1989 by environmental activists including Zsusza Beres, grew out of the Blue Danube Circle. Ironically, the activists' success in stopping the dam hurt the political fortunes of the HGP in the 1990 elections. Lacking a single issue to bring them together, party members divided into various factions. In addition, the victory against the dam convinced other political parties to incorporate environmental messages into their campaigns and caused support for the greens to dissipate. Finally, the green groups were rumored to be a bastion for communists, leading to criticism of the HGP and other groups as "watermelons"—that is, green on the outside and red on the inside. As a result, the HGP failed to crack the electoral threshold to gain representation at the national level. In fact, the party had scored 4 percent in pre-election polls but gathered only 0.37 percent in the final vote (Frankland, "Green Revolutions? The Role of Green Parties in Eastern Europe's Transition," 1995).

Although they had limited electoral success in the 1990s, green parties remained important players in Hungarian politics by acting as moral voices on various issues. They also stayed active at the local level. In addition, Hungary supports a relatively strong environmental movement that is not connected to its green party and does not seek to enter politics. "The environmental movement in Hungary has enjoyed considerable success," one expert noted. "It has won many of its battles, succeeded in spreading awareness of environmental issues, achieved political influence at the local level and continuous access to the mass media, and it is courted by politicians eager to ensure their own re-election by being seen to be attentive to environmental issues or who see the movement as a useful ally in their own pursuit of environmental reforms" (Rootes, "Environmental Movements and Green Parties in Western and Eastern Europe," 1997).

Czechoslovakia

Environmental groups formed in Czechoslovakia as early as the 1970s. Such groups as the Brontosaurus Movement, the Czech Union of Environmentalists, the Slovak Union of Landscape and Nature Protectors, and Charter 77 were primarily concerned with exposing environmental problems under the communist government. During the push for democratic reforms in the late 1980s, these groups coalesced into three regional groups based in Bohemia, Moravia-Silesia, and Slovakia. The regional groups united informally as the Green Circle in late 1989, then formally became the Czechoslovak Party of Greens in preparation for the 1990 elections.

The Greens were successful in mobilizing the public around environmental issues prior to the elections, but their success ended up costing them votes as other parties coopted their message. For example, President Vaclav Havel began emphasizing the importance of the environment in his speeches and named prominent environmentalist Josef Vavrousek as the federal minister of environment. Like other green parties in Eastern Europe, the Czechoslovak Party of Greens also suffered from factionalism, rumors of communist infiltrators in the party, and a shift in public interest to economic issues during the transition to democracy. As a result, the Greens failed to capture any seats in the national or Czech legislatures in 1990, though they did win six seats in the Slovak National Council and numerous local posts.

When Czechoslovakia was divided in 1993, the Czech Green Party disappeared from the national political scene. The party remained active in local politics, however, particularly in heavily polluted regions such as Bohemia. Meanwhile, Slovak environmentalists have achieved several notable victories, such as stopping a major dam project on the Danube, but green parties have not improved their standing in the political arena.

Bulgaria

According to its propaganda, the communist former government of Bulgaria placed a high value on the environment. For instance, the constitution stated that the government and individuals had a duty to protect it. In practice, however, the government's policies did not match its rhetoric, and the environment often took a backseat to the needs of industry and the economy. The contrast between the government's official position and actual practice toward the environment eventually produced significant public dissatisfaction and provided fertile soil for environmental activism to germinate.

In 1988, 2,000 people marched on the city of Ruse—across the Danube River from the heavily polluted industrial town of Giurgiu, Romania—in an illegal antipollution protest. This action led to the formation of the Bulgarian Green Party and several other opposition groups. In 1989, zoologist Petar Baron created the Social Movement Ecoglasnost to draw attention to Bulgaria's environmental problems. Although these early groups often faced official repression and police harassment, they continued to mount peaceful protests and ultimately helped bring down the communist regime of Todor Zhivkov, who resigned a week after Ecoglasnost led a rally of 9,000 people in Sofia in November 1989.

In early 1990, Ecoglasnost and several other green groups formed a coalition and joined the Union of Democratic Forces (UDF) in opposition to the communists. The UDF received 35 percent of the vote and 111 seats in the 1990 elections. Of that total, the Bulgarian Green Party claimed 3.25 percent and thirteen seats, while Ecoglasnost took 4 percent and nineteen seats (Frankland, "Green Revolutions? The Role of Green Parties in Eastern Europe's Transition," 1995). The green coalition split apart the following year, however, and the groups were unable to maintain their positions in the national government. The Bulgarian Green Party received one seat in the 1997 parliamentary elections.

Romania

The hard-line communist regime of Nicolae Ceausescu suppressed the development of an environmental movement in Romania. When the regime began to falter in the late 1980s, however, several groups seized the opportunity to expose the environmental devastation that had taken place under Ceausescu. In 1988, for example, the Democratic Action Movement issued a report detailing the nation's environmental problems. When Ceausescu was removed from power and executed in December 1989, the new communist government attempted to address environmental concerns by creating an environment ministry.

Three major green political parties formed prior to the 1990 national elections: the Romanian Ecological Party (REP); the Ecological Humanist Party; and the Romanian Ecological Movement (REM). The REM was an official front formed by the secret police to take advantage of public interest in environmental issues. The green groups fared relatively well in the 1990 elections, with the REM claiming twelve parliament seats and the REP gaining eight. In addition, REP leader Marcian Bleahu was appointed as environment minister. Thanks in part to growing public awareness of such ecological problems as chemical pollution at Giurgiu on the Danube River, green parties have retained their influence in Romanian politics since that time, maintaining a stable support base and some representation in parliament. Green groups have achieved several victories, including stopping plans for concrete channeling of the Danube delta and pushing through a restoration project for the river.

Russia

Environmental activism in Russia, as in most other countries in Eastern Europe, arose during the reform protests of the late 1980s. Leaders of the environmental movement did well in the 1989 elections to the USSR parliament, but they lost clout afterward as interest in environmental issues waned and supporters moved into the democracy movement. During the 1990s, the continued instability of the Russian government helped to prevent a strong national environmental movement from taking shape. Protesters largely confined their activities to local actions against industrial facilities and municipalities because state agencies appeared to lack the will or means to respond to their demands (Rootes, "Environmental Movements and Green Parties in Western and Eastern Europe," 1997).

Environmental activism began to increase once again during the late 1990s. The Russian Federation became home to an estimated 100 environmental groups, including the All-Russian Wild Nature Protection Society, the Green Cross of Russia, and the Cedar Movement, as well as nonprofits such as the Center of Environmental Policy of Russia, the Russian Environmental Academy, and Ecojuris. In 2000 many of these groups joined together in sponsoring an appeal for a national referendum to oppose further destruction of the country's environment. Although the groups collected nearly 3 million signatures, the Kremlin applied political pressure to halt the referendum effort (Yablokov, "Ecology and Human Rights in Russia," 2000).

As environmental groups gained power during the late 1990s, the Russian government and secret service began targeting activists. In July 1999, President Vladimir Putin recommended that the Federal Security Police (FSB)—successors to the Soviet KGB—keep a close watch on environmental organizations because he believed that many of them had been infiltrated by spies. Since then, many organizations have reported that their offices have been ransacked or their leaders harassed. Such repressive government actions have taken a toll on the environmental movement. "Environmentalism in Russia today is isolated from other social movements, demoralized by the absence of the solidarity which comes from mass protests, suffers a growing resource deficit, and is totally alienated from its social environment in a political climate in which ecologism is aggressively attacked" (Rootes, "Environmental Movements and Green Parties in Western and Eastern Europe," 1997).

In 2000, Putin dissolved the Federal Forest Service and the State Committee on Environmental Protection and transferred their functions to the Ministry of Natural Resources. Although Putin claimed that the move was a cost-cutting measure, environmentalists felt that the president was responding to pressure from large corporations and the powerful Russian ministries of defense and nuclear energy. They argued that the new arrangement created a conflict of interest, as the Ministry of Natural Resources would be responsible for protecting the environment as well as licensing the extraction of resources such as timber, oil, and minerals. Immediately after Putin announced the changes, a coalition of sixty-seven Russian and international environmental

Russian Antinuclear Activist Aleksandr Nikitin

The Soviet Union built and operated a large fleet of nuclear-powered submarines during the Cold War. As of 2000, Russia had sixty-nine retired nuclear submarines, as well as sixty others that remained on active duty. Many of these vessels were constructed on the Kola Peninsula along the Barents Sea, which is home to 18 percent of the world's nuclear reactors—the largest concentration anywhere. The proximity of this area to the Norwegian border attracted the attention of the Bellona Foundation, a Norwegian environmental NGO working to expose the environmental problems in northwestern Russia. Bellona set out to assess the danger of radioactive contamination from eroding submarines or accidents in waste storage facilities in Russia.

Assisting Bellona in this effort was Aleksandr Nikitin, a former naval captain in the Soviet Northern Fleet who served as chief engineer on nuclear submarines through 1985. After completing his military service, he worked for the Defense Department as a senior inspector for the Nuclear and Radiation Safety Inspection Department. Upon his retirement in 1992, Nikitin still felt a strong responsibility to help Russia handle its decommissioned submarines and nuclear waste safely. He decided to work with the Bellona Foundation to identify and map radioactive sources throughout the region. "I thought that by solving the problems, I would be helping my country," he explained (Sains, "Nordic Nations Hail Environmental Hero," 2000).

In 1995, Bellona published a report entitled *The Russian Northern Fleet: Sources of Radioactive Contamination.* Nikitin contributed two chapters on safety problems at naval reactor installations and the potential for nuclear submarine accidents. The report warned that "without international cooperation and financing, a grave situation could arise which can be pictured as a Chernobyl in slow motion. If safety measures are not implemented, major accidents and the release of fissile material will be unavoidable" ("Russia: Environmentalists Denounced as Western Spies" 2000).

The Russian Federal Security Police (FSB), successors to the Soviet KGB, cracked down immediately after the report was published. They ransacked Bellona's Moscow offices, confiscated research materials, and banned the report in Russia. In February 1996, Nikitin was arrested and charged with high treason and divulging state secrets, despite the fact that his contributions to the report were based on public information. Although he was released in December, he was not allowed to leave St. Petersburg. Nikitin was soon acquitted of the charges by a lower court, but the prosecutor general immediately launched an appeal. He ended up being charged eight times with the same crime, as upon each acquittal his case was sent back for reinvestigation.

(continues)

Thanks to the efforts of Bellona, Nikitin's case came to international attention. In 1997 members of U.S. environmental and human rights groups sent 600,000 letters urging then-president Boris Yeltsin to end state harassment of environmentalists. Nikitin also won the Goldman Environmental Prize for his work that year. In 2000 he was featured in a joint Sierra Club/Amnesty International report on persecuted environmentalists around the world. The U.S. Justice Department also weighed in on the matter, issuing a statement that said that the endless appeals of Nikitin's acquittal "adds to the appearance of political manipulation of the legal system and further suggests that law enforcement agencies may be harassing government critics" (ibid.).

Finally, in September 2000, Nikitin's acquittal was upheld by the Russian Supreme Court. With all appeals exhausted, it appeared that Nikitin was finally a free man. "I am convinced that ecology cannot be secret," he stated. "Environmental openness is an inalienable human right. Any attempt to conceal any information about harmful impact on people and the environment is a crime against humanity" (ibid.). Following his final acquittal, Nikitin began working to establish a new environmental organization called the Coalition for the Environment and Human Rights, dedicated to defending Russian environmentalists with a lower profile than himself. "During these last five years, the Sierra Club, Bellona, and the Union of Concerned Scientists have been working together to solve my case. But there are still many other people sitting in prison," he explained (Rauber, "The Green Menace," 2000).

Sources:

"Goldman Environmental Prize Recipient Profile: Alexander Nikitin." http://www.goldmanprize.org/recipients/recipientprofile.cfm?recipientID=38 (accessed June 2002).

Rauber, Paul. 2000. "The Green Menace: Vladimir Putin Finds a New Class Enemy in Environmentalism." *Sierra* 85 (November–December).

"Russia: Environmentalists Denounced as Western Spies, Despite Political Transition to a Free Civil Society." 2000. *Environmentalists under Fire: Ten Urgent Cases of Human Rights Abuses.* Washington, DC: Amnesty International USA/Sierra Club.

Sains, Ariane. 2000. "Nordic Nations Hail Environmental Hero." *Europe* (November).

organizations called for the World Bank to halt further loans to Russia. Upon investigating the situation, however, the World Bank claimed that it was satisfied with the new system of environmental monitoring and regulation.

Western Europe

The modern environmental movement got its start in Western Europe in the late 1960s. Such factors as rapid technological development, rising education levels, and a change in economic orientation from manufacturing to service helped transform Western Europe into a postindustrial society. Assured that their basic material needs would be met, citizens could concern themselves with broader quality-of-life issues such as environmental protection (Bomberg, *Green Parties and Politics in the European Union,* 1998).

Public concern about the environment grew during the 1970s as Western European nations increasingly saw the damaging effects of acid rain on forests, crops, and historic buildings. The first elections to the European Parliament (EP) in 1979 encouraged environmental groups in several countries—including Belgium, France, the United Kingdom, and West Germany—to form "green" political parties in order to participate. Many environmental activists turned their focus to nuclear issues during the 1980s, especially after the devastating accident at the Chernobyl nuclear facility in Ukraine in 1986.

By 1992 surveys showed that 85 percent of citizens of the European Union (EU) regarded reducing pollution and protecting the environment as matters of immediate concern (Commission of the European Communities, *Eurobarometer,* 1992). In addition, Western Europeans increasingly recognized the transnational nature of environmental issues and came to view the EU as the appropriate forum to set environmental policy. In fact, studies showed that up to 80 percent of citizens in each EU member state favored a common European environmental policy (Bomberg, *Green Parties and Politics in the European Union,* 1998). In response, the EU gradually expanded its role until it became the principal source of environmental policy in Western Europe.

Environmental Policy at the EU Level

When the EU was first established under the Treaty of Rome, it had no formal authority to create environmental policy for its member states. But a number of factors convinced the EU to increase its role in this area. For example, mounting evidence of the transboundary nature of environmental problems—such as water pollution, air pollution, and acid rain—led the citizens of Western Europe to seek ways to address these problems in a regional manner. In addition, the people of Western Europe were increasingly concerned about global environmental issues and felt that setting policy at the EU level might give them more say in the international arena. Finally, several EU nations lobbied for uniform environmental standards in order to eliminate trade distortions that would allow states with lax rules to profit at the expense of those with more stringent regulations (ibid.).

The 1973 Environmental Action Programme (EAP) is widely viewed as the EU's first foray into environmental policy. Objectives of the program included improving environmental quality, reducing pollution, and encouraging the EU to work with international bodies toward environmental protection. The

Single European Act (SEA) of 1987 added a special title on the environment to the Treaty of Rome and officially granted the EU authority to act on behalf of member states in matters other than trade. The EU gained even greater powers under the Treaty on European Union (TEU), which was signed in Maastricht in 1992. Since then, the EU has become the main source of environmental policy in Western Europe. But implementation of EU directives on the environment is left to member states, and compliance varies as a result.

Setting environmental policy at the EU level has created both opportunities and dilemmas for environmental activists. "The incentives for Greens to work with Europe are great, yet how can they work through institutions that . . . inherently violate green principles?" wrote Jeremy Richardson in his introduction to *Green Parties and Politics in the European Union* by Elizabeth Bomberg. "In many ways the EU is a singularly unfavorable political system for 'purist' organisations such as the Greens, because of its messy style of policy-making. This demands cooperation with sometimes strange bedfellows and last-minute compromises on fundamental principles. Yet, the EU is also an attractive opportunity structure—if only because it is a transnational decision-making system and is more suited, therefore, to solving environmental problems."

Since it can be difficult to coordinate transnational environmental activism, many NGOs and green political parties concentrate their focus on the national level. However, several organizations have formed to help environmentalists from countries across Europe work together. The European Environment Bureau (EEB) is an umbrella organization for 135 NGOs from twenty-four countries. Established in 1974, the EEB promotes environmental protection and sustainable use of natural resources at the EU level. It acts as a consultant to the European Commission, European Parliament, and Council of Europe, which has led to some criticism for its close ties to government and its willingness to compromise. The European Federation of Green Parties (EFGP) is a federation of green political parties from thirty-one countries across Europe. Created in 1993 from the former European Green Coordination, the EFGP works toward forging common platforms for European elections, supporting the efforts of small green parties in Europe, and establishing ties with green parties outside of Europe.

United Kingdom

As in other parts of Western Europe, environmental activism arose in the UK during the 1970s. The British Green Party, founded in 1973, is among the oldest in Europe. The environment gained strength as a political issue throughout the 1980s, thanks largely to the activities of environmental NGOs. In 1988 public concern about the environment prompted conservative prime minister Margaret Thatcher to surprise many observers by supporting urgent action to protect the ozone layer, prevent global warming, and reduce acid rain. The following year, the British government released an influential white paper on the environment called "This Common Inheritance" and began working to incorporate environmental concerns into its economic growth strategies.

Concern about the environment reached a peak in the late 1980s, with 35 percent of British citizens rating the environment as the most important issue for the government to address in 1989 (Rootes, "Environmental Movements and Green Parties in Western and Eastern Europe," 1997). That same year, the British Green Party received 14.9 percent of the vote in the elections to the European Parliament (Bomberg, *Green Parties and Politics in the European Union,* 1998), though the UK's plurality electoral system prevented them from claiming any seats. By 1995, however, only 5 percent of British citizens rated the environment as among the most important issues. But interest in the environment may have only shifted toward local concerns rather than disappeared during this period, as the percentage of citizens who reported taking environmentally friendly actions increased from 14 percent in 1988 to 29 percent in 1995 (Rootes, "Environmental Movements and Green Parties in Western and Eastern Europe," 1997).

Environmental NGOs increased in size and number in the UK during the 1990s. Although much of the environmental movement had become institutionalized and worked through formal channels by the mid-1990s, Great Britain also experienced a surge in grassroots activity that was more confrontational in nature. On the forefront of this trend was the radical green network Earth First! (UK), which was founded in 1991 by students Jake Burbridge and Jason Torrence. Like the founders of Earth First! in the United States, Burbridge and Torrence had become disillusioned with what they viewed as the institutionalized nature of other environmental groups, such as Friends of the Earth and Greenpeace, and they wanted to take a new approach involving deep ecology and direct action (Wall, "Mobilizing Earth First! in Britain," 1999).

One of the earliest protests launched by Earth First! (UK) involved a blockade of the Dungeness nuclear power station. A short time later, the new group tried to stop a ship loaded with rain forest timber from docking on the Thames. Then the activists moved into anticar "reclaim the streets" protests, which corresponded with widespread antiroads campaigns. In the mid-1990s, Earth First! (UK) began using confrontational strategies such as digging holes in road surfaces and burning construction machinery in their protests against new roads.

Germany

Germany is widely viewed as among the most progressive of the world's industrialized nations in terms of environmental policy. It boasts many of the most stringent environmental regulations in the world and has become a leader in the global environmental movement. Not surprisingly, Germany has a long history of environmental activism. Citizens became involved in local conservation initiatives as early as the late nineteenth century. Concern about the environment waned during the 1930s as the nation geared up its economy during wartime, and economic and physical recovery from the wartime destruction was the top priority through the 1950s. Although an umbrella organization of German conservation groups, Deutscher Naturschutzring (DNR), formed in 1950, its lobbying efforts did not have much effect in the postwar period.

Public awareness and concern about environmental issues began growing in Germany once again during the late 1960s. When the reform government came to power in 1969, it responded to such concerns by establishing a separate policy field for the environment. The government put forth a program to address environmental issues in 1970 and followed up with a detailed Environmental Programme and the Federal Nature Conservation Act in 1976. These initiatives established an integrated approach to environmental management and conservation that still forms the basis of German policy today. The national government regulates such issues as waste disposal and air quality with the help of scientific advisory bodies, while the implementation of laws and regulations affecting the environment are left to individual German states and municipalities (Brand, "Dialectics of Institutionalization: The Transformation of the Environmental Movement in Germany," 1999).

The German government continued to act as the driving force behind environmental protection through the mid-1970s, and its policies received broad support from the German people and even from industry groups. As Germany began to feel the effects of the oil crisis and accompanying global recession, however, the government backed off on some of its environmental policies and began sponsoring a nuclear energy program. At this point, the German people sprang into action and developed a strong environmental movement through thousands of local grassroots initiatives. As environmental protests became increasingly visible, environmental issues attracted news media attention and gained priority in the mind of the public. Over time, the German people developed a strong environmental consciousness as they rallied around such issues as nuclear safety and widespread damage to the nation's forests as a result of air pollution and acid rain.

The German government reacted to the 1986 accident at the Chernobyl nuclear power plant by bringing all of its environmental protection offices together as the Ministry for Environment, Nature Protection and Nuclear Safety. Klaus Topfer took over the ministry in 1987 and proved to be a progressive environmentalist. Although environmental initiatives took a backseat during reunification, Germany entered the 1990s with a renewed focus that extended to global environmental problems and sustainable development.

Germany has enacted numerous policies aimed at reducing pollution, conserving natural resources, and creating a sustainable economy. Industry has joined in these efforts, viewing it as an opportunity to improve efficiency, reduce operating expenses, and gain a competitive advantage over Japan and the United States in world markets. For example, Germany established a goal of retrofitting all of its power plants in order to reduce the emissions of pollutants that cause acid rain by 80 percent, and that goal was achieved in 1989. In 1991, Germany instituted a program that requires industry to collect and recycle all components of their products, including packaging. In addition, Germany banned the chemicals that harm the ozone layer and contribute to global warming in 1995—five years earlier than the rest of the world. Initiatives in progress include closing inner cities to automobile traffic and encouraging the use of energy-efficient mass transit (Moore, "Green Revolution in the Making," 1995).

Despite the progressive nature of German environmental policy, the German environmental movement remained strong at the beginning of the twenty-first century. Some environmental groups joined the mainstream and participate in government as a political party. The German Greens (die Grunen) formed as a political party in 1980 and entered the national parliament in 1983, winning 5.6 percent of the national vote and twenty-seven seats. The following year, the green party captured 8 percent of the vote in elections to the European Parliament and claimed seven seats. By 1989, die Grunen surpassed the 5 percent threshold to win seats in eight of the eleven Land assemblies. The party experienced a setback in the 1990 federal elections because of internal strife and their unpopular stance against reunification. They formed an alliance with the East German Greens (Bundnis 90) in 1993 and underwent a reorganization in both structure and priorities. In 1994, Bundnis 90/die Grunen claimed more than 10 percent of the vote and twelve seats in the EP elections, and also returned to the national parliament with 7.3 percent of the vote and forty-nine seats (Bomberg, *Green Parties and Politics in the European Union,* 1998).

At the same time, Germany remains home to a radical environmental movement that operates outside of the political arena. Some of the issues adopted by these activists include animal rights, genetic engineering, and the transport and storage of nuclear waste (Rucht and Roose, "The German Environmental Movement at a Crossroads?" 1999). Finally, German citizens maintain a strong environmental consciousness. Two-thirds of German consumers report that

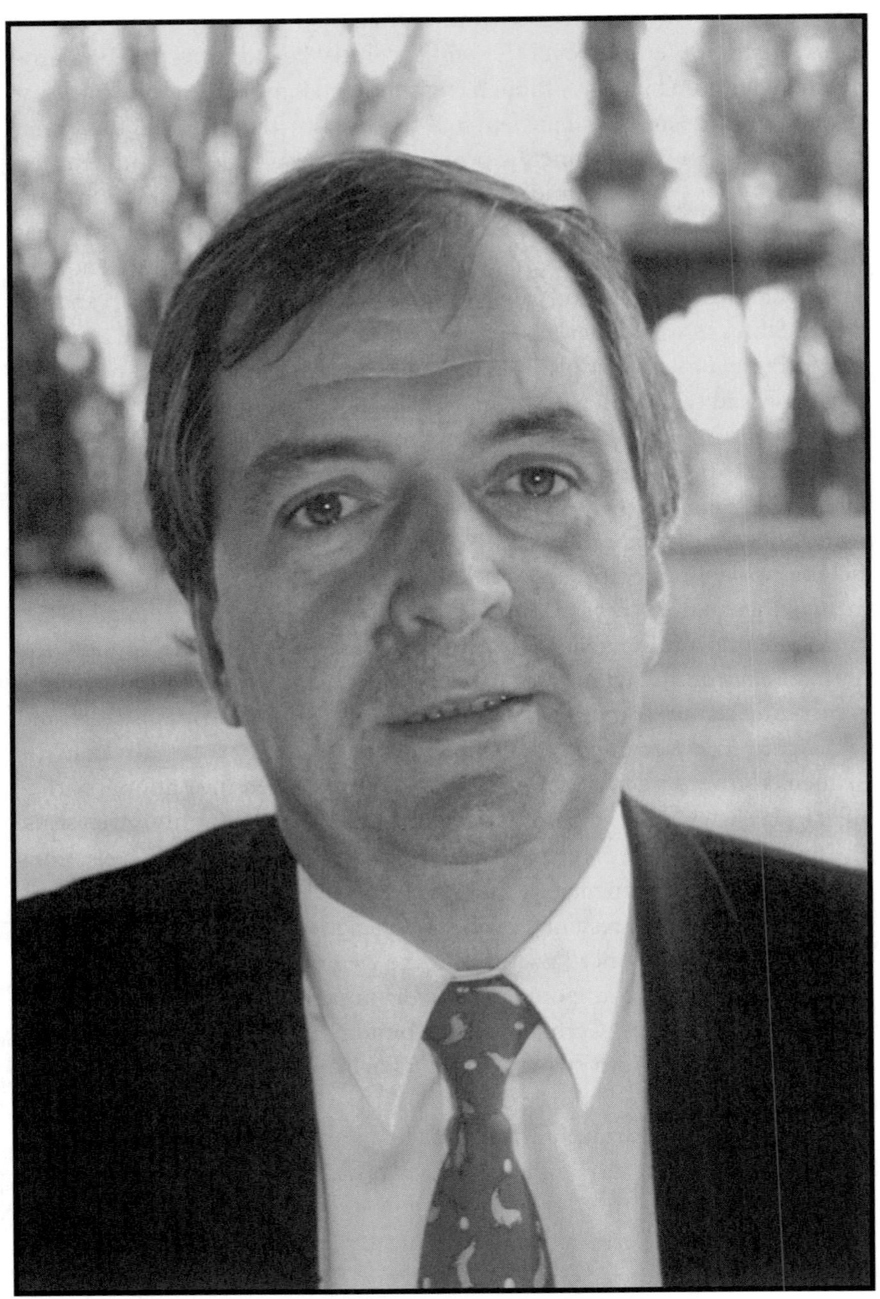

Portrait of Klaus Topfer VERNIER JEAN BERNARD/CORBIS SYGMA

they specifically shop for environmentally friendly products, for example, which has turned Germany into a test market for environmentally safe products from around the world. "Most German citizens and businesses remain convinced both that environmental protection is essential and that the technological innovation stimulated by stringent environmental requirements will, over the long term, strengthen their national productivity and competitiveness" (Moore, "Green Revolution in the Making," 1995).

Sources:

Barry, John, and E. Gene Frankland, eds. 2002. *International Encyclopedia of Environmental Politics.* London: Routledge.

Bomberg, Elizabeth. 1998. *Green Parties and Politics in the European Union.* London: Routledge.

Brand, Karl-Werner. 1999. "Dialectics of Institutionalization: The Transformation of the Environmental Movement in Germany." In Christopher Rootes, ed., *Environmental Movements: Local, National, and Global.* London: Frank Cass.

Commission of the European Communities. 1992. *Eurobarometer.* Luxembourg: Office for Official Publications of the European Communities.

Frankland, Erich G. 1995. "Green Revolutions? The Role of Green Parties in Eastern Europe's Transition, 1989–1994." *East European Quarterly* 29 (September).

French, Hilary F. 1991. "Green Revolutions: Environmental Reconstruction in Eastern Europe and the Soviet Union." *Columbia Journal of Business* (spring).

Jehlicka, Petr, and Tomas Kostelecky. 1992. "The Development of the Czechoslovak Green Party since the 1990 Elections." *Environmental Politics* 5 (spring).

Jimenez, Manuel. 1999. "Consolidation through Institutionalization? Dilemmas of the Spanish Environmental Movement in the 1990s." In Christopher Rootes, ed., *Environmental Movements: Local, National, and Global.* London: Frank Cass.

Jordan, Carlo. 1991. "Greenway 1989–90: The Foundation of the East European Green Parties." In Sara Parkin, ed., *Green Light on Europe.* London: Heretic.

Kousis, Maria. 1999. "Sustaining Local Environmental Mobilizations: Groups, Actions, and Claims in Southern Europe." In Christopher Rootes, ed., *Environmental Movements: Local, National, and Global.* London: Frank Cass.

Moore, Curtis. 1995. "Green Revolution in the Making." *Sierra* 80 (January–February).

Moore, Curtis, and Alan Miller. 1994. *Green Gold: Japan, Germany, the United States, and the Race for Environmental Technology.* Boston: Beacon Press.

Rootes, Christopher A. 1997. "Environmental Movements and Green Parties in Western and Eastern Europe." In Michael Redclift and Graham Woodgate, eds., *The International Handbook of Environmental Sociology.* Cheltenham, UK: Edward Elgar.

Rucht, Dieter, and Jochen Roose. 1999. "The German Environmental Movement at a Crossroads?" In Christopher Rootes, ed., *Environmental Movements: Local, National, and Global.* London: Frank Cass.

Wall, Derek. 1999. "Mobilizing Earth First! in Britain." In Christopher Rootes, ed., *Environmental Movements: Local, National, and Global.* London: Frank Cass.

Wapner, Paul. 1996. *Environmental Activism and World Civic Politics.* Albany: State University of New York Press.

Yablokov, Alexey V. 2000. "Ecology and Human Rights in Russia." Center of Environmental Policy in Russia. http://gadfly.igc.org/russia/yablokov1.

Appendix: International Environmental and Developmental Agencies, Organizations, and Programs

African-Eurasian Migratory Waterbird Agreement (AEWA)
http://www.unep-wcmc.org/AEWA/index2.html

Albertine Rift Conservation Society (ARCOS)
http://www.unep-wcmc. org/arcos/

Association of Southeast Asian Nations (ASEAN)
http://www.asean.or.id/

Biodiversity Planning Support Programme (BPSP)
http://www.undp.org/bpsp/

BirdLife International (BI)
http://www.birdlife.net

Botanic Gardens Conservation International (BGCI)
http://www.bgci.org.uk/

CAB International (CABI)
http://www.cabi.org/

Centre for International Forestry Research (CIFOR)
http://www.cifor.org/

Circumpolar Protected Areas Network (CPAN)
http://www.grida.no/caff/cpanstratplan.htm

Commission for Environment Cooperation (CEC) (North American Agreement on Environmental Cooperation)
http://www.cec.org/

Commission on Genetic Resources for Food and Agriculture (CGRFA)
http://www.fao.org/ag/cgrfa/default.htm

Commission for Sustainable Development (CSD)
http://www.un.org/esa/sustdev/csd.htm

Committee on Trade and Environment (CTE), World Trade Organization
http://www.wto.org/egnlish/tratop_e/envir_e/issu1_e.htm

Conservation International (CI)
http://www.conservation.org/

Consultative Group on International Agricultural Research (CGIAR)
http://www.cgiar.org/

Convention on Biological Diversity (CBD)
http://www.biodiv.org/

Convention on International Trade in Endangered Species of Wild Fauna and Flora (CITES)
http://www.cites.org/

Convention on Migratory Species of Wild Animals (CMS)
http://www.unep-wcmc.org/cms

European Centre for Nature Conservation (ECNC)
http://www.ecnc.nl/

European Community (EC)
http://europa.eu.int/

European Environment Agency (EEA)
http://www.eea.eu.int/

Forest Stewardship Council (FSC)
http://www.fscoax.org/index.html

Foundation for International Environmental Law and Development (FIELD)
http://www.field.org.uk/

Global Assessment of Soil Degradation (GLASOD)
http://www.isric.nl/GLASOD.htm

Global Biodiversity Information Facility (GBIF)
http://www.gbif.org/index.html

Global Coral Reef Monitoring Network (GCRMN)
http://coral.aoml.noaa.gov/gcrmn/

Global Forest Resources Assessment 2000 (FRA 2000), UN Food and Agriculture Organization
http://www.fao.org/forestry/fo/fra/index.jsp

Global International Waters Assessment (GIWA), UN Environment Programme
http://www.giwa.net/

Global Invasive Species Programme (GISP)
http://jasper.stanford.edu/GISP/home.htm

Global Resource Information Database (GRID), UN Environment Programme
http://www.grid.no

Inter-American Biodiversity Information Network (IABIN)
http://www.iabin.org/

Intergovernmental Oceanographic Commission (IOC), UN Educational, Scientific, and Cultural Organization
http://ioc.unesco.org/iocweb/

Intergovernmental Panel on Climate Change (IPCC)
http://www.ipcc.ch/index.html

International Center for Agricultural Research in the Dry Areas (ICARDA)
http://www.icarda.cgiar.org/

International Centre for Living Aquatic Resources Management (ICLARM)
http://www.cgiar.org/iclarm/

International Centre for Research in Agroforestry (ICRAF)
http://www.icraf.cgiar.org/

International Cooperative Biodiversity Groups (ICBG)
http://www.nih.gov/fic/programs/icbg.html

International Coral Reef Action Network (ICRAN)
http://www.unep.ch/earthw/icran.htm

International Coral Reef Information Network (ICRIN)
http://www.environnement.gouv.fr/icri/index.html

International Council for the Exploration of the Sea (ICES)
http://www.ices.dk/

International Council for Science (ICSU)
http://www.icsu.org/

International Food Policy Research Institute (IFPRI)
http://www.ifpri.org/

International Forum on Forests (IFF), Commission on Sustainable Development
http://www.un.org/esa/sustdev/forests.htm

International Fund for Agricultural Development (IFAD)
http://www.ifad.org/

International Geosphere-Biosphere Programme (IGBP)
http://www.igbp.kva.se/

International Institute of Tropical Agriculture (IITA)
http://www.iita.org/index3.htm

International Maritime Organization (IMO)
http://www.imo.org/

International Rivers Network (IRN)
http://www.irn.org/

International Union of Biological Sciences (IUBS)
http://www.iubs.org/

Man and the Biosphere Program (MAB), UN Educational, Scientific, and Cultural Organization
http://www.unesco.org/mab/index.htm

Marine Stewardship Council (MSC)
http://www.msc.org/

Organization of African Unity (OAU)
http://www.oau-oau.org/

Organization for Economic Cooperation and Development (OECD)
http://www.oecd.org/

Ozone Secretariat Homepage
http://www.unep.ch/ozone/

Pan-European Biological and Landscape Diversity Strategy (PEBLDS)
http://www.strategyguide.org/

Program for the Conservation of Arctic Flora and Fauna (CAFF), Arctic Council
http://www.grida.no/caff/

Protocol Concerning Specially Protected Areas and Wildlife (SPAW)
http://www.cep.unep.org/law/cartnut.html

Ramsar Convention on Wetlands of International Importance (RAMSAR)
http://www.ramsar.org/

South African Development Community (SADC)
http://www.sadc.int/

South Pacific Regional Environmental Programme (SPREP)
http://www.sprep.org.ws/

Species Survival Commission (SSC), World Conservation Union
http://iucn.org/themes/ssc/index.htm

TRAFFIC (the joint wildlife trade monitoring programme of World Wide Fund for Nature and World Conservation Union)
http://www.traffic.org

United Nations Centre for Human Settlements (UNCHS)
http://www.unchs.org

United Nations Children's Fund (UNICEF)
http://www.unicef.org

United Nations Conference on Environment and Development (UNCED), Rio de Janeiro, June 1992
http://www.un.org/esa/sustdev/agenda21.htm

United Nations Conference on Trade and Development (UNCTAD)
http://www.unctad.org/

United Nations Convention to Combat Desertification (UNCCD)
http://www.unccd.int/main.php

United Nations Convention on the Law of the Sea (UNCLOS)
http://www.un.org/Depts/los/index.htm

United Nations Development Programme (UNDP)
http://www.undep.org/

United Nations Educational, Scientific, and Cultural Organization (UNESCO)
http://www.unesco.org/

United Nations Environment Programme (UNEP)
http://www.unep.org/

United Nations Food and Agriculture Organization (FAO)
http://www.fao.org/

United Nations Forum on Forests (UNFF)
http://www.un.org/esa/sustdev/forests.htm

United Nations Framework Convention on Climate Change (UNFCCC)
http://www.unfccc.de/index.html

United Nations Industrial Development Organization (UNIDO)
http://www.unido.org/

World Agricultural Information Centre (WAIC), UN Food and Agriculture Organization
http://www.fao.org/waicent/search/default.htm

World Bank (WB)
http://www.worldbank.org

World Commission on Dams (WCD)
http://www.dams.org/

World Commission on Protected Areas (WCPA), World Conservation Union
http://www.wcpa.iucn.org/

World Conservation Monitoring Centre (WCMC)
http://www.unep-wcmc.org

World Conservation Union (IUCN)
http://www.iucn.org/

World Health Organization (WHO)
http://www.who.int

World Heritage Convention (WHC)
http://www.unesco.org/whc/index.htm

World Resources Institute (WRI)
http://www.wri.org/wri/

World Summit on Sustainable Development (WSSD), Johannesburg, South Africa, September 2002
http://www.johannesburgsummit.org/

World Trade Organization (WTO)
http://www.wto.org/

World Water Council (WWC)
http://www.worldwatercouncil.org/

World Wide Fund for Nature (WWF)
http://www.panda.org/

WorldWatch Institute
http://www.worldwatch.org/

Index

(*Note:* Page numbers in italic type refer to illustrations)